Leaving Certificate Maths

Text & Tests

Higher Level Maths

5

O.D. Morris • Paul Cooke • Frances O'Regan

The Celtic Press

Acknowledgements
The authors would like to thank Paul Behan and Frances O'Regan for their valuable contributions to the original texts.
We also wish to express our deep gratitude to Aidan Roantree, a highly experienced and well-regarded Maths teacher and fellow author, for his thorough reading of the text and for his insightful suggestions, many of which helped to shape this new edition.

First Published in April 2018 by
The Celtic Press
Ground Floor – Block B
Liffey Valley Office Campus
Dublin 22

This reprint April 2021

ISBN: 978-0-7144-2465-1

Contents

Preface

This substantially revised book is the second of two volumes that amalgamate the previous editions of *Text & Tests 4, 5, 6* and *7* into two books for the Higher Level Leaving Certificate Project Maths course. *Text & Tests 5* completes the course.

This Sixth-Year textbook follows on from *Text & Tests 4*. The topics of geometry, differential calculus, probability and statistics are completed. A chapter on functions is introduced and revises many of the graphs already encountered during the course.

The book fully reflects the overall approach to the teaching of Maths as stated in the learning outcomes for Project Maths. It encourages the development of not only the students' knowledge and skills but also the understanding necessary to apply these skills.

The extensive range of imaginatively written and probing questions on each topic will help students understand the concepts involved and develop their problem-solving skills. Every attempt has been made to grade the questions in order of difficulty.

At the beginning of each chapter, there is a list of Key Words that the students are expected to know and understand when the chapter is completed.

Each chapter concludes with a three-part revision exercise section consisting of (a) Core, (b) Advanced, and (c) Extended Response questions

O. D. Morris, Paul Cooke
February 2018

Complex numbers

Key words

Section 1.1 Irrational numbers

In your study of maths so far, you will have met these number systems:

(i)   Natural numbers: N = {1, 2, 3, 4, ...} ... whole positive numbers.

(ii) Integers: Z = {......−3, −2, −1, 0, 1, 2, 3, ...} ... whole, positive and negative numbers including zero.

(iii) Rational numbers: Q = $\{\frac{a}{b} \mid a, b \in Z, b \neq 0\}$, i.e. fractions, e.g. $\frac{1}{2}, \frac{7}{3}, \frac{-3}{5}, \frac{6}{1}, \frac{10}{9}, \frac{-4}{2}$ etc.

   Note: The set Q includes decimals that can be written as fractions.

If we try to solve the equation $x^2 + 2 = 7$, we get
$$x^2 = 7 - 2 = 5$$
$$x = \sqrt{5}$$

$\sqrt{5}$ is a number that is not an element of any of the above sets of numbers.

Using a calculator, we find $\sqrt{5} = 2.236067978... ...$, a non-repeating, non-terminating decimal.

Because $\sqrt{5}$ cannot be written as a ratio (fraction), it is called an **irrational number**.

Examples of irrational numbers are $\sqrt{2}, \sqrt{3}, \sqrt{5}, \sqrt{6}, \sqrt{7}$ ...

Note: We have already described these numbers as **surds**.

One of the most famous irrational numbers is π, the ratio of the circumference of a circle to its diameter.

$$\pi = 3.141592654.........$$

Another is Euler's number, *e*, the base number of the natural logarithms.

$$e = 2.71828182845.........$$

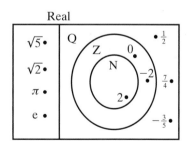

Definition: An irrational number is any real number that **cannot** be expressed in the form $\frac{a}{b}$, where *a* and *b* are integers, and *b* is not zero.

Since there can be no numbers common to the rational and irrational sets, together the sets of natural numbers, integers, rational and irrational numbers form the **partitioned** set of Real numbers (R).

It is clear that $N \subset Z \subset Q$.

Also, $R \setminus Q$ = the set of irrational numbers.

Note: Not all square roots are irrational numbers, e.g. $\sqrt{4} = 2, \sqrt{9} = 3$ etc.

As outlined in the section on surds, irrational numbers can be simplified by finding a pair of factors, one factor of which is a perfect square.

E.g. $\sqrt{18} = \sqrt{9 \times 2} = \sqrt{9} \times \sqrt{2} = 3\sqrt{2}$.

Example 1

Simplify each of the following, giving your answers in the form $a\sqrt{b}, a, b \in Z$.

    (i) $\sqrt{48} + \sqrt{75}$ (ii) $\sqrt{180} - \sqrt{20}$

(i)
$$\sqrt{48} = \sqrt{16 \times 3} = \sqrt{16} \times \sqrt{3} = 4\sqrt{3}$$
$$\sqrt{75} = \sqrt{25 \times 3} = \sqrt{25} \times \sqrt{3} = 5\sqrt{3}$$
$$\therefore \ \sqrt{48} + \sqrt{75} = 4\sqrt{3} + 5\sqrt{3} = 9\sqrt{3}$$

(ii)
$$\sqrt{180} = \sqrt{36 \times 5} = 6\sqrt{5}$$
$$\sqrt{20} = \sqrt{4 \times 5} = 2\sqrt{5}$$
$$\therefore \ \sqrt{180} - \sqrt{20} = 6\sqrt{5} - 2\sqrt{5} = 4\sqrt{5}$$

Constructing a line of length $\sqrt{2}$

Although $\sqrt{2} = 1.414214...$ is a non-terminating decimal, it is possible to construct a line of length $\sqrt{2}$ on the number line as the following example shows.

Example 2

Using a compass and straightedge only, construct a line segment of length $\sqrt{2}$ and hence mark $\sqrt{2}$ on the number line.

   (i) Using a straightedge, draw a line segment [AM].

  (ii) Starting at A, mark equal spaces 0, 1, 2... (A, B, C) using a compass.

 (iii) Using a compass, construct the perpendicular bisector of [AC], that is, draw a perpendicular line through B.

 (iv) Join D and E.

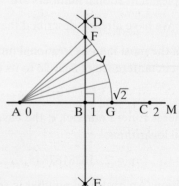

(v) Mark the point F on [DE] so that |AB| = |BF|.

(vi) Using A as the centre and |AF| as radius, draw an arc FG to the number line.

(vii) Mark G on the number line, √2.

Proof: Consider the triangle *ABF*:

$|AB| = 1, |BF| = 1, ABF = 90°$

Using Pythagoras' theorem: $|AF|^2 = |AB|^2 + |FB|^2$

$$\therefore |AF|^2 = 1^2 + 1^2 = 2$$

$$\therefore |AF| = \sqrt{2} \Rightarrow |AG| = \sqrt{2}$$

Note: Using similar constructions, other irrational numbers can be plotted on the number line.

  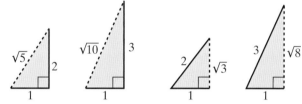

Example 3

Construct a line segment of length √3 on the number line.

(i) Mark a point A on a straight line AB.

(ii) Using a compass, mark equal spaces |AJ| and |JC| (each 1 unit) along AB.

(iii) Using A as centre and |AC| as radius, draw an arc.

(iv) Using C as centre and |CA| as radius, draw an arc.

(v) Join the points of intersection of the arcs HI.

(vi) From our geometry theorems, we know that HI is perpendicular to AB and bisects [AC] at J.

Consider the triangle AJH.

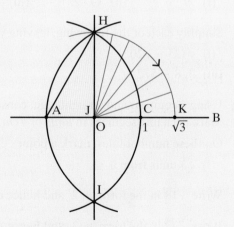

$|AJ| = 1, |AH| = 2, \angle AJH = 90°$

$\therefore\ |AH|^2 = |AJ|^2 + |JH|^2$ ...using Pythagroas's theorem

$\therefore\ 2^2 = 1^2 + |JH|^2$

$\therefore\ 4 = 1 + |JH|^2$

$\therefore\ 3 = |JH|^2 \Rightarrow |JH| = \sqrt{3}$

Using J as centre and $|JH|$ as radius, draw an arc HK intersecting the horizontal line at K. $|JK| = \sqrt{3}$

Exercise 1.1

1. By finding factors, one of which is a perfect square, write each of the following in its simplest form:

   (i) $\sqrt{18}$ (ii) $\sqrt{12}$ (iii) $\sqrt{45}$ (iv) $\sqrt{28}$

2. Simplify each of the following, giving your answer in the form $a\sqrt{b}, a, b \in Z$.

   (i) $\sqrt{18} + \sqrt{50}$ (ii) $\sqrt{48} + \sqrt{147}$

3. Given that N is the set of natural numbers,

   Z is the set of integers,

   Q is the set of rational numbers,

   and R is the set of real numbers, give two elements of each of the following sets:

   (i) $Z \setminus N$ (ii) $Q \setminus Z$ (iii) $R \setminus Q$

4. Describe in words each of the following sets:

   (i) Z (ii) $Q \setminus Z$ (iii) $Q \setminus N$ (iv) $R \setminus Z$ (v) $R \setminus Q$

5. Simplify each of the following, leaving your answer in the form $a\sqrt{b}, a, b \in Z$:

   (i) $\sqrt{125} - \sqrt{20}$ (ii) $\sqrt{32} - \sqrt{18} - \sqrt{8}$

   (iii) $3\sqrt{8} + 5\sqrt{2}$ (iv) $4\sqrt{18} - 2\sqrt{27} + 3\sqrt{3} - \sqrt{288}$

6. Using a compass and straightedge, construct two line segments each of length 12 cm. Mark each line segment in *units of 4 cm* (0, 1, 2, 3).

   On these number lines, mark a point

   (i) $\sqrt{3}$ units from 0   (ii) $\sqrt{2}$ units from 0.

7. Write $\sqrt{18}$ in the form $a\sqrt{2}$ and hence draw a line $\sqrt{18}$ in length.

8. Write $\sqrt{12}$ in the form $a\sqrt{3}$ and hence draw a line $\sqrt{12}$ in length.

9. Given a line segment [AB] of length $\sqrt{2}$, describe how to make a line segment of length $\sqrt{3}$ using a compass and straightedge only.

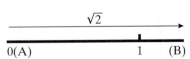

10. Find the length of the perimeter of this triangle.

Give your answer in the form $a\sqrt{b}$, $a, b \in N$.

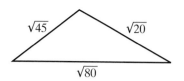

11. Which of the following are irrational numbers:

$$\sqrt{3}\,,\ \pi\,,\ \tfrac{1}{3}\,,\ e\,,\ 0\,,\ \sqrt[5]{2}\,,\ \tfrac{22}{7}\,,\ \sqrt{36}$$

12. Find the length of each of the sides *a, b, c, d, e, f* and *g*.

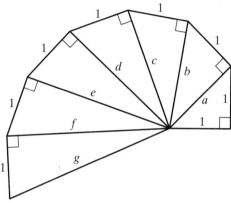

Which of these lengths is not an irrational number?

13. A stairs makes an angle of 45° with the horizontal.

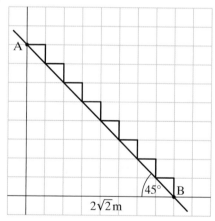

If the base of the stairs measures $2\sqrt{2}$ m, as shown, find the length of the carpet needed to cover the stairs from A to B. Give your answer in the form $a\sqrt{2}$.
If the angle of the stairs is increased to 60°, find how much extra carpet is needed.
Give your answer in the form $2(\sqrt{a} - \sqrt{b})$.

14. (i) Write down one value of *x* for which the expression $\sqrt{3-x}$ is rational.

(ii) Describe in words the set of values of *x* for which the expression $\sqrt{3-x}$ is rational.

Section 1.2 Complex numbers

To solve an equation such as $x^2 - 9 = 0$, we could proceed as follows:

$$x^2 - 9 = 0$$
$$x^2 = 9$$
$$x = \sqrt{9} = \pm 3$$

However, if $x^2 + 9 = 0$

$$x^2 = -9$$
$$x = \sqrt{-9}$$

and since no real number multiplied by itself gives -9, no real number can satisfy this equation.

To deal with the square root of a negative number, a new number $\sqrt{-1}$ is created. This number is called i.

Hence, $\sqrt{-9} = \sqrt{9 \times -1} = \sqrt{9} \times \sqrt{-1} = \pm 3i$.

Similarly, $\sqrt{-16} = \sqrt{16 \times -1} = \sqrt{16} \times \sqrt{-1} = \pm 4i$

and $\sqrt{-5} = \sqrt{5 \times -1} = \sqrt{5} \times \sqrt{-1} = \pm\sqrt{5}i$.

$$i = \sqrt{-1}$$
$$\Rightarrow i^2 = -1$$

Square roots of negative numbers are called **imaginary numbers** and are written in the form of bi, where b is a real number, e.g. $3i$.

Example 1

Solve the equation $x^2 + 25 = 0$.

$$x^2 + 25 = 0$$
$$x^2 = -25$$
$$x = \sqrt{-25} = \sqrt{25 \times -1} = \sqrt{25} \times \sqrt{-1}$$
$$x = \pm 5i$$

Example 2

Solve the equation $x^2 + 2x + 2 = 0$.

Using the quadratic formula, we have $a = 1, b = 2, c = 2$.

Hence, $x = \dfrac{-b \pm \sqrt{b^2 - 4ac}}{2a}$

$$x = \frac{-2 \pm \sqrt{2^2 - 4(1)(2)}}{2(1)}$$

$$x = \frac{-2 \pm \sqrt{-4}}{2} = \frac{-2 \pm \sqrt{4 \times -1}}{2} = \frac{-2 \pm 2i}{2}$$

$$x = -1 \pm i$$

Therefore, $x = -1 + i, -1 - i$.

Numbers such as $-1 + i$ are called **complex numbers** and are normally denoted by the letter *z*.

A complex number such as $z = 3 + 6i$, has two parts (dimensions); a **real part** and an **imaginary part**.

The first part of this complex number is the real constant 3.

The second part of this complex number is imaginary; the real constant 6 multiplied by *i*.

3 is referred to as the real part and is given by **Re(z) = 3**.

6 is referred to as the imaginary part and is given by **Im(z) = 6**.

The set of complex numbers is denoted by **C**.

> Complex number (*z*):
> $z = x + iy$
> $Re(z) = x$ and $Im(z) = y$

Complex number (*z*)	Real part, Re(*z*)	Imaginary part, Im(*z*)
$4 + 3i$	4	3
$3 - i$	3	-1
-5	-5	0
$2i$	0	2
$3 - \sqrt{5}i$	3	$-\sqrt{5}$

Adding and subtracting complex numbers

When adding or subtracting complex numbers, we add (or subtract) the real and imaginary parts separately.

For example: (i) $(4 + 3i) + (3 - 2i) = 4 + 3i + 3 - 2i$
$$= (4 + 3) + (3i - 2i)$$
$$= 7 + i$$

(ii) $(3 + 7i) - (4 - 5i) = 3 + 7i - 4 + 5i$
$$= 3 - 4 + 7i + 5i$$
$$= -1 + 12i$$

Multiplying complex numbers

For example: (i) $(3 + 5i)(4 - 3i) = 3(4 - 3i) + 5i(4 - 3i)$
$$= 12 - 9i + 20i - 15i^2$$
$$= 12 - 9i + 20i - 15(-1)$$
$$= 12 - 9i + 20i + 15$$
$$= 12 + 15 - 9i + 20i$$
$$= 27 + 11i$$

> $i^2 = -1$

(ii) $(2 + 4i)(2 - 4i) = 2(2 - 4i) + 4i(2 - 4i)$
$$= 4 - 8i + 8i - 16i^2$$
$$= 4 - 16(-1)$$
$$= 20$$

Example 3

If $z_1 = 2 + 3i$, $z_2 = 3 - 4i$ and $z_3 = 1 + 5i$, express each of the following complex numbers in the form $a + bi$.

(i) $z_1 + z_3$ (ii) $z_2 . z_3$ (iii) $z_1(z_2 + z_3)$

(i) $z_1 + z_3 = 2 + 3i + 1 + 5i$
$= 2 + 1 + 3i + 5i = 3 + 8i$

(ii) $z_2 . z_3 = (3 - 4i)(1 + 5i)$
$= 3 + 15i - 4i - 20i^2$
$= 3 + 20 + 15i - 4i = 23 + 11i$

(iii) $z_1(z_2 + z_3) = (2 + 3i)(3 - 4i + 1 + 5i)$
$= (2 + 3i)(4 + i)$
$= 8 + 2i + 12i + 3i^2$
$= 8 - 3 + 2i + 12i$ $... + 3i^2 = -3$
$= 5 + 14i$

Exercise 1.2

1. Write each of the following numbers in terms of i:

   (i) $\sqrt{-4}$ (ii) $\sqrt{-36}$ (iii) $\sqrt{-27}$ (iv) $\sqrt{-20}$

2. Solve each of the following equations, giving your answer in the form bi, where b is a real number.
   (i) $x^2 + 9 = 0$ (ii) $x^2 + 12 = 0$

3. Express each of the following in the form $a + bi$:

   (i) $(3 + 2i) + (5 - i)$ (ii) $(7 - 2i) + (3 - 4i)$ (iii) $(-3 + 4i) + (6 - 4i)$
   (iv) $(-3 - i) + (-2 + 6i)$ (v) $(5 - 3i) + (-5 + 6i)$ (vi) $(1 + i) + (2 - 3i)$

4. Simplify each of the following:

   (i) $(2 + 6i) - (1 + 4i)$ (ii) $(3 - 5i) - (2 + 4i)$ (iii) $(4 - 7i) - (-1 + 3i)$
   (iv) $3 - (1 + 4i)$ (v) $(3 - 6i) - 4i$ (vi) $(-3 - 2i) - (4 - 7i)$

5. Multiply each of the following complex numbers and give your answer in the form $a + bi$, $a, b \in R$:

   (i) $(3 + 2i)(2 + 3i)$ (ii) $(4 + i)(3 - 5i)$ (iii) $(5 - 2i)(3 - 5i)$
   (iv) $(3 + 4i)(3 - 4i)$ (v) $(5 - i)(5 + i)$ (vi) $(3 - 2i)^2$

6. If $z_1 = 2 + 4i$, $z_2 = 3 - i$ and $z_3 = 4 - 2i$, express each of the following in the form of $a + bi$, $a, b \in R$.
   (i) $3z_1$ (ii) $z_2 + z_3$ (iii) $2z_1 + z_2$ (iv) $-3z_2$
   (v) $z_1 . z_2$ (vi) $z_2 . z_3$ (vii) $i(z_3)$ (viii) $z_2(z_1 - z_2)$

7. Solve each of the following equations using the quadratic formula and give your answer in the form $a + bi, a, b \in R$:

$$x = \frac{-b \pm \sqrt{b^2 - 4ac}}{2a}$$

    (i) $x^2 - 2x + 17 = 0$ (ii) $x^2 - 4x + 13 = 0$

    (iii) $x^2 - 10x + 26 = 0$ (iv) $x^2 - 8x + 52 = 0$

8. Solve the equation $2z^2 - 8z + 9 = 0$.

9. Complete the table, given that $i = \sqrt{-1}$ and $i^2 = -1$.

    i $= i^1 = i$

    $i \times i$ $= i^2 = -1$

    $i \times i \times i$ $= i^3 =$

    $i \times i \times i \times i$ $= i^4 =$

    $i \times i \times i \times i \times i$ $= i^5 =$

    $i \times i \times i \times i \times i \times i = i^6 =$

Describe the pattern formed from this sequence.

What strategy could be used to simplify $i^n, n \in N$? [e.g., i^{29} and i^{32}.]

10. Simplify each of the following:

    (i) i^{30} (ii) i^{11} (iii) i^{19} (iv) i^{21} (v) i^{-4}

11. Simplify the following:

    (i) $i^{16} + i^{10} + i^6 - i^{12}$ (ii) $i^3 - i^{11} + i^{17} - i^{29}$

12. Simplify the following:

    (i) $i^2.i^6.i^5$ (ii) $3i^3.2i^5.4i^2$ (iii) $(2i^7)^3$

13. Write $4i^3 + 7i^9$ in the form bi where $b \in Z$.

Section 1.3 Division and Equality of complex numbers ⎯⎯

Complex numbers can be divided by a real number as follows.

$$\frac{2 + 5i}{2} = \frac{2}{2} + \frac{5}{2}i = 1 + \frac{5}{2}i$$

To divide a complex number by another non-real complex number, we must change the denominator into a real number using a **complex conjugate**.

Complex conjugate ⎯⎯⎯⎯⎯⎯⎯⎯⎯⎯

Given any complex number $z = a + bi$, then the complex conjugate of z, written $\bar{z}$, is $a - bi$.

For example, if $z = 3 + 4i$,

        then $\bar{z} = 3 - 4i$, where $\bar{z}$ is the complex conjugate of z.

The product $z.\bar{z} = (3 + 4i)(3 - 4i)$
$$= 9 - \cancel{12}i + \cancel{12}i - 16i^2$$
$$= 9 + 16$$
$$= 25, \text{ a real number}$$

Complex conjugate: If $z = a + bi$, then $\bar{z} = a - ib$
$$\text{and } z\bar{z} = (a + bi)(a - bi)$$
$$= a^2 + b^2$$

Note:

z	$\bar{z}$
$3 + 7i$	$3 - 7i$
$2 - 4i$	$2 + 4i$
$-3 + i$	$-3 - i$
$+4i$	$-4i$

Using the complex conjugate, we can divide complex numbers as shown in the following example.

Example 1

Write $\dfrac{3 + 4i}{2 - 5i}$ in the form $a + bi$.

$$\frac{3 + 4i}{2 - 5i} = \frac{3 + 4i}{2 - 5i} \times \frac{2 + 5i}{2 + 5i}$$

$$= \frac{6 + 15i + 8i + 20i^2}{4 + \cancel{10}i - \cancel{10}i - 25i^2}$$

$$= \frac{6 + 23i - 20}{4 + 25} \quad \text{...since } i^2 = -1$$

$$= \frac{-14 + 23i}{29} = -\frac{14}{29} + \frac{23i}{29}$$

Equality of complex numbers

For two complex numbers to be equal, their real parts must be equal and their imaginary parts must be equal.

If $(x + 2) + 4i = 6 + (y - 2)i$,

then $x + 2 = 6$ and $4 = y - 2$

$\Rightarrow x = 4$ and $6 = y$

If $a + bi = x + yi$,

then $a = x$ and $b = y$

Example 2

Find x and y if $x + 2i + 2(3 - 5yi) = 8 - 13i$.

$$x + 2i + 2(3 - 5yi) = 8 - 13i$$
$$\Rightarrow \quad x + 2i + 6 - 10yi = 8 - 13i$$
$$\Rightarrow \quad x + 6 + (2 - 10y)i = 8 - 13i$$

Equating the real parts:

$$x + 6 = 8$$
$$x = 2$$

Equating the imaginary parts:

$$2 - 10y = -13$$
$$-10y = -15$$
$$10y = 15$$
$$y = \frac{15}{10} = \frac{3}{2}$$

Example 3

Given that $(z + 1)(2 - i) = 3 - 4i$, find z in the form $x + yi$, where $x, y \in R$.

$$(z + 1)(2 - i) = 3 - 4i$$
$$\Rightarrow \quad z + 1 = \frac{3 - 4i}{2 - i} \times \frac{2 + i}{2 + i}$$
$$= \frac{3 - 4i}{2 - i} \times \frac{2 + i}{2 + i} = \frac{6 + 3i - 8i - 4i^2}{4 + 2i - 2i - i^2}$$
$$= \frac{10 - 5i}{5}$$
$$z + 1 = 2 - i$$
$$\therefore \quad z = 2 - i - 1$$
$$= 1 - i$$

Example 4

Express $\sqrt{5 + 12i}$ in the form of $a + bi$, where $a, b \in R$.

Let
$$a + bi = \sqrt{5 + 12i}$$
$$(a + bi)^2 = 5 + 12i$$
$$\Rightarrow a^2 + 2abi + b^2i^2 = 5 + 12i$$
$$\Rightarrow \quad a^2 - b^2 + 2abi = 5 + 12i$$
$$\therefore \quad a^2 - b^2 = 5 \quad \text{and} \quad 2ab = 12$$
$$\Rightarrow \quad a = \frac{12}{2b} = \frac{6}{b}$$

$$\therefore \left(\frac{6}{b}\right)^2 - b^2 = 5$$

$$6^2 - b^4 = 5b^2$$

$$\Rightarrow \quad b^4 + 5b^2 - 36 = 0$$

$$(b^2 + 9)(b^2 - 4) = 0 \quad \Rightarrow \quad b^2 = -9 \quad \text{or} \quad b^2 = 4$$

$$b = \sqrt{-9} \qquad b = \pm 2$$

$$b = \pm 3i$$

Since $a = \dfrac{6}{b}$, when $b = +2$, $a = \dfrac{6}{2} = 3$　　　　　[Note: $b \neq 3i$ since $b \in R$]

when $b = -2$, $a = \dfrac{6}{-2} = -3$

$$\therefore \quad \sqrt{5 + 12i} = (3 + 2i) \quad \text{or} \quad (-3 - 2i)$$

Exercise 1.3

1. Write down the complex conjugate of each of the following complex numbers.
   - (i) $3 + 4i$
   - (ii) $2 - 6i$
   - (iii) $-5 - 2i$
   - (iv) $-8 + 3i$

2. Given z, find $\bar{z}$ in each of the following cases.
   - (i) $z = 2 + 5i$
   - (ii) $z = -3 - 4i$
   - (iii) $z = 1 + 7i$
   - (iv) $z = -5 + i$

3. Express each of the following in the form of $a + bi$, where $a, b \in R$:
   - (i) $\dfrac{2 + 3i}{4 - i}$
   - (ii) $\dfrac{4 + 3i}{5 + i}$
   - (iii) $\dfrac{8 - i}{2 + 3i}$
   - (iv) $\dfrac{2 + 5i}{-3 + 2i}$

4. If $z = 2 + 6i$, express each of the following in the form of $a + bi$, where $a, b \in R$:
   - (i) $z.\bar{z}$
   - (ii) $z + \bar{z}$
   - (iii) $z - \bar{z}$
   - (iv) z^2

5. Simplify each of the following.
   - (i) $\dfrac{(3 + 4i) + (2 + i)}{4 - i}$
   - (ii) $\dfrac{(2 - 6i) - (3 + 2i)}{2 + 2i}$
   - (iii) $\dfrac{3(2 + 4i)}{5i}$
   - (iv) $\dfrac{(2 + i) + (3 - 2i)}{(4 + i) - (3 + 2i)}$
   - (v) $\dfrac{(3 + 2i)(1 - i)}{2 + 4i}$
   - (vi) $\dfrac{(3 + i)(2 - i)}{(4 + i)(2 + i)}$

6. Find the values of x and y in each of the following:
   - (i) $x + yi = 4 - 2i$
   - (ii) $x + yi = (2 + i)(3 - 2i)$
   - (iii) $x + yi = \dfrac{7 + i}{2 - i}$
   - (iv) $x + yi = (2 - 3i)^2$

7. Find the values of a and b in each of the following:
   (i) $a + bi + 3 - 2i = 4(-2 + 5i)$
   (ii) $a(1 + 2i) - b(3 + 4i) = 5$

8. If $z = x + yi$ and $3(z - 1) = i(3 + i)$, find the values of x and y.

9. If $z_1 = -3 + 4i$ and $z_2 = 1 + 2i$ are two complex numbers and $z_1 + (p + iq)z_2 = 0$ where $p, q \in R$, find the values of p and q.

   Hint: $0 = 0 + 0i$

10. Given $z = \sqrt{3 + 4i}$, find z in the form of $a \pm bi$, where $a, b \in R$.

11. If $(x + iy)^2 = 8 - 6i$, find the values of x and y, $x, y \in R$.

12. Express each of the following in the form $a + bi$, $a, b \in R$:
    (i) $\sqrt{-12 - 16i}$ (ii) $\sqrt{-15 + 8i}$ (iii) $\sqrt{9 - 40i}$

13. Given $z_1 = 2 + 3i$ and $z_2 = -1 - 5i$, find
    (i) $\overline{z_1 + z_2}$ (ii) $\overline{z_1 z_2}$

Section 1.4 Argand diagram – Modulus

The **Argand diagram** gives a geometric representation of a complex number as a point in the complex plane.

Real numbers can be plotted on a single number line but complex numbers, with two parts consisting of a real part and an imaginary part, need a plane of points to represent them.

The complex plane is similar to the Cartesian plane, with the real part $Re(z)$ of a complex number represented by the x-axis, and the imaginary part $Im(z)$ represented by the y-axis.

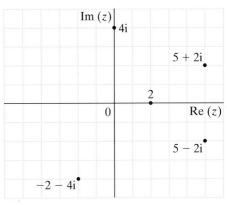

In this diagram we have plotted the complex numbers
    (i) $z_1 = 5 + 2i$
    (ii) $z_2 = 0 + 4i = 4i$
    (iii) $z_3 = 2 + 0i = 2$
    (iv) $z_4 = -2 - 4i$
    (v) $\overline{z}_1 = 5 - 2i$

Modulus of a complex number

The **modulus** of a complex number is the distance from the origin to the point in the plane representing the number.

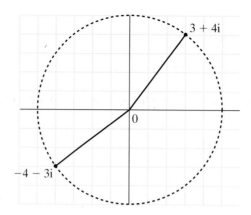

The modulus of $z_1 = 3 + 4i$ is given by:

$$|z_1| = \sqrt{3^2 + 4^2}$$
$$= \sqrt{25} = 5$$

Notice that the modulus of $z_2 = -4 - 3i$, is

$$|z_2| = \sqrt{(-4)^2 + (-3)^2}$$
$$= \sqrt{16 + 9}$$
$$= \sqrt{25} = 5$$

> If $z = a + bi$, then the modulus of z, written as $|z|$, is given by
> $$|z| = \sqrt{a^2 + b^2}.$$

This shows that $3 + 4i$ and $-4 - 3i$ have equal moduli and hence lie on the circumference of the same circle (with centre at the origin).

Example 1

Given that $z_1 = 4 + i$ and $z_2 = -2 + 2i$, plot the following on an Argand diagram:

$$0, z_1, z_2 \text{ and } (z_1 + z_2).$$

Also calculate $|z_1|, |z_2|$ and $|z_1 + z_2|$.
Is $|z_1| + |z_2| = |z_1 + z_2|$?

$$z_1 = 4 + i \Rightarrow |z_1| = \sqrt{4^2 + 1^2}$$
$$= \sqrt{17}$$

$$z_2 = -2 + 2i \Rightarrow |z_2| = \sqrt{(-2)^2 + (2)^2}$$
$$= \sqrt{4 + 4}$$
$$= \sqrt{8}$$

$$z_1 + z_2 = 4 + i + (-2 + 2i) \qquad \Rightarrow |z_1| + |z_2| = \sqrt{17} + \sqrt{8}$$
$$= 2 + 3i \qquad\qquad\qquad |z_1 + z_2| = \sqrt{13}$$
$$|z_1 + z_2| = \sqrt{2^2 + 3^2}$$
$$= \sqrt{13} \qquad\qquad \Rightarrow |z_1| + |z_2| \neq |z_1 + z_2|.$$

Exercise 1.4

1. Plot each of the following complex numbers on an Argand diagram:

   (i) $z_1 = 3 + 5i$ (ii) $z_2 = -3 + i$ (iii) $z_3 = 5i$ (iv) $z_4 = -1 - 3i$

2. Given $z_1 = 2 + i$ and $z_2 = -4 + 3i$, plot each of the following numbers on an Argand diagram:

   (i) z_1 (ii) z_2 (iii) $\bar{z}_1$ (iv) $\bar{z}_2$

   (v) $z_1 + z_2$ (vi) $z_1 - z_2$ (vii) $z_1 z_2$ (viii) $\dfrac{z_1}{z_2}$

3. If $z_1 = 3 - i$ and $z_2 = 2 + 4i$, plot each of the following numbers on an Argand diagram:

   (i) $z_1.\bar{z}_1$ (ii) $z_1 + \bar{z}_1$ (iii) $\dfrac{1}{z_1}$ (iv) $z_1 z_2$

4. (a) Given $z_1 = 3 + i$ and $z_2 = -1 + 3i$, plot the numbers z_1, z_2 and $z_1 + z_2$ on an Argand diagram. Join the points $0, z_1, z_2,$ and $z_1 + z_2$.
   (b) Given $z_3 = 2 - 2i$ and $z_4 = -1 - 4i$, plot the numbers z_3, z_4 and $z_3 + z_4$ on an Argand diagram. Join the points $0, z_3, z_4,$ and $z_3 + z_4$.
   (c) What geometrical observation could you make about the relationship between $0, z_1, z_2,$ and $z_1 + z_2$?

5. If $z = 1 + 3i$, plot each of the following complex numbers on an Argand diagram.

   (i) 2 (ii) $2 + z$ (iii) $3i$ (iv) $3i + z$
   (v) $1 + i$ (vi) $1 + i + z$ (vii) $-3i + z$ (viii) $-2 - i + z$

   What geometrical observation can be made about adding the same complex number z to other complex numbers?

6. If $z = 3 + 2i$, find each of the following complex numbers in the form $a + bi$:

   (i) iz (ii) $i^2 z$ (iii) $i^3 z$

   Plot the complex numbers $z, iz, i^2 z, i^3 z$.

7. Find the modulus of each of the following complex numbers:

   (i) $5 + 2i$ (ii) $4 - 2i$ (iii) $-2 - 4i$ (iv) $-3 + i$

8. Plot the number $z_1 = 2 + 5i$.

   Write down three different complex numbers that have the same modulus as z_1.

9. Evaluate each of the following:

   (i) $\left| \dfrac{3 + i}{-2 - 3i} \right|$ (ii) $|(4 + 2i)(3 - i)|$ (iii) $\left| \dfrac{1}{3 + 5i} \right|$

10. Given $z_1 = -2 - 3i$ and $z_2 = 3 + i$, find the complex number $\dfrac{z_1}{z_2}$.

   Investigate if $\dfrac{|z_1|}{|z_2|} = \left| \dfrac{z_1}{z_2} \right|$

11. The complex numbers u, v and w are related by the equation
$$\frac{1}{u} = \frac{1}{v} + \frac{1}{w}.$$
Given that $v = 3 + 4i$ and $w = 4 - 3i$, find u in the form $x + yi$.

12. If $z = 4 - 2i$, find $|z|$, $|2z|$ and $|3z|$. Is $2|z| = |2z|$?
Explain your answer.

13. Investigate if $|z| = |\bar{z}|$ for all $z \in C$.

14. Let $z_1 = s + 8i$ and $z_2 = t + 8i$, where $s, t \in R$ and $i^2 = -1$.
(i) Given that $|z_1| = 10$, find the value of s.
(ii) Given that $|z_2| = 2|z_1|$, find the value of t.

15. Find the modulus of $\dfrac{i}{1 - i}$.

16. Describe the set of solutions of $|z - 1||z - 1| = 1$.

17. Given any two complex numbers z_1, and z_2 as shown.
Indicate on an Argand diagram z_1, z_2 and $(z_1 + z_2)$.
Under what conditions would $|z_1 + z_2| = |z_1| + |z_2|$?

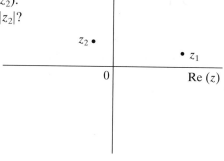

> **ICT:** Use computer software such as
> Geogebra to investigate Q17.
> Take the y-axis as the imaginary axis.
> Use the polygon function to plot 0, z_1, z_2
> and $(z_1 + z_2)$ as a parallelogram.
> By moving $(z_1 + z_2)$, investigate the
> conditions under which $|z_1 + z_2| = |z_1| + |z_2|$.

Section 1.5 Transformations of complex numbers

1. Multiplying a complex number by a real number

If a complex number $z_1 = 3 + 2i$ is multiplied by 4,
we get $4z_1 = 4(3 + 2i) = 12 + 8i$.
The real part is increased by a factor of 4 and the
imaginary part is also increased by a factor of 4.

The complex number appears to be **stretched**
along a line from the origin by a factor of 4.
For example, $3 + 2i$ is mapped onto $12 + 8i$.

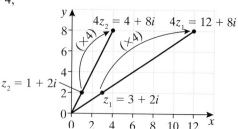

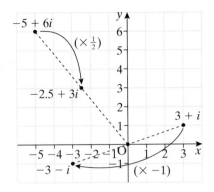

If the complex number is multiplied by $\frac{1}{2}$, a **contraction** occurs.
For example, $(-5 + 6i)$ is mapped onto $-2.5 + 3i$.

Multiplying by (-1) **changes the direction**, that is, the number is reflected through the origin. For example, $(3 + i) \times (-1)$ is mapped onto $-3 - i$.

If $z = x + iy$, then the transformation az has the following results:

  (i) $|a| > 1$, results in stretching away from the origin
 (ii) $0 < |a| < 1$, results in a contraction towards the origin
(iii) $a < 0$, then az is reflected in the origin and stretched or contracted as in (i) or (ii)

2. Adding complex numbers

  (i) When a complex number z is added separately
      to other complex numbers – z_1, z_2, z_3 –
      it creates a **translation of the plane.**

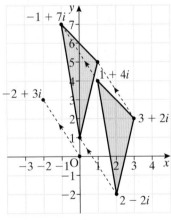

      Let $z = -2 + 3i$
      and $z_1 = 3 + 2i, \; z_2 = 1 + 4i, \; z_3 = 2 - 2i.$
      Then $z + z_1 = -2 + 3i + 3 + 2i = 1 + 5i$
              $z + z_2 = -2 + 3i + 1 + 4i = -1 + 7i$
              $z + z_3 = -2 + 3i + 2 - 2i = i$

Notice that the complex number z_1 translates to $z_1 + z$.

Translation mapping $z_1 \longrightarrow z_1 + z$

 (ii) When z_1 is added to z_2 to create the new complex number $(z_1 + z_2)$, the three
      complex numbers form a parallelogram with the origin $(0 + 0i)$.

17

Let $z_1 = -2 + 2i$ and $z_2 = 3 + 2i$,

then $z_1 + z_2 = -2 + 2i + 3 + 2i$

$\qquad = 1 + 4i.$

$0 + 0i, -2 + 2i, 3 + 2i$ and $1 + 4i$ form a parallelogram, as shown.

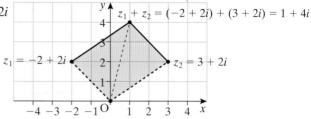

3. Multiplying complex numbers

(i) When a complex number such as $4 + i$ is multiplied by i, the complex number **rotates anti-clockwise about the origin by a quarter of a turn.**

For example, $(4 + i).i = 4i + i^2$

$\qquad\qquad\qquad = 4i - 1$

$\qquad\qquad\qquad = -1 + 4i$

$\qquad\qquad\qquad$ ... a rotation of $90°$

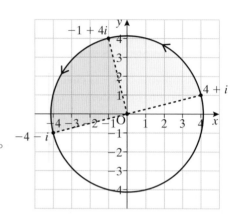

Also, $(4 + i)(i^2) = (4 + i)(i)(i)$

$(-1 + 4i)(i) = -i + 4i^2$

$\qquad\qquad\quad = -i - 4$

$\qquad\qquad\quad = -4 - i$

$\qquad\qquad\qquad$ ... a rotation of $180°$

Note: $(-4 - i)(-i) = +4i + i^2$

$\qquad\qquad\qquad = +4i - 1$

$\qquad\qquad\qquad = -1 + 4i$

$\qquad\qquad\qquad$ ... a rotation of $-90°$

> $z \times i$, z rotates by $90°$
> $z \times (i)^2$, z rotates by $180°$
> $z \times (i)^3$, z rotates by $270°$
> $z \times (i)^4$, z rotates by $360°$
> $z \times (-i)$, z rotates by $(-90°)$

(ii) When $z_1 = 2 + i$ is multiplied by $z_2 = 3 + i$, the product can be seen as a combination of a stretching and rotation transformation as follows.

$z_1 z_2 = (2 + i)(3 + i)$

$\qquad = 2(3 + i) + i(3 + i)$

$2(3 + i)$ produces a **stretching effect** from $(3 + i)$ to $6 + 2i$.

$i(3 + i)$ produces **a rotation** of $90°$ from $(3 + i)$ to $-1 + 3i$.

$2(3 + i) + i(3 + i) = 6 + 2i + 3i - 1$

$\qquad\qquad\qquad\qquad = 5 + 5i$

This combines both transformations.

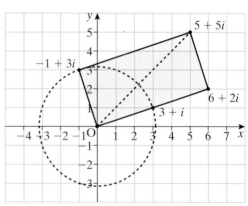

Example 1

(i) Plot the complex numbers $z_1 = 3 + 2i$, $z_2 = 3 + 3i$, $z_3 = 4 + 2i$ on the Argand diagram.

(ii) Using the same axes, plot the complex numbers $3z_1$, $3z_2$ and $3z_3$.

(iii) Plot the rotation $z_1(i)^2$, $z_2(i)^2$ and $z_3(i)^2$.

(iv) The complex numbers $4 - i, 4, 5 - i$ are the images of z_1, z_2, z_3 by the translation $a + bi$. Find the values of a and b.

(i)

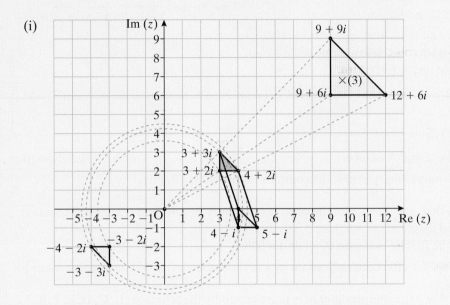

(ii) If $z_1 = 3 + 2i$, $3z_1 = 9 + 6i$

If $z_2 = 3 + 3i$, $3z_2 = 9 + 9i$

If $z_3 = 4 + 2i$, $3z_3 = 12 + 6i$

(iii) $z_1(i)^2 = (3 + 2i)(-1) = -3 - 2i$

$z_2(i)^2 = (3 + 3i)(-1) = -3 - 3i$

$z_3(i)^2 = (4 + 2i)(-1) = -4 - 2i$

(iv) $z_1 + a + bi = 4 - i$

$a + bi = 4 - i - z_1$

$a + bi = 4 - i - (3 + 2i)$

$= 1 - 3i$

$\Rightarrow\quad a = 1, b = -3$

[Checking z_3: $4 + 2i + (1 - 3i) = 5 - i$ ... which is correct.]

Example 2

Describe the transformation in each of the following:

(i) $z_1, z_2 \longrightarrow z_3, z_4$

(ii) $z_1, z_2 \longrightarrow z_5, z_6$

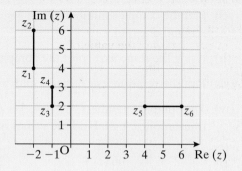

Solution:

(i) $z_1, z_2 \longrightarrow z_3, z_4$

a contraction by $\frac{1}{2}$

$\therefore \quad z_3 = \left(\frac{1}{2}\right)z_1$

(ii) $z_1, z_2 \longrightarrow z_5, z_6$

a rotation clockwise by $90°$

$\therefore \quad z_5 = (-i)z_1$

Exercise 1.5

1. Plot the complex numbers $z_1 = 1 + i, z_2 = 3 + 2i, z_3 = 4 - i$ on an Argand diagram. On the same diagram, plot the complex numbers $3z_1, 3z_2, 3z_3$.

2. Given that $z_1 = 2 - i$, plot the complex numbers $3z_1, 4z_1$ and $-2z_1$ on the same Argand diagram.

   State the feature common to all of the points $z_1, 3z_1, 4z_1$ and $-2z_1$.

   Describe the effect multiplication, by a real number, has on these complex numbers.

3. Write down the complex numbers represented by the letters A, B, C, D, E, F, N.

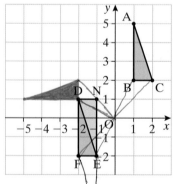

   (i) What transformation in the complex plane moves the triangle ABC onto DEF?
   (ii) Copy this diagram and indicate the image of ABC by the transformation (ABC)(i).
   (iii) What rotation followed by a translation is needed to transform ABC onto DEN?

4. Plot the complex numbers, $z_1 = 4 + i, z_2 = 7 + 2i, z_3 = 5 + 5i$.

   If $w = -3 - 4i$, plot the complex numbers $z_1 + w, z_2 + w, z_3 + w$.

   State the transformation generated here.

5. Plot the complex number (i) $z_1 = 6 - 2i$ (ii) $z_2 = (z_1)i$ (iii) $z_3 = (z_1)i^2$.
   What transformation is created by this multiplication?

6. Given that
   (i) $z_2 = a\,z_1$, find the value of a
   (ii) $z_3 = b\,z_1$, find the value of b
   (iii) $z_4 = c\,z_1$, find the value of c.

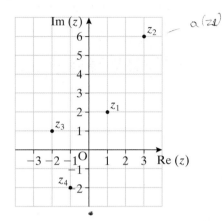

7. Copy this diagram and plot the complex number, w.

   Plot the complex number, $-w$, and hence plot the complex number $z - w$.

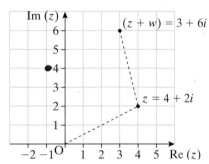

8. Describe each of the following transformations of the complex plane.
   (i) $z \longrightarrow z + k$, where $k = a + bi$.
   (ii) $z \longrightarrow k\,z$, where $k \in R, k \neq 0$.
   (iii) $z \longrightarrow k\,z$, where $k \in C, k \neq 0$.

9. A rectangle is represented in the complex plane by the numbers z_1, z_2, z_3, z_4.

   Copy this diagram and mark in the diagram the image of this rectangle under the following transformations
   (i) $z \longrightarrow 2z$
   (ii) $z \longrightarrow (i)z$
   (iii) $z \longrightarrow (2 + i)z$

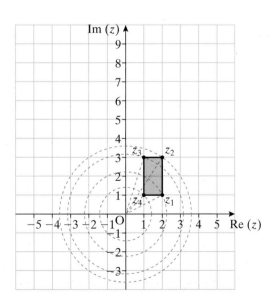

21

10. A triangle formed by the complex numbers z_1, z_2, z_3 is shown in the diagram.

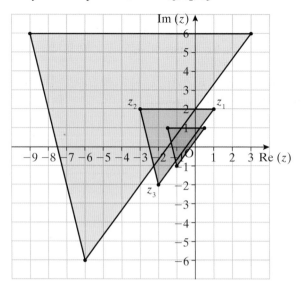

Describe the transformations needed to create the other triangles.

Section 1.6 Conjugate roots theorem _____

When dealing with complex numbers, it is usual to use z instead of x as a variable. The quadratic equation then takes the form $az^2 + bz + c = 0$.

Consider the quadratic equation $z^2 + 2z + 2 = 0$.

Using the quadratic formula where $a = 1, b = 2$ and $c = 2$.

$$\Rightarrow z = \frac{-b \pm \sqrt{b^2 - 4ac}}{2a}$$

$$= \frac{-2 \pm \sqrt{2^2 - 4(1)(2)}}{2(1)}$$

$$= \frac{-2 \pm \sqrt{-4}}{2} = \frac{-2 \pm 2i}{2} = -1 \pm i$$

The roots of this equation are $z_1 = -1 + i$ and $z_2 = -1 - i$ which we note are the complex conjugates of each other.

The sum of the roots $= (-1 + i) + (-1 - i) = -2$ (a real number).

The product of the roots $= (-1 + i)(-1 - i) = 1 + i - i - i^2$
$$= 1 + 1$$
$$= 2 \text{ (a real number)}.$$

$\therefore \quad z^2 - (\text{Sum of roots})z + (\text{Product of roots}) = z^2 - (-2)z + 2 = 0$
$$= z^2 + 2z + 2 = 0.$$

Therefore, the roots of a quadratic equation with real coefficients occur in conjugate pairs.

Example 1

If $z = 1 + 5i$ is a root of the equation $az^2 + bz + c = 0$, where $a, b, c \in R$, find a possible set of values for values of a, b, c.

Given $1 + 5i$ is one root and since the coefficients are real, therefore the roots occur in conjugate pairs; the other root is $1 - 5i$.

$\therefore$ the two roots are $1 + 5i$ and $1 - 5i$

$\therefore$ $z^2 - (\text{Sum of roots})z + \text{Product of roots} = 0$

$\Rightarrow$ $z^2 - (1 + 5i + 1 - 5i)z + (1 + 5i)(1 - 5i) = 0$

$\Rightarrow$ $z^2 - 2z + 1 - \cancel{5i} + \cancel{5i} - 25i^2 = 0$

$z^2 - 2z + 26 = 0$

$\therefore$ $a = 1, b = -2$ and $c = 26$

Example 2

Given that $z = 2 + i$ is a root of $z^2 - 4z + 5 = 0$, show that $\bar{z}$ is also a root.

$z = 2 + i \Rightarrow \bar{z} = 2 - i$

Since $f(z) = z^2 - 4z + 5 = 0$

$\Rightarrow$ $f(2 - i) = (2 - i)^2 - 4(2 - i) + 5$

$= 4 - \cancel{4i} + i^2 - 8 + \cancel{4i} + 5$

$= 4 - 1 - 8 + 5 = 0$

$\therefore$ $2 - i$ is also a root of $z^2 - 4z + 5 = 0$.

We can now generalise this result to include all polynomials with real coefficients and state the conjugate roots theorem as follows:

Conjugate roots theorem

If z is a root of $az^n + bz^{n-1} + \ldots dz + c = 0$ where $a, b, c, d, \ldots$ are all $\in R$, then $\bar{z}$ is also a root of this equation.

Example 3

Given that $z = 1 + 2i$ is a root of $z^3 - z^2 + 3z + 5 = 0$, show that $\bar{z}$ is also a root. Hence find the third root.

Since the coefficients are real, $z = 1 + 2i$ is a root

$\Rightarrow$ $\bar{z} = 1 - 2i$ is also a root.

Proof: $f(z) = z^3 - z^2 - 3z + 5$

$$f(1 - 2i) = (1 - 2i)^3 - (1 - 2i)^2 + 3(1 - 2i) + 5$$
$$= -11 + 2i - (-3 - 4i) + 3 - 6i + 5$$
$$= -\cancel{11} + \cancel{2i} + \cancel{3} + \cancel{4i} + \cancel{3} - \cancel{6i} + \cancel{5}$$
$$= 0$$

$\therefore$ $1 - 2i$ is also a root.

If $1 + 2i$ and $1 - 2i$ are roots $\Rightarrow z^2 - (1 + 2i + 1 - 2i)z + (1 + 2i)(1 - 2i) = 0$

$\Rightarrow z^2 - 2z + 5 = 0$ is a quadratic equation formed from two of the roots.

$\therefore$ The third factor can be obtained by dividing the cubic expression by the quadratic expression.

$$
\begin{array}{r}
z + 1 \\
z^2 - 2z + 5 \overline{)\, z^3 - z^2 + 3z + 5} \\
\underline{z^3 - 2z^2 + 5z} \\
z^2 - 2z + 5 \\
\underline{z^2 - 2z + 5} \\
0
\end{array}
$$

or $(z + a)(z^2 - 2z + 5)$
$\equiv z^3 - z^2 + 3z + 5$

$\Rightarrow$ $5a \equiv 5 \dots$ equating coefficients

$a = 1$

$\therefore$ $(z + 1)$ *is the third factor*

$\therefore$ $z + 1 = 0$

and $z = -1$ is the third root.

$\therefore$ $(z + 1) = 0$

and $z = -1$ is the third root.

Exercise 1.6

1. Show that $-2 + 4i$ is a root of the equation $z^2 + 4z + 20 = 0$ and write down the second root.

2. Solve these equations, giving your answers in the form $a \pm bi, a, b \in R$.
   (i) $z^2 - 2z + 17 = 0$　　　　　　(ii) $z^2 + 4z + 7 = 0$

3. Form a quadratic equation, given a pair of roots in each case.
   (i) $1 \pm 3i$　　　　(ii) $-2 \pm i$　　　　(iii) $4 \pm 2i$　　　　(iv) $\pm 5i$

4. If $z = 4 - i$ is a root of the equation $z^2 - 8z + 17 = 0$, show that $\bar{z}$ is also a root.

5. Show that $-2 + 2i$ is a root of the equation $z^3 + 3z^2 + 4z - 8 = 0$ and find the other roots.

6. Given that $2 + 3i$ is one root of the equation $2z^3 - 9z^2 + 30z - 13 = 0$, find the other two roots.

7. Show that $1 + 2i$ is a root of the equation $z^2 + (-1 + 5i)z + 14 - 7i = 0$. Show also that the conjugate $1 - 2i$ is not a root of this equation. Explain why.

8. $\dfrac{1 + 2i}{1 - 2i}$ is a root of $az^2 + bz + 5 = 0$, where $a, b \in R$. Find a value for a and for b.

9. Given that $z^3 - 1 = (z - 1)(z^2 + az + b)$, find a and b and hence solve the equation $z^3 - 1 = 0$, giving the complex roots in the form $a + bi$.

10. Form the quadratic equation whose roots are $-2 \pm i$. If $-2 + i$ is a root of $z^3 + z^2 - 7z - 15 = 0$, find the other two roots.

11. Form the quadratic equation whose roots are $-3 \pm 2i$.

    Hence form the cubic equation whose roots are $-3 \pm 2i$ and 2.

12. Form a cubic equation with real coefficients, two of whose roots are 2 and $-1 + i$.

13. The roots of the equation $z = 1^{\frac{1}{3}}$ are called the cube roots of unity.
    If these roots are $1, \alpha, \beta$, find α and β and prove that

    Hint: see Q9.

    (i) $\alpha^2 = \beta$ (ii) $1 + \alpha + \beta = 0$

Section 1.7 Polar form of a complex number

By studying this diagram, we can see that there are two ways to locate a point in the complex plane.

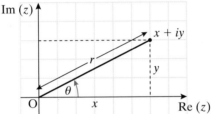

(i) Cartesian coordinates (x, y) or   (ii) Polar coordinates (r, θ)

$$\sin \theta = \frac{y}{r} \implies y = r \sin \theta$$

$$\cos \theta = \frac{x}{r} \implies x = r \cos \theta$$

Therefore, any complex number $x + yi$ can be written as $r \cos \theta + ri \sin \theta$.

$\implies x + iy = r(\cos \theta + i \sin \theta)$

We note also from the diagram that

(i) $r = \sqrt{x^2 + y^2}$ = modulus of the number

(ii) $\tan \theta = \dfrac{y}{x}$

    $\theta = \tan^{-1}\left(\dfrac{y}{x}\right), 0 \le \theta < 90°$, where θ is called the **argument** of the number.

> Rectangular form / Cartesian form: $x + iy$
>
> Polar form / Modulus argument form: $r(\cos \theta + i \sin \theta)$

Example 1

Express in the form $x + iy$ these complex numbers:

(a) $z_1 = 12\left(\cos \dfrac{\pi}{6} + i \sin \dfrac{\pi}{6}\right)$

(b) $z_2 = 5\left(\cos \dfrac{\pi}{8} + i \sin \dfrac{\pi}{8}\right)$

(a) $\cos \dfrac{\pi}{6} = \dfrac{\sqrt{3}}{2}$ and $\sin \dfrac{\pi}{6} = \dfrac{1}{2}$ ... (*Formulae and Tables*, p. 13)

$$z_1 = 12\left(\cos \dfrac{\pi}{6} + i \sin \dfrac{\pi}{6}\right)$$
$$= 12\left(\dfrac{\sqrt{3}}{2} + i \dfrac{1}{2}\right)$$
$$= 6\sqrt{3} + 6i$$

> 1. The argument of a complex number can be given in *degrees* or *radians*.
> $180° = \pi$ (3.1415....) radians
> 2. When using π use the *rad mode* on the calculator.

(b) $\sin \dfrac{\pi}{8} = 0.382$ and $\cos \dfrac{\pi}{8} = 0.924$

$$z_2 = 5\left(\cos \dfrac{\pi}{8} + i \sin \dfrac{\pi}{8}\right)$$
$$= 5[0.924 + i(0.382)]$$
$$= 4.62 + 1.92i$$

Example 2

Express $(-1 + i\sqrt{3})$ in the form $r(\cos \theta + i \sin \theta)$.

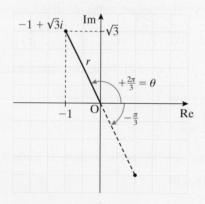

$r = \sqrt{x^2 + y^2} = \sqrt{(-1)^2 + (\sqrt{3})^2} = \sqrt{4} = 2$

$\theta = \tan^{-1}\left(\dfrac{y}{x}\right) = \tan^{-1}\left(\dfrac{\sqrt{3}}{-1}\right) = -\dfrac{\pi}{3}$ or $+\dfrac{2\pi}{3}$

$\left[\text{Note: } \tan\left(-\dfrac{\pi}{3}\right) = \tan\left(\pi - \dfrac{\pi}{3}\right) = \tan\left(\dfrac{2\pi}{3}\right) = -1.7321\right]$

By plotting the complex number, we see that the argument required is $\dfrac{2\pi}{3}$.

$\therefore \quad r(\cos \theta + i \sin \theta) = 2\left(\cos \dfrac{2\pi}{3} + i \sin \dfrac{2\pi}{3}\right).$

Note 1: When calculating the argument of a complex number, the principal value of θ is taken to be between $-\pi$ and $+\pi$, that $-\pi < \theta \leq \pi$.

Note 2: When using a calculator to find the argument (θ), it is important to check that the angle given by the calculator locates the correct quadrant for the particular complex number.

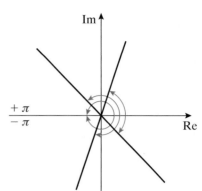

By first plotting the complex number on an Argand diagram, it can help to solve this problem.

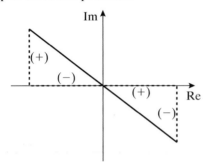

The tan ratio is negative in both 2nd and 4th quadrants.

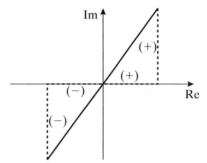

The tan ratio is positive in both the 1st and 3rd quadrants.

Example 3

Write the complex number $1 - i\sqrt{3}$ in modulus/argument form.

$x + iy = 1 - i\sqrt{3}$

Modulus $r = \sqrt{x^2 + y^2}$
$= \sqrt{1^2 + (-\sqrt{3})^2}$
$= \sqrt{4} = 2$

Argument $\theta = \tan^{-1}\dfrac{y}{x}$
$= \tan^{-1}\dfrac{-\sqrt{3}}{1}$
$= \dfrac{-\pi}{3}$

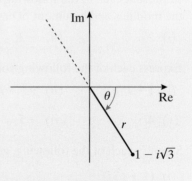

Since the complex number is in the 4th quadrant, $\dfrac{-\pi}{3}$ is the correct argument.

$\Rightarrow \quad (r, \theta) = \left(2, \dfrac{-\pi}{3}\right)$

$\therefore \quad 1 - i\sqrt{3} = \left[2\cos\left(\dfrac{-\pi}{3}\right) + i\sin\left(\dfrac{-\pi}{3}\right)\right]$

Example 4

Write $-\sqrt{3} - i$ in polar form.

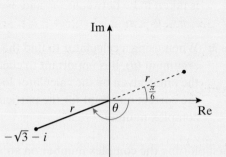

$$x + iy = -\sqrt{3} - i$$

Modulus $r = \sqrt{x^2 + y^2}$

$$= \sqrt{(-\sqrt{3})^2 + (-1)^2}$$

$$= \sqrt{3 + 1} = 2$$

Argument $\theta = \tan^{-1}\dfrac{y}{x}$

$$= \frac{-1}{-\sqrt{3}} = \frac{1}{\sqrt{3}}$$

$$= \frac{\pi}{6} \,(30°) \ ......$$

$\left(\begin{array}{l}\text{since the number is in the 3rd quadrant,} \\ \qquad \theta = \dfrac{\pi}{6} - \pi = \dfrac{-5\pi}{6}\end{array}\right)$

$$\Rightarrow \qquad \theta = \frac{-5\pi}{6}\,(-150°)$$

$$\therefore \quad -\sqrt{3} - i = 2\left[\cos\left(\frac{-5\pi}{6}\right) + i \sin\left(\frac{-5\pi}{6}\right)\right]$$

Exercise 1.7

1. Express each of the following in the form $a + bi$.

   (i) $4\left(\cos\dfrac{\pi}{2} + i \sin\dfrac{\pi}{2}\right)$

   (ii) $2\left(\cos\dfrac{5\pi}{6} + i \sin\dfrac{5\pi}{6}\right)$

   (iii) $\sqrt{2}\left(\cos\dfrac{3\pi}{4} + i \sin\dfrac{3\pi}{4}\right)$

   (iv) $2\left(\cos\dfrac{\pi}{3} + i \sin\dfrac{\pi}{3}\right)$

2. Represent each of the following complex numbers on an Argand diagram, indicating the modulus and argument of each number.

   (i) $2 + 2i$ (ii) $-3i$ (iii) 4 (iv) $-\sqrt{3} + i$

3. Express each of the following complex numbers in polar form.

   (i) $1 + i$ (ii) $\sqrt{3} + i$ (iii) $-2 + \sqrt{2}i$ (iv) $-2 - \sqrt{2}i$

   (v) $4i$ (vi) -5 (vii) $-3i$ (viii) $\dfrac{1}{2} - \dfrac{\sqrt{3}}{2}i$

4. Simplify each of the following, giving your answer in the form $r(\cos\theta + i \sin\theta)$.

   (i) $(1 + \sqrt{3}i)^2$ (ii) $\dfrac{-2}{-\sqrt{3} + i}$

5. If $z = 1 + \sqrt{3}i$, find the complex numbers:

   (i) iz (ii) i^2z (iii) i^3z

   Plot each of the numbers z, iz, i^2z and i^3z on an Argand diagram.

   Find the argument (θ) of each number: (i) z (ii) iz (iii) i^2z (iv) i^3z

   What geometrical observation can be made about multiplying a complex number by i?

6. Express each of the following in polar form:

    (i) $2i$ (ii) $-3 - \sqrt{3}i$ (iii) $\dfrac{2}{-1 + i}$

7. Solve the equation $z^2 - 2z + 2 = 0$ and express your answer in the form $r(\cos \theta + i \sin \theta)$.

8. Let $z_2 = t + 8i, t \in R$ and $i^2 = -1$. Given that $\arg(z_2) = \dfrac{3\pi}{4}$, find the value of t.

Section 1.8 Products and quotients of complex numbers in polar form

Consider the complex numbers $z_1 = r_1(\cos \theta_1 + i \sin \theta_1)$ and $z_2 = r_2(\cos \theta_2 + i \sin \theta_2)$.

Then $z_1.z_2 = r_1(\cos \theta_1 + i \sin \theta_1).r_2(\cos \theta_2 + i \sin \theta_2)$

$$= r_1r_2[\cos \theta_1 \cos \theta_2 + i \cos \theta_1 \sin \theta_2 + i \sin \theta_1 \cos \theta_2 + i^2 \sin \theta_1 \sin \theta_2]$$
$$= r_1r_2[\cos \theta_1 \cos \theta_2 - \sin \theta_1 \sin \theta_2 + i(\sin \theta_1 \cos \theta_2 + \cos \theta_1 \sin \theta_2)]$$
$$= r_1r_2[\cos(\theta_1 + \theta_2) + i \sin (\theta_1 + \theta_2)] \quad \text{... (Formulae and Tables, p. 15)}$$

$\Rightarrow$ Modulus of $z_1.z_2 = r_1.r_2$ and argument of $z_1.z_2 = \theta_1 + \theta_2$

Also, $\dfrac{z_1}{z_2} = \dfrac{r_1(\cos \theta_1 + i \sin \theta_1)}{r_2(\cos \theta_2 + i \sin \theta_2)}$

$$= \dfrac{r_1(\cos \theta_1 + i \sin \theta_1)}{r_2(\cos \theta_2 + i \sin \theta_2)} \times \dfrac{(\cos \theta_2 - i \sin \theta_2)}{(\cos \theta_2 - i \sin \theta_2)}$$

$$= \dfrac{r_1}{r_2} \dfrac{[\cos \theta_1 \cos \theta_2 - i \cos \theta_1 \sin \theta_2 + i \sin \theta_1 \cos \theta_2 - i^2 \sin \theta_1 \sin \theta_2]}{[\cos^2 \theta_2 - i\cos \theta_2 \sin \theta_2 + i\sin \theta_2 \cos \theta_2 - i^2 \sin^2 \theta_2]}$$

$$= \dfrac{r_1}{r_2} \left[\dfrac{\cos \theta_1 \cos \theta_2 + \sin \theta_1 \sin \theta_2 + i (\sin \theta_1 \cos \theta_2 - \cos \theta_1 \sin \theta_2)}{\cos^2 \theta_2 + \sin^2 \theta_2}\right]$$

$$= \dfrac{r_1}{r_2} \left[\dfrac{\cos(\theta_1 - \theta_2) + i \sin (\theta_1 - \theta_2)}{1}\right] \quad \text{... (Formulae and Tables, p. 15)}$$

$\Rightarrow$ Modulus of $\dfrac{z_1}{z_2} = \dfrac{r_1}{r_2}$ and the argument of $\dfrac{z_1}{z_2} = \theta_1 - \theta_2$.

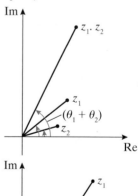

If	$z_1 = r_1(\cos \theta_1 + i \sin \theta_1)$
and	$z_2 = r_2(\cos \theta_2 + i \sin \theta_2)$,
then	$z_1.z_2 = r_1.r_2[\cos(\theta_1 + \theta_2) + i \sin(\theta_1 + \theta_2)]$
and	$\dfrac{z_1}{z_2} = \dfrac{r_1}{r_2} [\cos(\theta_1 - \theta_2) + i \sin(\theta_1 - \theta_2)]$.

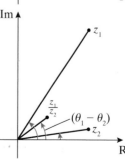

Note: $\dfrac{z_1}{z_2} = z_1\left(\dfrac{1}{z_2}\right) = \dfrac{r_1}{r_2} [\cos(\theta_1 - \theta_2) + i \sin(\theta_1 - \theta_2)]$

$\Rightarrow \quad \dfrac{1}{z_2} = \dfrac{1}{r_2} [\cos(-\theta_2) + i \sin(-\theta_2)]$

If $z = r (\cos \theta + i \sin \theta)$, $\dfrac{1}{z} = \dfrac{1}{r} [\cos(-\theta) + i \sin (-\theta)]$

If $z_1 = 2\left(\cos \frac{\pi}{4} + i \sin \frac{\pi}{4}\right)$ and $z_2 = 5\left(\cos \frac{5\pi}{12} + i \sin \frac{5\pi}{12}\right)$, find

(i) $z_1 z_2$ (ii) $\dfrac{z_2}{z_1}$ in the form $a + ib$.

(i) $z_1 z_2 = \left[2\left(\cos \frac{\pi}{4} + i \sin \frac{\pi}{4}\right)\right] \cdot \left[5\left(\cos \frac{5\pi}{12} + i \sin \frac{5\pi}{12}\right)\right]$

$= (2 \times 5)\left[\cos\left(\frac{\pi}{4} + \frac{5\pi}{12}\right) + i \sin\left(\frac{\pi}{4} + \frac{5\pi}{12}\right)\right]$

$= 10\left(\cos \frac{2\pi}{3} + i \sin \frac{2\pi}{3}\right) = 10\left(-\frac{1}{2} + \frac{\sqrt{3}}{2} i\right)$

$= -5 + 5\sqrt{3}i$

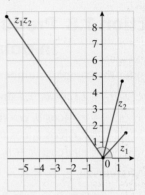

(ii) $\dfrac{z_2}{z_1} = \dfrac{5\left(\cos \frac{5\pi}{12} + i \sin \frac{5\pi}{12}\right)}{2\left(\cos \frac{\pi}{4} + i \sin \frac{\pi}{4}\right)}$

$= \left(\frac{5}{2}\right)\left[\cos\left(\frac{5\pi}{12} - \frac{\pi}{4}\right) + i \sin\left(\frac{5\pi}{12} - \frac{\pi}{4}\right)\right]$

$= \frac{5}{2}\left[\cos \frac{\pi}{6} + i \sin \frac{\pi}{6}\right] = \frac{5}{2}\left(\frac{\sqrt{3}}{2} + i \frac{1}{2}\right)$

$= \frac{5\sqrt{3}}{4} + \frac{5}{4} i$

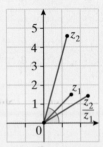

Note: the transformations using Argand diagrams.

Exercise 1.8

1. If $z_1 = 4\left(\cos \frac{3\pi}{4} + i \sin \frac{3\pi}{4}\right)$ and $z_2 = 2\left(\cos \frac{\pi}{4} + i \sin \frac{\pi}{4}\right)$, find

   (i) $z_1 . z_2$ (ii) $\dfrac{z_1}{z_2}$, giving your answer in the form $r(\cos \theta + i \sin \theta)$.

2. Given $z = 2\left(\cos \frac{\pi}{3} + i \sin \frac{\pi}{3}\right)$, find z^2 in the form $r(\cos \theta + i \sin \theta)$.

3. Given $z_1 = 3\left(\cos \frac{\pi}{2} + i \sin \frac{\pi}{2}\right)$ and $z_2 = 4\left(\cos \frac{\pi}{3} + i \sin \frac{\pi}{3}\right)$, find the modulus and argument of

   (i) z_1 (ii) z_2 (iii) $z_1 . z_2$ (iv) $\dfrac{z_1}{z_2}$

4. Multiply $4\left(\cos\frac{\pi}{6} + i\sin\frac{\pi}{6}\right)$ by $3\left(\cos\frac{\pi}{3} + i\sin\frac{\pi}{3}\right)$.

5. Divide $9\left(\cos\frac{5\pi}{6} + i\sin\frac{5\pi}{6}\right)$ by $6\left(\cos\frac{\pi}{3} + i\sin\frac{\pi}{3}\right)$.

6. Simplify $2\left(\cos\frac{\pi}{9} + i\sin\frac{\pi}{9}\right) \cdot \frac{1}{3}\left(\cos\frac{\pi}{9} + i\sin\frac{\pi}{9}\right) \cdot 6\left(\cos\frac{\pi}{9} + i\sin\frac{\pi}{9}\right)$, giving your answer in the form $a + bi$.

7. Simplify $\left(\cos\frac{3\pi}{7} + i\sin\frac{3\pi}{7}\right)\left(\cos\frac{2\pi}{7} + i\sin\frac{2\pi}{7}\right)^2$.

8. Simplify (a) $\left[2\left(\cos\frac{\pi}{3} + i\sin\frac{\pi}{3}\right)\right]^3$ (b) $\left[2\left(\cos\frac{\pi}{3} + i\sin\frac{\pi}{3}\right)\right]^4$

9. If $z = 3(\cos\pi + i\sin\pi)$, express $\frac{1}{z}$ in the form
    (i) $r(\cos\theta + i\sin\theta)$ (ii) $a + bi$.

10. Express $z = -2 + 2\sqrt{3}i$ in polar form.
    Hence express (a) z^2 (b) z^3 in (i) polar form   (ii) cartesian form.

11. Show that if $z = \cos\theta + i\sin\theta$, then $\frac{1}{z} = \bar{z}$.

12. Given $z.\left(\cos\frac{\pi}{4} + i\sin\frac{\pi}{4}\right) = 1$, find z in the form $a + ib$.

13. If $z = \cos\theta + i\sin\theta$, show that $z + \frac{1}{z} = 2\cos\theta$.

Section 1.9 De Moivre's theorem ─────────

In the previous section, we saw that

$$(\cos\theta + i\sin\theta)(\cos\theta + i\sin\theta) = \cos(\theta + \theta) + i\sin(\theta + \theta)$$
$$= \cos 2\theta + i\sin 2\theta$$

That is $(\cos\theta + i\sin\theta)^2 = \cos 2\theta + i\sin 2\theta$

Also $(\cos\theta + i\sin\theta)^3 = \cos 3\theta + i\sin 3\theta$

The general case of this result is known as **de Moivre's theorem**.

De Moivre's theorem $(\cos\theta + i\sin\theta)^n \equiv \cos n\theta + i\sin n\theta,$
                        for all real values of n.

Proof of de Moivre's Theorem by Induction

When n is a positive integer, prove $(\cos\theta + i\sin\theta)^n = (\cos n\theta + i\sin n\theta)$

(i) Let $n = 1 \Rightarrow (\cos\theta + i\sin\theta)^1 = \cos\theta + i\sin\theta \ldots$ which is true

(ii) Assume that $(\cos\theta + i\sin\theta)^k = \cos k\theta + i\sin k\theta$

(iii) Prove true for $n = k + 1$, i.e.,

$$(\cos\theta + i\sin\theta)^{k+1} = [\cos(k+1)\theta + i\sin(k+1)\theta]$$

Proof: $(\cos\theta + i\sin\theta)^{k+1} = (\cos\theta + i\sin\theta)^k (\cos\theta + i\sin\theta)$

$$= (\cos k\theta + i\sin k\theta)(\cos\theta + i\sin\theta)\ldots \text{assumed}$$

$$= \cos k\theta\cos\theta + i\cos k\theta\sin\theta + i\sin k\theta\cos\theta - \sin k\theta\sin\theta$$

$$= \cos k\theta\cos\theta - \sin k\theta\sin\theta + i(\cos k\theta\sin\theta + \sin k\theta\cos\theta)$$

$$= \cos(k+1)\theta + i\sin(k+1)\theta$$

Therefore, if it is true for $n = k$, it is true for $n = k + 1$.

But it is true for $n = 1$.

Thus, it is true for $n = 1 + 1 = 2$.

Therefore, the theorem is true for $n = 1, 2, 3, \ldots$ i.e. $n \in N$.

> If $z = r(\cos\theta + i\sin\theta)$, then using de Moivre's Theorem:
>
> $z^n = [r(\cos\theta + i\sin\theta)]^n$
>
> $\quad = r^n(\cos n\theta + i\sin n\theta)$ for all $n \in N$.

Example 1

Find the value of $\left(\cos\dfrac{\pi}{6} + i\sin\dfrac{\pi}{6}\right)^3$.

$$\left(\cos\frac{\pi}{6} + i\sin\frac{\pi}{6}\right)^3 = \cos\frac{3\pi}{6} + i\sin\frac{3\pi}{6}$$

$$= \cos\frac{\pi}{2} + i\sin\frac{\pi}{2}$$

$$= 0 + i = i$$

Example 2

Write $1 + \sqrt{3}i$ in polar form and hence find the value of $(1 + \sqrt{3}i)^9$.

$$x + iy = 1 + \sqrt{3}i$$

Modulus $r = \sqrt{x^2 + y^2} = \sqrt{1^2 + (\sqrt{3})^2} = 2$

Argument $\theta = \tan^{-1}\dfrac{y}{x} = \tan^{-1}\dfrac{\sqrt{3}}{1} = \dfrac{\pi}{3}$ ≈ 60

$\therefore \quad z = 1 + \sqrt{3}i = 2\left(\cos\dfrac{\pi}{3} + i\sin\dfrac{\pi}{3}\right)$

$\therefore \quad z^9 = (1 + \sqrt{3}i)^9 = 2^9\left(\cos\dfrac{\pi}{3} + i\sin\dfrac{\pi}{3}\right)^9$

$$= 2^9\left(\cos\dfrac{9\pi}{3} + i\sin\dfrac{9\pi}{3}\right)$$

$$= 2^9\left(\cos 3\pi + i\sin 3\pi\right)$$

$$= 2^9\left(-1 + i.0\right)$$

$$= -2^9 = -512$$

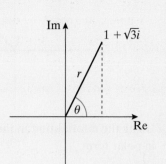

Im ▲ $1 + \sqrt{3}i$

r

θ Re

Exercise 1.9

1. Use de Moivre's theorem to simplify each of the following, expressing your answers in the form $a + bi$:

   (i) $\left(\cos\left(\dfrac{\pi}{8}\right) + i\sin\left(\dfrac{\pi}{8}\right)\right)^4$ (ii) $\left(\cos\left(\dfrac{\pi}{6}\right) + i\sin\left(\dfrac{\pi}{6}\right)\right)^7$

   (iii) $\left(\cos\dfrac{\pi}{12} + i\sin\dfrac{\pi}{12}\right)^8$ (iv) $\left(\cos\dfrac{2\pi}{3} + i\sin\dfrac{2\pi}{3}\right)^3$

   (v) $\left(\cos\dfrac{\pi}{4} + i\sin\dfrac{\pi}{4}\right)^{-6}$ (vi) $\left(\cos\dfrac{2\pi}{5} + i\sin\dfrac{2\pi}{5}\right)^{10}$

   (vii) $\left(\cos\dfrac{-\pi}{18} + i\sin\dfrac{-\pi}{18}\right)^9$ (viii) $\left(\cos\dfrac{\pi}{6} + i\sin\dfrac{\pi}{6}\right)^{-3}$

2. Given $z = \sqrt{2}\left(\cos\dfrac{\pi}{3} + i\sin\dfrac{\pi}{3}\right)$, express z^4 in the form $a + bi$.

3. Given $z = 3\left(\cos\dfrac{\pi}{10} + i\sin\dfrac{\pi}{10}\right)$, express z^5 in the form $a + bi$.

4. Express (i) $\left(\cos\dfrac{\pi}{3} + i\sin\dfrac{\pi}{3}\right)^2$ (ii) $\left(\cos\dfrac{2\pi}{3} + i\sin\dfrac{2\pi}{3}\right)^4$ in the form $\cos\theta + i\sin\theta$.

   Hence express $\left(\cos\dfrac{\pi}{3} + i\sin\dfrac{\pi}{3}\right)^2\left(\cos\dfrac{2\pi}{3} + i\sin\dfrac{2\pi}{3}\right)^4$ in the form $a + bi$.

5.

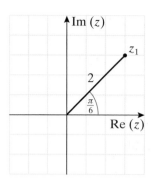
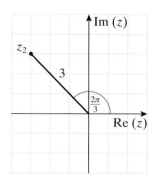

Using the information in the Argand diagrams above, express each of the following in polar form.

(i) z_1

(ii) z_2

(iii) $\bar{z}_1$

(iv) $\bar{z}_2$

(v) $z_1 . z_2$

(vi) $\dfrac{z_1}{z_2}$

6. Change each of the following to polar form and then use de Moivre's theorem to express your answers in the form $a + bi$:

(i) $(1 - i)^4$

(ii) $(1 + \sqrt{3}i)^3$

(iii) $(-2 - 2i)^4$

7. Find the value of $(1 + i)^4$.

8. Express $4 - 4i$ in polar form.

Hence find the value of $\dfrac{1}{(4 - 4i)^3}$.

9. Simplify (i) $(3 - \sqrt{3}i)^6$ (ii) $(2 + 2\sqrt{3}i)^6$.

10. Express $\dfrac{\sqrt{3} + i}{1 + \sqrt{3}i}$ in the form $r(\cos \theta + i \sin \theta)$.

Hence evaluate $\left(\dfrac{\sqrt{3} + i}{1 + \sqrt{3}i}\right)^6$.

Section 1.10 Applications of de Moivre's Theorem

Simplifying expressions of the form $(\cos \theta - i \sin \theta)^n$

de Moivre's theorem applies to $(\cos \theta + i \sin \theta)$ and not to $(\cos \theta - i \sin \theta)$.

However, since $-\sin \theta = \sin (-\theta)$ and $\cos \theta = \cos (-\theta)$,

then $\cos \theta - i \sin \theta = \cos (-\theta) + i \sin (-\theta)$.

Hence, $(\cos \theta - i \sin \theta)^n = [\cos (-\theta) + i \sin (-\theta)]^n$

$$= [\cos (-n\theta) + i \sin (-n\theta)]$$

Example 1

Simplify $\left(\cos \frac{\pi}{3} - i \sin \frac{\pi}{3}\right)^6$, giving your answer in rectangular form $(x + iy)$.

$$\cos \frac{\pi}{3} - i \sin \frac{\pi}{3} = \cos\left(-\frac{\pi}{3}\right) + i \sin\left(-\frac{\pi}{3}\right)$$

$$\Rightarrow \quad \left(\cos \frac{\pi}{3} - i \sin \frac{\pi}{3}\right)^6 = \left(\cos\left(-\frac{\pi}{3}\right) + i \sin\left(-\frac{\pi}{3}\right)\right)^6$$

$$= \cos\left(-\frac{6\pi}{3}\right) + i \sin\left(-\frac{6\pi}{3}\right)$$

$$= \cos(-2\pi) + i \sin(-2\pi)$$

$$= 1 + i.0$$

$$= 1$$

Expressing $\cos n\theta$ and $\sin n\theta$ in terms of $\cos \theta$ and $\sin \theta$

Example 2

Express   (a) $\cos 2\theta$ in terms of $\cos \theta$ (b) $\sin 3\theta$ in terms of $\sin \theta$.

(a) $\cos 2\theta$: $(\cos \theta + i \sin \theta)^2 = \cos 2\theta + i \sin 2\theta$

$$\Rightarrow \quad \cos 2\theta + i \sin 2\theta = (\cos \theta + i \sin \theta)^2$$

$$= \cos^2 \theta + 2i \cos \theta \sin \theta + i^2 \sin^2 \theta$$

$$\cos 2\theta + i \sin 2\theta = \cos^2 \theta - \sin^2 \theta + i(2 \cos \theta \sin \theta)$$

Equating real parts: $\cos 2\theta = \cos^2 \theta - \sin^2 \theta$

$$= \cos^2 \theta - [1 - \cos^2 \theta] \quad \ldots [\sin^2 \theta + \cos^2 \theta = 1]$$

$$\cos 2\theta = 2 \cos^2 \theta - 1$$

(**Note:** If we need $\sin 2\theta$, we equate the imaginary parts.)

(b) $\sin 3\theta$: $(\cos \theta + i \sin \theta)^3 = \cos 3\theta + i \sin 3\theta$

$$\Rightarrow \quad \cos 3\theta + i \sin 3\theta = (\cos \theta + i \sin \theta)^3$$

$$= \cos^3 \theta + 3i \cos^2 \theta \sin \theta$$
$$+ 3i^2 \cos \theta \sin^2 \theta + i^3 \sin^3 \theta$$

$$\ldots \text{(using a Binomial expansion)}$$

$$= \cos^3 \theta - 3 \cos \theta \sin^2 \theta$$
$$+ i(3 \cos^2 \theta \sin \theta - \sin^3 \theta)$$

Equating imaginary parts:

$$\sin 3\theta = 3 \cos^2 \theta \sin \theta - \sin^3 \theta$$

$$= 3[1 - \sin^2 \theta] \sin \theta - \sin^3 \theta \quad \ldots [\cos^2 \theta = 1 - \sin^2 \theta]$$

$$= 3 \sin \theta - 3 \sin^3 \theta - \sin^3 \theta$$

$$\sin 3\theta = 3 \sin \theta - 4 \sin^3 \theta$$

How to find the nth root of a complex number

If $z^n = a + bi \Rightarrow z = (a + bi)^{\frac{1}{n}}$, the nth root of $a + bi$.

Then (i) $z^3 = 1 + i \Rightarrow z = (1 + i)^{\frac{1}{3}}$, the cube root of $(1 + i)$

   (ii) $z^4 = 0 + 8i \Rightarrow z = (0 + 8i)^{\frac{1}{4}}$, the fourth root of $8i$.

To use de Moivre's theorem to find the nth root of a complex number, we need to express the complex number in **general** polar form.

Because the trigonometric functions cosine and sine are periodic functions, with period 2π,

$$\cos\theta = \cos(\theta + 2n\pi) \text{ and}$$
$$\sin\theta = \sin(\theta + 2n\pi) \text{ for } n \in Z.$$

$\therefore a + bi = r[\cos(\theta + 2n\pi) + i\sin(\theta + 2n\pi)].$

> Given $z = a + bi$,
> then $z = r[\cos(\theta + 2n\pi) + i\sin(\theta + 2n\pi)]$
> where $n \in Z$ is the **general polar form** of z.

Example 3

Solve the equation $z^3 = 8i$.

$$z^3 = 8i \Rightarrow z = (8i)^{\frac{1}{3}}$$

Modulus $r = \sqrt{x^2 + y^2}$

$$= \sqrt{0^2 + 8^2} = 8$$

Argument $\theta = \frac{\pi}{2}$

$\therefore 0 + 8i = 8\left(\cos\frac{\pi}{2} + i\sin\frac{\pi}{2}\right)$ ... in polar form.

$8i = 8\left(\cos\left(\frac{\pi}{2} + 2n\pi\right) + i\sin\left(\frac{\pi}{2} + 2n\pi\right)\right)$

... in general polar form.

$$\Rightarrow z = (8i)^{\frac{1}{3}} = 8^{\frac{1}{3}}\left(\cos\left(\frac{\pi}{2} + 2n\pi\right) + i\sin\left(\frac{\pi}{2} + 2n\pi\right)\right)^{\frac{1}{3}}$$

$$= 2\left(\cos\frac{1}{3}\left(\frac{\pi}{2} + 2n\pi\right) + i\sin\frac{1}{3}\left(\frac{\pi}{2} + 2n\pi\right)\right) \quad \text{... using de Moivre's theorem}$$

Let $n = 0$: $z = 2\left(\cos\frac{1}{3}\left(\frac{\pi}{2}\right) + i\sin\frac{1}{3}\left(\frac{\pi}{2}\right)\right) = 2\left(\cos\frac{\pi}{6} + i\sin\frac{\pi}{6}\right)$

$$= 2\left(\frac{\sqrt{3}}{2} + i\frac{1}{2}\right)$$

$$= \sqrt{3} + i$$

Let $n = 1$: $z = 2\left(\cos\frac{1}{3}\left(\frac{\pi}{2} + 2\pi\right) + i\sin\frac{1}{3}\left(\frac{\pi}{2} + 2\pi\right)\right)$

$$= 2\left(\cos\left(\frac{5\pi}{6}\right) + i\sin\left(\frac{5\pi}{6}\right)\right)$$

$$= 2\left(\frac{-\sqrt{3}}{2} + i\frac{1}{2}\right)$$

$$= -\sqrt{3} + i$$

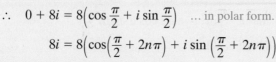

Let $n = 2$: $z = 2\left(\cos\frac{1}{3}\left(\frac{\pi}{2} + 4\pi\right) + i\sin\frac{1}{3}\left(\frac{\pi}{2} + 4\pi\right)\right)$

$\qquad = 2\left(\cos\frac{9\pi}{6} + i\sin\frac{9\pi}{6}\right)$

$\qquad = 2\left(\cos\frac{3\pi}{2} + i\sin\frac{3\pi}{2}\right)$

$\qquad = 2(0 + i(-1))$

$\qquad = -2i$

The cube roots of $8i$ are

$\qquad \sqrt{3} + i, \quad -\sqrt{3} + i, \quad -2i.$

Example 4

Solve the equation $z^2 = -2 - 2\sqrt{3}i$.

$z^2 = -2 - 2\sqrt{3}i \quad\Rightarrow\quad z = (-2 - 2\sqrt{3}i)^{\frac{1}{2}}$

Modulus $r = \sqrt{x^2 + y^2}$

$\qquad = \sqrt{(-2)^2 + (-2\sqrt{3})^2} = 4$

Argument $\theta = \tan^{-1}\frac{y}{x}$

$\qquad = \tan^{-1}\frac{-2\sqrt{3}}{-2} = \tan^{-1}\sqrt{3} = \frac{\pi}{3}$

Tan θ is positive in the first and third quadrants.

$\qquad\Rightarrow\quad \theta = -\frac{2\pi}{3}$

$-2 - 2\sqrt{3}i = 4\left(\cos\left(-\frac{2\pi}{3}\right) + i\sin\left(-\frac{2\pi}{3}\right)\right)$

$z = (-2 - 2\sqrt{3}i)^{\frac{1}{2}} = 4^{\frac{1}{2}}\left(\cos\left(-\frac{2\pi}{3} + 2n\pi\right) + i\sin\left(-\frac{2\pi}{3} + 2n\pi\right)\right)^{\frac{1}{2}}$

$\qquad = 2\left(\cos\frac{1}{2}\left(-\frac{2\pi}{3} + 2n\pi\right) + i\sin\frac{1}{2}\left(-\frac{2\pi}{3} + 2n\pi\right)\right)$

Let $n = 0$: $z = 2\left(\cos\frac{1}{2}\left(-\frac{2\pi}{3}\right) + i\sin\frac{1}{2}\left(-\frac{2\pi}{3}\right)\right)$

$\qquad = 2\left(\cos\left(-\frac{2\pi}{6}\right) + i\sin\left(-\frac{2\pi}{6}\right)\right) = 2\left(\frac{1}{2} - \frac{i\sqrt{3}}{2}\right) = 1 - \sqrt{3}i$

Let $n = 1$: $z = 2\left(\cos\frac{1}{2}\left(-\frac{2\pi}{3} + 2\pi\right) + i\sin\frac{1}{2}\left(-\frac{2\pi}{3} + 2\pi\right)\right)$

$\qquad = 2\left(\cos\left(\frac{2\pi}{3}\right) + i\sin\left(\frac{2\pi}{3}\right)\right) = 2\left(-\frac{1}{2} + \frac{i\sqrt{3}}{2}\right) = -1 + \sqrt{3}i$

$\qquad\therefore\quad z = 1 - \sqrt{3}i, \; -1 + \sqrt{3}i$

Exercise 1.10

1. Simplify each of the following, giving your answer in the form $a + bi$:

   (i) $(\cos \pi - i \sin \pi)^5$

   (ii) $\left(\cos \frac{\pi}{5} - i \sin \frac{\pi}{5}\right)^{10}$

   (iii) $\dfrac{1}{\left(\cos \frac{\pi}{3} - i \sin \frac{\pi}{3}\right)^3}$

   (iv) $\left(\cos \frac{\pi}{2} - i \sin \frac{\pi}{2}\right)^4$

2. Using de Moivre's theorem, express

   (i) $\sin 2\theta$ in terms of $\sin \theta$ and $\cos \theta$

   (ii) $\cos 3\theta$ in terms of $\cos \theta$.

3. Use the identity $(\cos 4\theta + i \sin 4\theta) = (\cos \theta + i \sin \theta)^4$ to show that

   (i) $\cos 4\theta = 8 \cos^4 \theta - 8 \cos^2 \theta + 1$

   (ii) $\sin 4\theta = 4 \cos^3 \theta \sin \theta - 4 \cos \theta \sin^3 \theta$.

4. Use de Moivre's theorem to solve the equation $z^3 = 8$.

5. Find the values of z for which $z^3 = -8$, giving your answer in $a + bi$ form.

6. Plot the point $2 + 2\sqrt{3}i$ on an Argand diagram.

   Use this diagram to express $2 + 2\sqrt{3}i$ in the form $r(\cos \theta + i \sin \theta)$

   Hence find the solution set of $z^2 = 2 + 2\sqrt{3}i$.

7. The complex number $z = 1$ is plotted on this Argand diagram.

   Write down the modulus and argument of this number.

   (a) Express $z = 1$ in general polar form and hence find the cube roots of unity, that is, find the values of z for which $z = 1^{\frac{1}{3}}$.

   (b) Prove that the sum of these roots is zero.

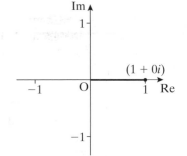

8. Find the cube roots of $27i$.

9. Use de Moivre's theorem to solve,

   (i) $z^2 = 1 + \sqrt{3}i$

   (ii) $z^2 = 2 - 2\sqrt{3}i$

   (iii) $z^2 = 4i$.

10. Use de Moivre's theorem to find, in polar form, the five roots of the equation $z^5 = 1$.

    Choose one of the roots w, where $w \neq 1$, and prove that $w^2 + w^3$ is real.

Revision Exercise 1 (Core)

1. Simplify $\sqrt{80} - \sqrt{20}$, expressing your answer in the form $a\sqrt{b}$ where $a, b \in \mathbb{N}$.

2. $(x - 1) + yi = y + 4i$; find x and y.

3. Solve the equation $z^2 + 4z + 3 = 0$, giving your answer in the form $a + bi$.

4. Given $z_1 = 5 + i$ and $z_2 = -2 + 3i$.
   (i) Find $(z_1)^2$ (ii) Show that $|z_1|^2 = 2|z_2|^2$

5. Let z be the complex number $-1 + \sqrt{3}i$.
   (i) Express z^2 in the form $a + bi$.
   (ii) Find the value of the real number p such that $z^2 + pz$ is real.

6. Express the complex number $z = 1 + i$ in the form $r(\cos\theta + i\sin\theta)$ and hence find a value for z^4 in the form $p + qi$ where $p, q \in \mathbb{R}$.

7. Express $-1 + \sqrt{3}i$ in the form $r(\cos\theta + i\sin\theta)$.

8. Show that $2 + 3i$ is a root of $z^2 - 4z + 13 = 0$.
   Hence find the other root.

9. If $z_1 = 2 + 3i$ and $z_2 = 1 - 4i$, investigate if $|z_1|.|z_2| = |z_1.z_2|$

10. Write $\dfrac{5 - 5i}{2 + i}$ in the form $a + bi, a, b \in \mathbb{R}$.

11. Simplify $4i^{13} + 3i^3$.

12. Given that $f(z)$ has roots $z_1 = 2 + 3i$ and $z_2 = -1 + 4i$, find $f(z)$.

13. Plot the complex numbers $a = 3 + 3i$ and $b = 1 - 2i$ on an Argand diagram.
    Plot the complex number $a + b$ on the same diagram.
    Find the complex number, c, that would translate
    (i) a to $a + b$ (ii) b to $a + b$ (iii) a to b.

14. In this diagram, describe the transformations needed for these:
    (i) $R \rightarrow S$
    (ii) $S \rightarrow T$
    (iii) If $z \in R$, find z_1 so that $zz_1 \in S$.
    (iv) If $z \in R$, find z_3
    so that $zz_1 + z_3 \in T$.

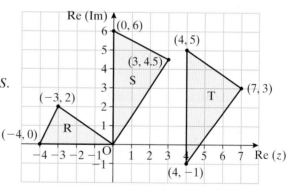

Revision Exercise 1 (Advanced)

1. If $z = x + iy$ and $3(z - 1) = i(z + 1)$, find the value of x and the value of y.

2. Given that $2 + 3i$ is a root of $2z^3 - 9z^2 + 30z - 13 = 0$, find the other two roots.

3. Express $\sqrt{3} + i$ in the form $r(\cos\theta + i\sin\theta)$.
   Use de Moivre's theorem to simplify $(\sqrt{3} + i)^{11}$.

4. The roots of the quadratic equation $z^2 + pz + q = 0$ are $1 + i$ and $4 + 3i$. Find the values of p and q.

5. If $w_1 = -\dfrac{1}{2} + \dfrac{\sqrt{3}}{2}i$ and $w_2 = (w_1)^2$, find w_2.

   Prove that $w_1 + w_2 = -1$.

6. If $p = 2\left(\cos \dfrac{\pi}{3} + i \sin \dfrac{\pi}{3}\right)$, find $\bar{p}$, the complex conjugate of p. Prove that $p\bar{p}$ is a real number.

7. Express $\dfrac{(1 + 2i)^2}{1 - i}$ in the form $a + bi$.

8. Find the value of k if the real part of $\dfrac{-3 + i}{1 + ki}$ is -3, $k \neq 0$.

9. Simplify $\left(\cos \dfrac{\pi}{3} + i \sin \dfrac{\pi}{3}\right)\left(\cos \dfrac{\pi}{12} + i \sin \dfrac{\pi}{12}\right)^2$.

10. Show that $1 + 2i$ is a root of the equation $z^2 - (3 + 3i)z + 5i = 0$ and find the other root.

11. Simplify the following expression giving your answer in the form $a + bi$, $a, b \in \mathbb{R}$:
$$\left(\cos \dfrac{\pi}{3} + i \sin \dfrac{\pi}{3}\right)^2\left(\cos \dfrac{2\pi}{3} + i \sin \dfrac{2\pi}{3}\right)^4$$

12. One of the roots of $z^3 + z^2 + 4z + \rho = 0$, where ρ is real, is $1 - 3i$. Find the value of ρ and the other two roots.

13. Given $x + iy = \sqrt{8 - 6i}$.
    By squaring both sides of this equation, use simultaneous equations to find the values of x and y.

14. Find the value of t for which ti is a solution of the equation
$$z^4 - 2z^3 + 7z^2 - 4z + 10 = 0.$$
    Hence find all the solutions of this equation.

15. Given that $\bar{z}$ is the conjugate of z and $z = a + bi$ where a and b are real, find the possible values of z if $z\bar{z} - 2iz = 7 - 4i$.

16. Determine the real p and q for which $(p + iq)^2 = 15 - 8i$.
    Hence solve the equation $(1 + i)z^2 + (-2 + 3i)z - 3 + 2i = 0$

Revision Exercise 1 (Extended Response Questions)

1. Given that $p = 3\left(\cos \dfrac{\pi}{6} + i \sin \dfrac{\pi}{6}\right)$ and $q = 2 - 2\sqrt{3}i$.
   (i) Find pq in the form $a + bi$.   (ii) Find $|p|, |q|, |pq|, |p + q|$.

2. The complex number $z = \dfrac{1 + i\sqrt{3}}{1 - i\sqrt{3}}$.

    (i) Express z in the form $a + bi$.   (ii) Plot z on an Argand diagram.

    (iii) Express z in the form of $r(\cos\theta + i\sin\theta)$.   (iv) Show that $z^3 = 1$.

3. The complex number $z = (1 + 3i)(p + qi)$, where p and $q \in R$ and $p > 0$.

    (i) Write z in the form $a + bi$.

        Given that the argument of $z = \dfrac{\pi}{4}$, show that $p + 2q = 0$.

    (ii) Given also that $|z| = 10\sqrt{2}$, find the values of p and q.

4. $z_1 = 3\left(\cos\dfrac{\pi}{6} + i\sin\dfrac{\pi}{6}\right)$ and $z_2 = \left(\cos\dfrac{\pi}{4} + i\sin\dfrac{\pi}{4}\right)$; find

    (i) $|z_1 z_2|$ (ii) $\arg(z_1 z_2)$ (iii) $|z_1|^2$

    (iv) $|z_2|^2$ (v) $\arg(z_1^2)$ (vi) $\arg(z_2^2)$

    (vii) Determine if each of the following statements is true or false for any two complex numbers $z, w \in C$.

        (a) $|zw| = |z||w|$ (b) $\arg(zw) = \arg(z) + \arg(w)$

5. If $z = 2\left(\cos\dfrac{\pi}{6} + i\sin\dfrac{\pi}{6}\right)$, find z^2, z^4 and z^6.

    (i) Plot z^2, z^4, z^6.

    (ii) Describe the transformation that occurs as z^2 is multiplied each time.

6. Express $\dfrac{\sqrt{3} + i}{1 + \sqrt{3}i}$ in the form $r(\cos\theta + i\sin\theta)$. Hence evaluate $\left(\dfrac{\sqrt{3} + i}{1 + \sqrt{3}i}\right)^6$.

7. Plot any two complex numbers z_1, z_2.
    By completing the parallelogram, find the complex number $z_1 + z_2$.
    Using this parallelogram, describe geometrically a proof for the triangle inequality $|z_1 + z_2| \leqslant |z_1| + |z_2|$.
    Under what conditions is $|z_1 + z_2| = |z_1| + |z_2|$?

8. z is said to be the reciprocal of w if $zw = 1$.

    (i) By letting $z = a + bi$ and $w = c + di$, find two algebraic relationships between the real parts and imaginary parts a, b, c and d.

    (ii) Using simultaneous equations, find a and b in terms of c and d.

    (iii) Prove that $\dfrac{1}{z} = \dfrac{\bar{z}}{|z|^2}$.   (iv) Plot z, $\dfrac{1}{z}$ and $\bar{z}$ on the same Argand diagram.

    (v) Prove that $\dfrac{1}{z}$ and $\bar{z}$ are always collinear with $0 + 0i$.

9. By letting $z = (a + bi)$, prove that:

    (i) the conjugate of a sum of complex numbers is equal to the sum of the conjugates

    (ii) the conjugate of the difference of complex numbers is equal to the difference of the conjugates

    (iii) the conjugate of a quotient of complex numbers is equal to the quotient of the conjugates.

    (iv) the conjugate of a product of complex numbers is equal to the product of the conjugates.

10. (a) Given $w = -1 + \sqrt{3}i$, where $i^2 = -1$.

    (i) Write w in polar form.

    (ii) Use de Moivre's theorem to solve $z^2 = -1 + \sqrt{3}i$, giving your answer in rectangular form.

(b) Four complex numbers z_1, z_2, z_3 and z_4 are shown on an Argand diagram. They satisfy the following conditions:

$$z_2 = i z_1$$
$$z_3 = k z_1, \text{ where } k \in R$$
$$z_4 = z_2 + z_3.$$

(Note: the same scale was used on both axes.)

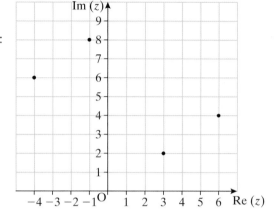

    (i) Identify which number is which by labelling each point in the diagram.

    (ii) Write down an appropriate value of k.

    (iii) State which condition helped to identify the numbers first. Explain your answer.   (Adapted from SEC *project maths* paper 1, 2011)

11. (a) (i) Write the complex number $1 - i$ in polar form.

    (ii) Use de Moivre's theorem to evaluate $(1 - i)^9$, giving your answer in rectangular form.

(b) A complex number z has a modulus greater than 1. The three numbers z, z^2 and z^3 are shown on an Argand diagram. One of them lies on the imaginary axis, as shown.

    (i) Label the points to show which point corresponds to which number.

    (ii) Find θ, the argument of z.

    (iii) Explain the significance of knowing that the modulus of z is greater than 1.

(c) Consider the complex number $z = a + ai, a > 1, a \in R$.

    (i) Find the complex numbers z^2, z^4, z^6, etc., giving your answers in rectangular form.

    (ii) Describe geometrically the pattern formed by $z, z^2, z^4, z^6, \ldots$ (Adapted from SEC *project maths* paper 1, 2010)

12. (i) Given $z = \cos\theta + i\sin\theta$, use de Moivre's theorem to write down an expression for z^k in terms of θ, where k is a positive integer.

(ii) Hence show that $\dfrac{1}{z^k} = \cos k\theta - i\sin k\theta$.

(iii) Deduce expressions for $\cos k\theta$ and $\sin k\theta$ in terms of z^k.

(iv) Show that $\cos^2\theta\sin^2\theta = \dfrac{-1}{16}\left(z^2 - \dfrac{1}{z^2}\right)^2$.

(v) Hence show that $\cos^2\theta\sin^2\theta = a + b\cos 4\theta$, where a and b are constants.

Geometry 2: Enlargements and Constructions

Key words

enlargement   object   image   vertex   scale factor   centre of enlargement

bisector   perpendicular bisector   incircle   median   centroid   circumcircle

orthocentre   equidistant

Section 2.1 Enlargements

In this diagram the rectangle A′B′C′D′ is an **enlargement** of the rectangle ABCD.

Here $|AB| = 3$ and $|A'B'| = 9$
       $|AD| = 2$ and $|A'D'| = 6$

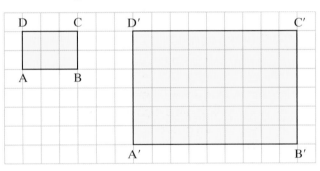

The sides of the rectangle A′B′C′D′
are three times as long as the sides
of the rectangle ABCD.
Here the **scale factor** is **3**.

Now consider the two triangles ABC and A′B′C′, shown below.

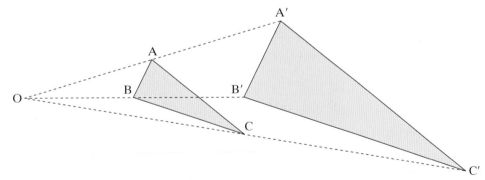

The triangle A′B′C′ is an enlargement of the triangle ABC.

The point O is called the **centre of enlargement**.

Since $|OA'| = 2|OA|$, the scale factor is 2.

Since the scale factor is 2, $|A'B'| = 2|AB|$, $|A'C'| = 2|AC|$ and $|B'C'| = 2|BC|$.

The given triangle ABC is called the **object**.

The triangle A′B′C′ is called the **image**.

The dotted lines are called guidelines or **rays**.

Drawing enlargements

To construct the image of a given figure under an enlargement, we need
  (i)   the centre of enlargement
  (ii) the scale factor of the enlargement.

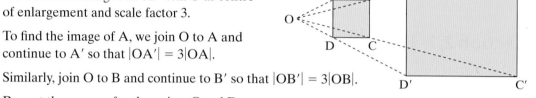

The diagram on the right shows a square ABCD and a centre of enlargement O.

We will now enlarge ABCD with O as centre of enlargement and scale factor 3.

To find the image of A, we join O to A and continue to A′ so that $|OA'| = 3|OA|$.

Similarly, join O to B and continue to B′ so that $|OB'| = 3|OB|$.

Repeat the process for the points C and D.

The square A′B′C′D′ is the image of the square ABCD.

Since the scale factor is 3, $|A'B'| = 3|AB|$ and $|A'D'| = 3|AD|$.

When a vertex is the centre of enlargement

The diagrams below show how to enlarge the shape ABCD by a scale factor of 2 using A as the centre of enlargement.

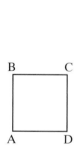 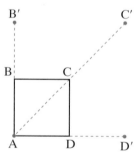 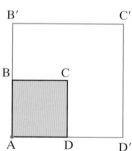

Notice that the centre of enlargement, A, does not move.

In the final figure, $|AB'| = 2|AB|$, $|AD'| = 2|AD|$ and $|AC'| = 2|AC|$.

The diagram on the right shows an enlargement where the centre of enlargement, X, is inside the figure.

In this enlargement, the scale factor is 2.

Draw the line [XA] and extend it so that $|XA'| = 2|XA|$.

Extend [XB] so that $|XB'| = 2|XB|$.

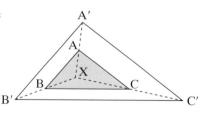

Repeat for [XC].

Each side of the enlarged triangle A'B'C' is twice the length of the corresponding side in ABC.

For any enlargement, the scale factor is found by dividing the length of the image side by the length of the corresponding object side.

> The scale factor is
> $$\frac{\text{length of image side}}{\text{length of corresponding object side}}$$

Enlargements with a Scale Factor less than 1

An enlargement with a scale factor less than 1 produces a smaller figure nearer to the centre of enlargement.

In the figure below, where A'B'C' is the image of ABC under an enlargement, the scale factor is $\frac{1}{2}$.

Thus $|OA'| = \frac{1}{2}|OA|$ and $|A'B'| = \frac{1}{2}|AB|$.

> If the scale factor is k, then
>   (i) if $k > 1$, the figure is enlarged
>   (ii) if $k < 1$, the figure is reduced.

When the scale factor is a positive fraction less than 1, the result is a reduction of the given figure.

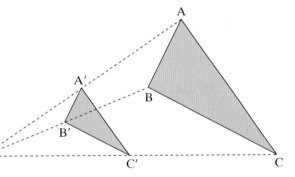

Finding the centre of enlargement

When a figure and its enlargement are given, then the centre of enlargement is found by joining two sets of corresponding points and continuing the lines until they meet.

In the diagram on the right, A'A and C'C meet at O.
The centre of enlargement is this point, O.

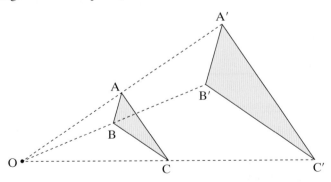

Example 1

In the given figure, AB'C' is an enlargement of the triangle ABC where A is the centre of enlargement.

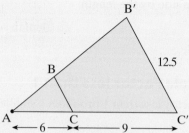

If |AC| = 6, |CC'| = 9 and |B'C'| = 12.5, find
  (i) the scale factor of the enlargement
 (ii) |BC|
(iii) the ratio |AB| : |AB'|.

(i) It may simplify your work if you draw the two triangles separately.

$$\text{The scale factor} = \frac{\text{image length}}{\text{object length}}$$

$$= \frac{|AC'|}{|AC|} = \frac{15}{6} = 2.5$$

(ii) Since the scale factor is $2\frac{1}{2}$, $|B'C'| = 2\frac{1}{2}|BC|$

$$|B'C'| = 2\frac{1}{2}|BC| \quad \Rightarrow \quad |BC| = \frac{|B'C'|}{2\frac{1}{2}} = \frac{12.5}{2.5} = 5$$

$$\therefore \qquad |BC| = 5$$

(iii) $|AB'| = 2\frac{1}{2}|AB|$

$$\therefore \qquad \frac{|AB'|}{|AB|} = 2\frac{1}{2} = \frac{5}{2}$$

$$\therefore \quad |AB'| : |AB| = 5 : 2$$

$$\Rightarrow \quad |AB| : |AB'| = 2 : 5$$

$$\frac{x}{y} = \frac{3}{4}$$
$$\Rightarrow \quad x : y = 3 : 4$$

Enlargement and area

The rectangle on the right is an enlargement of the rectangle on the left. The scale factor of the enlargement is k.

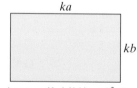

Area = ab Area = $(ka)(kb) = k^2ab$

The area of the enlarged figure is k^2 (area) of the given figure.

This illustrates an important general rule for all similar shapes.

When a figure is enlarged by a scale factor k, the area of the image figure is increased by a scale factor k^2.

Example 2

The figure P′Q′R′S′ is an enlargement
of the figure PQRS.
If the area of PQRS is 12 cm²
and the area of
P′Q′R′S = 48 cm², find the
scale factor of the enlargement.

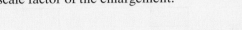
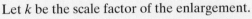
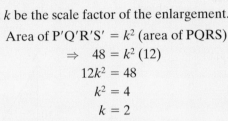

Let k be the scale factor of the enlargement.

$$\text{Area of P′Q′R′S′} = k^2 \,(\text{area of PQRS})$$
$$\Rightarrow \quad 48 = k^2\,(12)$$
$$12k^2 = 48$$
$$k^2 = 4$$
$$k = 2$$

∴   the scale factor of the enlargement is 2.

Example 3

Two similar triangles have areas 12 cm² and 27 cm², as shown.

If the base of the smaller triangle is 6 cm,
find the base of the larger triangle.

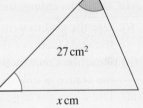

Let the scale factor of the
enlargement be k.

Area of larger triangle = k^2 (area of smaller triangle)

$$\Rightarrow \quad 27 = k^2(12)$$
$$\Rightarrow \quad k^2 = \tfrac{27}{12} = \tfrac{9}{4} \quad \Rightarrow \quad k = \tfrac{3}{2}$$

Length of larger side = k (length of smaller side)

$$\Rightarrow \quad x = 6k$$
$$\Rightarrow \quad x = 6\left(\tfrac{3}{2}\right)$$
$$\Rightarrow \quad x = 9 \text{ cm}$$

Length of base of larger triangle = 9 cm

Exercise 2.1

1. The diagram on the right shows a figure and its enlargement.

    (i) Use the grid to write down the scale factor of the enlargement.
    (ii) The lengths of two sides are given. Find the lengths of the sides marked x and y.
    (iii) If the scale factor is k, verify that the area of the enlarged figure is k^2 times the original figure.

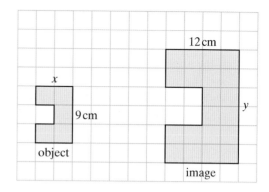

2. In the given diagram, the triangle $A'B'C'$ is the image of the triangle ABC under an enlargement with centre O and scale factor 2.

    If $|BC| = 4$, $|AC| = 6$ and $|A'B'| = 10$, find

    (i) $|B'C'|$ (ii) $|A'C'|$ (iii) $|AB|$.

    If the area of $\triangle A'B'C'$ is 30 square units, find the area of the triangle ABC.

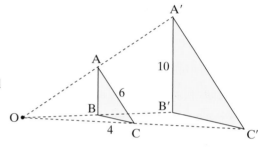

3. The given diagram shows the figure ABCD and its enlargement PQRS.

    (i) Use the grid to write down the scale factor of the enlargement.
    (ii) Describe how you would find the centre of enlargement.
    (iii) Use a straight edge to find the coordinates of the centre of enlargement.
    (iv) If the area of ABCD is 30 square units, find the area of PQRS.

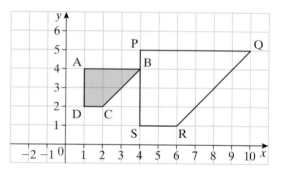

4. The triangle $AB'C'$ is the image of the triangle ABC under an enlargement with A as centre and scale factor $1\frac{1}{2}$.

    If $|AC| = 8$, $|B'C'| = 9$ and $|BB'| = 3$, find

    (i) $|AC'|$ (ii) $|BC|$ (iii) $|AB|$.

    If the area of $\triangle ABC = 20$ square units, find the area of $\triangle AB'C'$.

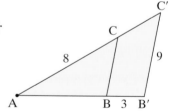

5. Make a copy of the given triangle PQR. Now draw an enlargement of the triangle with A as centre and scale factor 2.

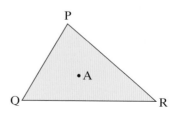

6. In the diagram below, the triangle X′Y′Z′ is the image of the triangle XYZ under an enlargement with O as centre.

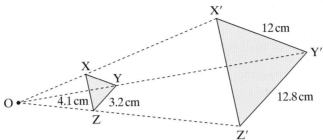

|YZ| = 3.2 cm, |XZ| = 4.1 cm, |X′Y′| = 12 cm and |Y′Z′| = 12.8 cm.

Find (i) the scale factor of the enlargement.
     (ii) |X′Z′|
     (iii) |XY|
     (iv) the ratio |OZ| : |ZZ′|
     (v) the area of the triangle XYZ if the area of the triangle X′Y′Z′ is 64 cm².

7. In the given figure, AB′C′ is an enlargement of the triangle ABC, where A is the centre of enlargement. If |AC| = 8, |CC′| = 12 and |B′C′| = 25, find

  (i) the scale factor of the enlargement
  (ii) |BC| (iii) the ratio |AB| : |AB′|
  (iii) the area of the △AB′C′ if the area of △ABC is 16 square units.

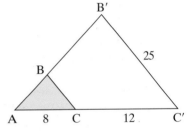

8. In the triangle ABC, XY∥BC and $\frac{|AB|}{|AX|} = \frac{3}{2}$.

If the area of the triangle AXY is 4 cm², find the area of the triangle ABC.

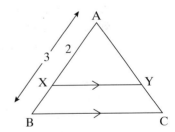

9. A design for a mosaic has an area of 176 cm².
The actual mosaic is an enlargement of the design with scale factor 2.5.
What is the area of the completed mosaic?

10. If you want to enlarge a photo so its area is multiplied by 4, what scale factor do you use for the enlargement?
What scale factor do you use if you want the area to be doubled?

11. The shapes shown on the right are similar.
Find the area of shape A.

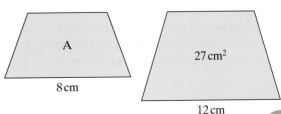

12. This diagram is reduced on a photocopier to $\frac{2}{3}$ of its original size.

   (i) If the height of the original diagram is 156 mm, how high will the reduced diagram be?

   (ii) If the label on the reduced diagram is 28 mm in height, find the height of the label on the original diagram.

13. The Eiffel Tower is 300 m high.
A model of the Eiffel Tower is 15 cm high and its base area is 25.5 cm². What is the base area of the actual tower?

14. A plan of a small garden is drawn to a scale of 1 : 25.

   (i) A pond covers 24 cm² on the plan. What is the area in m² of the real pond?

   (ii) The real lawn has an area of 17 m². What area in cm² will it cover on the plan?

15. The scale on a map is 1 : 1000.
Anna enlarges the map by a scale factor 2.

   (i) What is the scale for the enlarged map?

   (ii) On the original map, Anna's street is 6 cm long. What is the actual length of the street in real life? Give your answer in metres.

Sean borrowed Anna's original map and he enlarged it by a scale factor $\frac{1}{2}$.

   (iii) What is the scale on Sean's enlarged map?

   (iv) If the distance between two railway stations is 1 km, how far are they apart on Sean's enlarged map?

Section 2.2 Constructions

In your study of constructions for the Junior Cycle, you will have learned:
- How to bisect a line segment
- How to bisect an angle
- How to construct various triangles
- How to draw parallel and perpendicular lines.

In this section we will deal with seven new constructions that are on the Leaving Certificate course as well as the application of these constructions to real-life situations. For these constructions you will need a compass, straight edge and protractor.

When you use a compass you must leave the construction arcs as evidence that you have used the correct method.

1. Constructing an angle of 60°

Each angle in an equilateral triangle is 60°. We will now use this information to draw an angle of 60°.

> In an equilateral triangle, all the sides are equal in length.

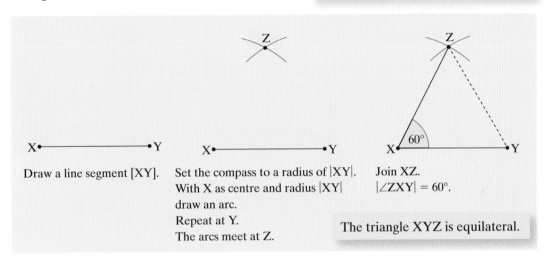

Draw a line segment [XY].

Set the compass to a radius of |XY|. With X as centre and radius |XY| draw an arc. Repeat at Y. The arcs meet at Z.

Join XZ. |∠ZXY| = 60°.

> The triangle XYZ is equilateral.

2. How to construct a tangent to a circle at a given point on it

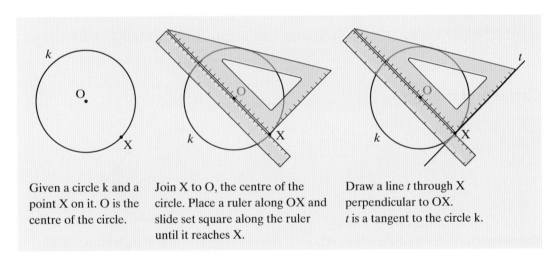

Given a circle k and a point X on it. O is the centre of the circle.

Join X to O, the centre of the circle. Place a ruler along OX and slide set square along the ruler until it reaches X.

Draw a line *t* through X perpendicular to OX. *t* is a tangent to the circle k.

3. How to construct a parallelogram, given the lengths of the sides and the measures of the angles

The instructions below show how to construct a parallelogram ABCD where |AB| = 3.5 cm, |AD| = 4 cm and |∠DAB| = 55°.

We first draw a rough sketch of ABCD.

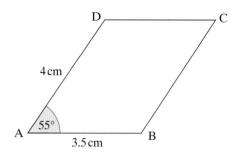

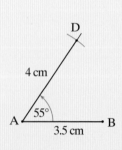

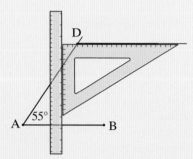

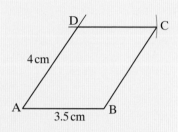

Draw a horizontal line [AB] = 3.5 cm. Use a protractor to measure an angle of 55° at A. Draw a line through A and measure |AD| = 4 cm.

Place set square along the line AB. Use a ruler to slide the set square up to the point D. Draw a line through D parallel to AB.

Use a compass with a radius of 3.5 cm (the same as |AB|) to draw an arc on the line. |DC| = 3.5 cm. Join BC. ABCD is the required parallelogram.

Circles and triangles

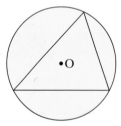

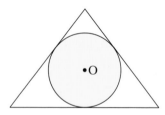

The **circumcircle** of a triangle is the circle which passes through the three vertices, as shown.

The centre, O, of this circle is called the **circumcentre** of the triangle.

A circle inscribed in a triangle such that all three sides touch the circle is called the **incircle** of the triangle. The centre of the incircle is called the **incentre** of the triangle. In the figure above, O is the incentre.

The construction of the circumcircle and incircle of a triangle will involve two constructions that you studied for your Junior Certificate examination.

The diagrams shown below will help you recall the steps involved in doing these constructions.

The perpendicular bisector of a line segment   The bisector of an angle

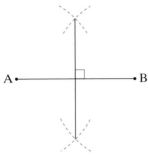

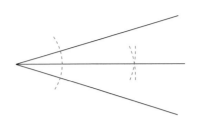

You should practise these constructions before attempting to draw the circumcircle and incircle of a triangle.

4. How to construct the circumcircle of a given triangle

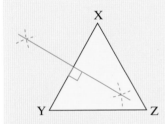

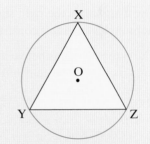

Construct the perpendicular bisector of [XY].

Construct the perpendicular bisector of [XZ]. The two bisectors meet at the point O, as shown.
O is the circumcentre.

With O as centre and |OX| as radius, draw a circle through X, Y and Z.
This is the circumcircle of the triangle.

5. How to construct the incircle of a given triangle

The construction of the incircle of a triangle involves constructing the bisector of an angle which is given on the previous page.

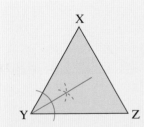

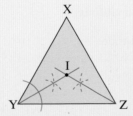

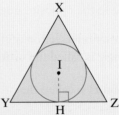

Construct the bisector of ∠XYZ, as shown.

Now construct the bisector of ∠XZY. The two bisectors meet at the point I.
I is the incentre.

Use a set square to draw a perpendicular from I to the line YZ.
The perpendicular meets YZ at H.
With |IH| as radius, draw a circle to touch the three sides.
This is the incircle of the triangle XYZ.

6. How to construct the centroid of a triangle

The line segment joining the vertex of a triangle to the midpoint of the opposite side is called a **median**.

In the triangle below, [XM] is a median.

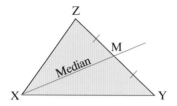

The point of intersection of the three medians of a triangle is called the **centroid** of the triangle.

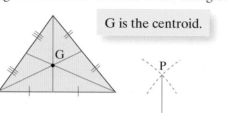

G is the centroid.

To find the midpoint of any line segment, we construct the perpendicular bisector of that line segment.

The diagram on the right should help you recall the steps involved in this construction.

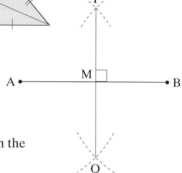

The three diagrams below illustrate the steps to be followed in the construction of the centroid of a triangle.

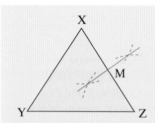

Construct the perpendicular bisector of [XZ], as shown. M is the midpoint of [XZ].

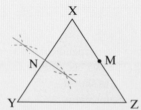

Now construct the perpendicular bisector of [XY]. N is the midpoint of [XY].

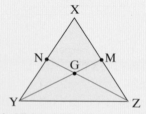

Join YM and ZN. They meet at the point G. G is the centroid of the triangle.

7. How to construct the orthocentre of a triangle

The perpendicular line segment drawn from the vertex of a triangle to the opposite side is called an **altitude**.

The point of intersection of the three altitudes of a triangle is called the **orthocentre**.

The point H is called the orthocentre.

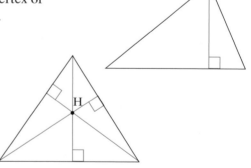

The diagrams below illustrate the steps involved in the construction of the orthocentre of a triangle.

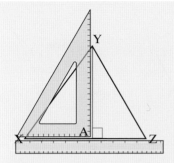 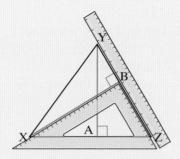 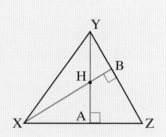

Place the ruler along XZ and use the set square to draw the line YA perpendicular to XZ.

Use the ruler and set square to draw the line XB perpendicular to YZ.

The lines YA and XB meet at the point H. H is the orthocentre of the triangle.

Applications of the given constructions

In the given diagram, the line ℓ is the perpendicular bisector of [AB].

Any point on this bisector is the same distance from A and B.

Thus |AX| = |XB|.

OP is the bisector of ∠AOB.

Any point on this bisector is equidistant from the arms of the angle. |XY| = |XZ|.

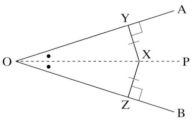

Take any three points X, Y and Z.
How do we find a point that is the same distance from all three points?

Construct the perpendicular bisectors of [XY] and [YZ].
Name these lines ℓ and m.
Any point on ℓ is equidistant from X and Y.
Any point on m is equidistant from Y and Z.
The lines ℓ and m intersect at K.
K is equidistant from X, Y and Z.

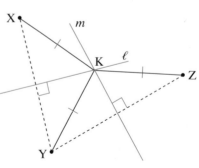

> Equidistant means 'the same distance'.

The **largest circle** that can be drawn inside a triangle is the **incircle**, that is, the circle that touches all three sides.

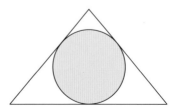

Exercise 2.2

1. (i) The diagram on the right shows a rough sketch of
        the parallelogram ABCD.
        Construct this parallelogram if its perpendicular
        height is 4 cm.
    (ii) Draw the diagonals [AC] and [BD].
        Does your construction verify that the diagonals
        bisect each other?
    (iii) Now prove that the diagonal [AC] bisects
        the diagonal [BD].

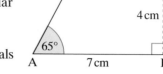

2. Draw the parallelogram ABCD in which the base [AB] = 4.5 cm, |BC| = 3 cm
    and |AC| = 6 cm. Measure ∠ABC.

3. Draw a triangle of sides 6 cm, 5 cm and 4 cm. Now construct the circumcircle of this
    triangle. Show all construction lines.

4. Draw the right-angled triangle, as shown on the right.
    Now construct the circumcircle of this triangle.
    What do you notice about the circumcentre of
    the triangle?

    Now draw any other right-angled triangle and
    construct the circumcircle.

    Did you get the same result as you got for the first triangle?
    What conclusion is suggested regarding the circumcentre of
    a right-angled triangle?

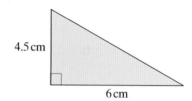

5. The diagram on the right shows a rough sketch of a
    triangle with sides 7 cm, 4.5 cm and 3.5 cm.

    Make an accurate drawing of this triangle and
    construct the circumcircle.

    You should find that the centre of the circumcircle
    is outside the triangle.

    What is the connection between the type of triangle
    you have drawn and the location of the circumcentre?

    Use the diagram on the right to explain why the
    circumcentre of an obtuse-angled triangle will always lie
    outside the triangle.

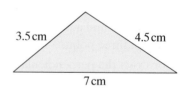

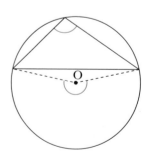

6. The diagram shows three villages, Drum, Moore and Tubber.
   The distances between the villages are shown.

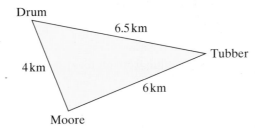

Drum
6.5 km
Tubber
4 km
6 km
Moore

Using the scale 1 cm = 1 km, make an accurate drawing of the diagram above.
It is planned to build a school that is equidistant from the three villages.
Show on your drawing where the school should be built.

7. Using a compass and ruler only, construct an angle of 60°.

8. Draw a triangle of sides 6.5 cm, 5 cm and 4 cm.
   Use the bisectors of any two angles of the triangle to find the centre of its incircle.
   Now draw the incircle.

9. ABC is a triangle with sides of length a, b and c, as shown.
   Its incircle has radius r and centre O.

   (i) Express the area of $\triangle BOC$ in terms of a and r.

   (ii) Hence show that the area of $\triangle ABC$ is
   $$\tfrac{1}{2}r\,(a + b + c).$$

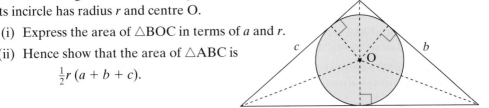

10. The line XD is the bisector of $\angle AXB$.
    K is a point on XD, KZ $\perp$ AX and KY $\perp$ XB.
    Show that the triangles XKZ and XKY
    are congruent.
    Hence show that $|KZ| = |KY|$.
    What conclusion can you come to
    regarding any point on the bisector
    of an angle?

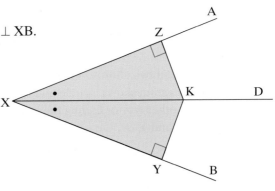

11. In the given diagram, p is a transversal intersecting two
    parallel lines ℓ and m.
    Draw a rough sketch to show the locations of the
    points X and Y, each of which is equidistant from
    the three lines.

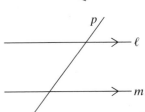

12. A campsite is in the shape of a triangle with busy roads running along all three sides of the site.
    The sides of the site are 110 m, 150 m and 170 m in length.

    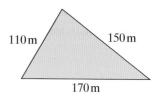

    (i) Using 20 m = 1 cm, draw a scaled diagram of this site.
    (ii) Show on the diagram the best position to pitch a tent so that it is as far away as possible from all three roads. Show your construction lines.

13. ABC is a right-angled triangle, as shown.

    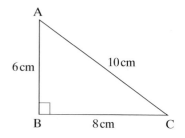

    (i) Write down the radius of the circumcircle without drawing and measuring it.
    (ii) Explain why the point B is the orthocentre of △ABC.

14. Draw any obtuse-angled triangle.
    Now construct the orthocentre of the triangle.
    Is the orthocentre inside or outside the triangle?
    Will this result hold for all obtuse-angled triangles? Explain why.

15. Draw a circle of radius 3 cm and mark the centre O. Mark a point X on this circle.
    Now use a ruler and set square to draw a tangent to this circle at the point X.

16. The given figure shows a circle and two chords [AB] and [CD].
    What can you say about the perpendicular bisector of [AB]?
    Now describe how these two chords can be used to find the centre of the circle.

    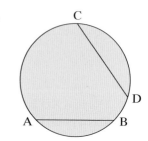

17. In Q16 we used two chords to find the centre of a circle.
    The given diagram shows a circle and two points on the circle.
    Describe another way of finding the centre of this circle using the points X and Y.

    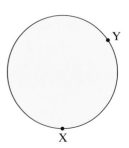

18. Construct an equilateral triangle of side 5 cm.

    (i) Now construct the circumcentre, O, of the triangle.
    (ii) Explain why O is also the incentre of the triangle.

Revision Exercise 2 (Core)

Note: For completeness several revision questions are based on the geometry that you have learnt in book 4. It is therefore advisable to revise Geometry 1 before proceeding with these revision questions.

1. The area of the parallelogram ABCD is 40 cm². If $|DB| = 15$ cm, find $|AE|$, where AE $\perp$ DB.

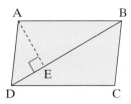

2. Gary, G, can just see the top of a radio mast, R, over a wall, W. Gary is 15 m from the wall. The wall is 45 m from the radio mast. The wall is 2.7 m high.

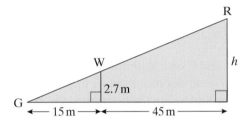

   Calculate the height of the radio mast, marked h on the diagram.

3. In the given triangles, the equal angles are marked.
   (i) Explain why the two triangles are similar.
   (ii) Find the values of x and y.

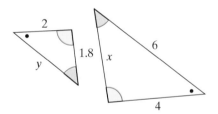

4. The triangle ABC has been enlarged positively and negatively as shown in diagram.
   (i) Find the scale factor used in each case.
      Calculate the area of the triangle ABC and hence
   (ii) deduce the area of triangles EFG and HIJ using the scale factors found in (i)

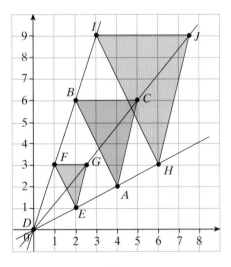

5. In the given circle, O is the centre.

    (i) Find the sizes of the angles marked x and y.

    (ii) Explain why a circle drawn on [AC] as diameter must pass through O.

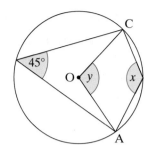

6. In the given figure, PQRS is a parallelogram. State whether each of the following is true or false, giving a reason for answer:

    (i) $|\angle TQR| + |\angle QRS| = 180°$

    (ii) $|\angle PQR| + |\angle RST| = 180°$

    (iii) $|\angle QTS| + |\angle QRS| = 180°$

    (iv) $|\angle QPS| + |\angle QRS| = 180°$.

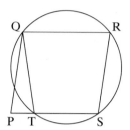

7. (i) Three people A, B and C on a shoreline see a boat at sea. The boat is the same distance from all three people. Describe how you would locate the position of the boat.

    (ii) In the triangle XYZ below, the angles XYZ and XZY are bisected.
If $|\angle YXZ| = 70°$, find $|\angle YPZ|$.

    (iii) Is P the incentre? Explain.

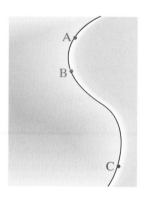

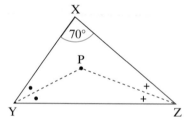

8. Draw a triangle of sides 5 cm, 6 cm and 7 cm.
Now construct the circumcircle of the triangle, showing all your construction lines.

9. In the given figure, AB′C′ is an enlargement of the triangle ABC, where A is the centre of enlargement.
If $|AC| = 8$, $|CC'| = 12$ and $|B'C'| = 15$, find

    (i) the scale factor of the enlargement

    (ii) $|BC|$

    (iii) the ratio $|AB| : |AB'|$.

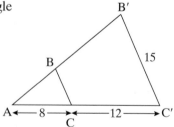

10. The height of a picture is $\frac{4}{3}$ its width. The picture is to be enlarged so as to have an area of 192 cm². Find the height and width of the enlarged picture.

Revision Exercise 2 (Advanced)

1. In the given triangles, the arrows indicate that the lines are parallel.
   Mark in the equal angles and hence use similar triangles to find the values of x and y.

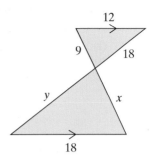

2. In the given figure, l, m and n are parallel lines.

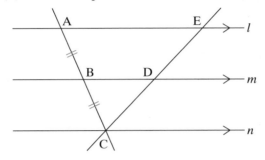

   (i) If $|AB| = |BC| = 7$ cm and $|CD| = 8$ cm, find $|DE|$.
   (ii) If $|AE| = 12$ cm, find $|BD|$.
   (iii) Explain why $\triangle ACE$ is an enlargement of $\triangle BCD$ and determine the scale factor and centre of enlargement.

3. In the given triangle ABC, I is the incentre and the radius of the incircle is 3 cm.
   What is the area of $\triangle BIC$?
   Hence find the area of $\triangle ABC$.

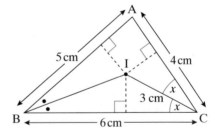

4. Shape B is similar to shape A.
   (i) What is the scale factor of the enlargement?
   (ii) Find a and b.
   (iii) A square of area 25 cm² is enlarged using a scale factor k. Find the scale factor k if the area of the enlarged square in cm² has the same numerical value as the perimeter of the enlarged square in cm.

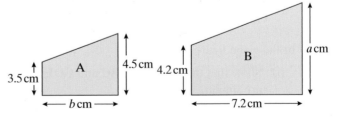

5. BC is parallel to DE.
   |AB| is twice as long as |BD|.
   |AD| = 36 cm and |AC| = 27 cm.

   (i) Work out the length of [AB].
   (ii) Work out the length of [AE].

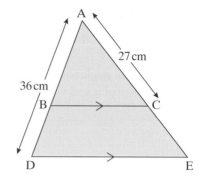

6. In the given circle, O is the centre and |AB| = 6 cm.
   The distance from O to AB is 4 cm and the
   distance from O to CD is 2 cm.
   Find the length of the chord [CD].

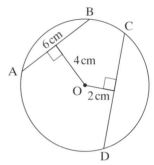

7. [PT] is a tangent to the semicircle with centre O. AOBP is a straight line.

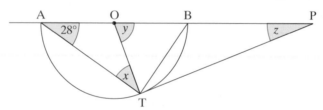

   If |∠TAO| = 28°, find the values of x, y and z.

8. (i) A ball of radius r cm has a surface area of 20 cm².
   Find, in terms of r, the radius of a ball with a surface area of 500 cm².

   (ii) The length of a rectangle is twice the width of
   the rectangle.
   The length of a diagonal of the rectangle is 25 cm.
   Work out the area of the rectangle.
   Give your answer as an integer.

9. In the given figure, AB ∥ DE.

   (i) Show that the triangles ABC and CDE
   are similar.
   (ii) If |AB| = 7 cm, |BC| = 6 cm, |AC| = 4 cm
   and |CE| = 12 cm, find |CD|.

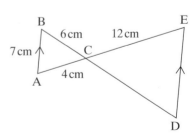

10. AOB is a diameter of the circle with centre O.
Find the values of x, y and z.

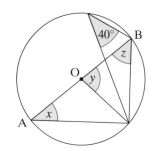

Revision Exercise 2 (Extended Response Questions)

1. (i) Plot the points $A(2, 2)$, $B(9, 2)$, $C(7, 7)$
   (ii) Show that the point $D(7, 4)$ is the orthocentre of the $\triangle ABC$.
   (iii) Show that $E(5.5, 3.5)$ is the circumcentre of the triangle and hence find the equation of the circumcircle.
   (iv) Construct the incentre F of $\triangle ABC$ showing all necessary construction lines.

2. In the given figure, JK $\parallel$ ML.

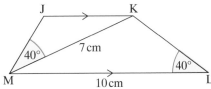

   (i) Explain why the triangles JKM and KML are similar.
   (ii) Find the length of [JK].
   (iii) An explorer wants to estimate the width of a river. He stands vertically opposite a tree growing on the other bank, at A, walks 50 m along the river bank to B where he places a stick, walks another 50 m to C, then walks at right angles to the river until he reaches a point D where the stick and the tree are in line. If $|CD| = 80$ m, how wide is the river?

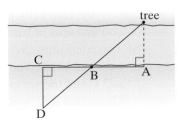

3. The lengths of the edges of two cubes are in the ratio $2 : 3$.

   (i) What is the ratio of their surface areas.
   (ii) If an edge of the larger cube is 12 cm, what is the length of an edge of the smaller cube?
   (iii) If the total surface area of the smaller cube is 54 cm², what is the total surface area of the larger cube?

4. In the given diagram [AB], [BC] and [CA] are tangents to the circle at P, Q and R respectively. If $|\angle BAC| = 70°$ and $|\angle BCA| = 50°$, find
   (i) $|\angle PRQ|$
   (ii) $|\angle BPQ|$
   (iii) $|\angle PQR|$.

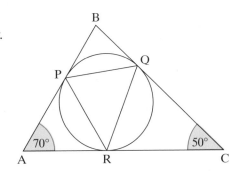

5. (i) *TP, TQ* are tangents touching the circle, centre *O*, at *P* and *Q*.
   (a) Find $|\angle POQ|$.
   (b) Explain why POQT is a cyclic quadrilateral.
   (c) Find $|\angle PTQ|$.

(ii) A class was asked to find the radius of a circular track laid out on the school playing field, without going inside the track or measuring the circumference. Pupils were allowed to use a 50-m tape besides their own mathematical equipment.

Sally went to a point outside the circle, used the tape to judge where the two tangents to the circle were, measured their lengths at 29 m and found the angle between the tangents to be 120°. What did she find the radius to be, and how far was she from the circumference of the circle? Can you suggest another method?

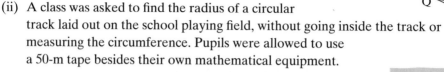

6. (a) [AB] is a chord of length 12 cm in a circle, centre O, of radius 8 cm, with [AC] as the diameter. Find
   (i) the distance of the centre of the circle from the chord [AB],
   (ii) the length of [BC],
   (iii) the distance from the centre of the circle to the chord [BC],
   (iv) the area of triangle ABC.
   (b) Two concentric circles (with the same centre) have radii 6 cm and 10 cm. The line ABCD cuts the first circle at B and C and the second at A and D. Given that $|BC| = 8$ cm, show that $|AB| = 4(\sqrt{5} - 1)$ cm.

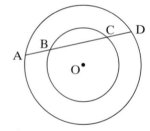

7. For the right-angled triangle shown:
   (i) Explain why $x + y = 24$.
   (ii) Write down two similar equations involving x and z, and y and z.
        Hence find x, y and z.
   (iii) Deduce the radius of the inscribed circle shown.

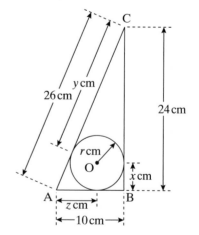

8. **(i)** AOB is a diameter of a circle, centre O.

$|\angle ABC| = 52°$.

    (a) Prove that OD bisects $\angle AOC$.

    (b) If AD and AC were joined, what is the size
of $\angle CAD$?

    (c) Prove that OD $\perp$ AC.

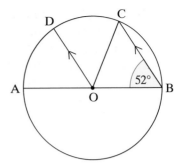

(ii) Two circles, with centres A and B, of radii 10 cm
and 17 cm respectively, intersect at P and Q,
where $|PQ| = 16$ cm.

How far apart are the centres of
the two circles?

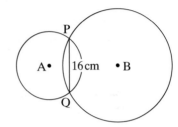

(iii) Prove that

    (a) the tangent at A bisects the line $[XY]$

    (b) $|\angle XAY| = 90°$

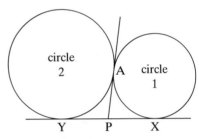

3 Integration

Key words

antidifferentiation   integration   integral   integrand   constant of integration
exponential function   velocity   acceleration   definite integral
indefinite integral   average value of a function   intervals

Section 3.1 Antidifferentiation

Consider the equation $y = x^2$.

Differentiating, we get $\dfrac{dy}{dx} = 2x$.

$2x$ is the derivative of the function $y = x^2$.

From this we can see that when given the derivative $2x$, we can write down the equation of the function, i.e. $y = x^2$.

The process of finding a function from its derivative is called **antidifferentiation**.

Now consider the functions shown: $y = x^2$, $y = x^2 + 1$ and $y = x^2 + 2$.

The derivative of each of these functions is $\dfrac{dy}{dx} = 2x$,

as represented by the line shown in red.

The expressions x^2, $x^2 + 1$ and $x^2 + 2$ are said to be **antiderivatives** of $2x$.

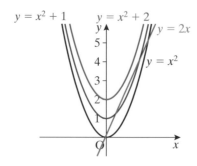

Starting with $\dfrac{dy}{dx} = 2x$, we have an infinite number of

possibilities for y, all of the form $y = x^2 + c$, where c is an unknown constant.

We use the notation $\int 2x\,dx = x^2 + c$ to state that 'the general antiderivative of $2x$ with respect to x is $x^2 + c$'.

$$y = \int dy$$

From the examples above, we can see that **antidifferentiation** is the reverse of differentiation.

Antidifferentiation is more commonly called **integration**.

> If $f'(x)$ is the derivative of $f(x)$, then $\int f'(x)\,dx = f(x) + c$.
>
> If $\dfrac{dy}{dx}$ is the derivative of y, then $\int \left(\dfrac{dy}{dx}\right) dx = y + c$.

Now consider the following functions and their derivatives:

$$f(x) = x^2 \Rightarrow f'(x) = 2x$$
$$f(x) = x^3 \Rightarrow f'(x) = 3x^2$$
$$f(x) = x^7 \Rightarrow f'(x) = 7x^6$$
....

Reversing this process, we have

$$\int 2x\,dx = x^2 \Rightarrow \int x\,dx = \tfrac{1}{2}x^2 + c$$
$$\int 3x^2\,dx = x^3 \Rightarrow \int x^2\,dx = \tfrac{1}{3}x^3 + c$$
$$\int 7x^6\,dx = x^7 \Rightarrow \int x^6\,dx = \tfrac{1}{7}x^7 + c$$
....

From this pattern, we can see that reversing the rule for differentiation produces a rule for integration as follows:

> In general, $\int x^n\,dx = \dfrac{x^{n+1}}{n+1} + c, \ n \neq -1$

In words

> To integrate a power of x, increase the power by 1 and divide by the new power.

Here are some useful results for integrating expressions that follow from the corresponding results for differentiation.

1. $\int af(x)\,dx = a\int f(x)\,dx$, that is, any constant factor may be taken outside the integral sign.

2. $\int (f(x) + g(x))\,dx = \int f(x)\,dx + \int g(x)\,dx$ ... integrate each term separately.

3. $\int a\,dx = ax + c$, since $\dfrac{d}{dx}(ax + c) = a$, where a is a constant.

To integrate a function $f(x)$ with respect to x, we write

$$\int f(x)\,dx.$$

We read this as 'the integral of $f(x)$ with respect to x'.

The function to be integrated, i.e. $f(x)$, is called the **integrand**.

Example 1

Find (i) $\int(3x^2 + 4x + 5)\,dx$ (ii) $\int(2x - 1)^2\,dx$.

(i) $\int(3x^2 + 4x + 5)\,dx = \dfrac{3x^3}{3} + \dfrac{4x^2}{2} + 5x + c$

$$= x^3 + 2x^2 + 5x + c \quad \text{... don't forget to include } c$$

(ii) $\int(2x - 1)^2\,dx = \int(4x^2 - 4x + 1)\,dx = \dfrac{4x^3}{3} - \dfrac{4x^2}{2} + x + c$

$$= \dfrac{4x^3}{3} - 2x^2 + x + c$$

Some expressions are not in the form ax^n or are not written as a sum or difference of functions of this form. In these cases, it is necessary to change the integrand so that each term is in the form ax^n.

Example 2

Find (i) $\displaystyle\int \dfrac{x^3 - 4x}{x}\,dx$ (ii) $\displaystyle\int \left(x^3 + \dfrac{1}{x^2} + \sqrt{x}\right)dx$ (iii) $\displaystyle\int \sqrt{x}(x + 4)\,dx$

(i) $\displaystyle\int \dfrac{x^3 - 4x}{x}\,dx = \int\left(\dfrac{x^3}{x} - \dfrac{4x}{x}\right)dx = \int(x^2 - 4)\,dx = \dfrac{x^3}{3} - 4x + c$

(ii) $\displaystyle\int \left(x^3 + \dfrac{1}{x^2} + \sqrt{x}\right)dx = \int(x^3 + x^{-2} + x^{\frac{1}{2}})\,dx$

$$= \dfrac{x^4}{4} + \dfrac{x^{-1}}{-1} + \dfrac{x^{\frac{3}{2}}}{\frac{3}{2}} + c$$

$$= \dfrac{x^4}{4} - \dfrac{1}{x} + \dfrac{2}{3}x^{\frac{3}{2}} + c$$

(iii) $\displaystyle\int \sqrt{x}(x + 4)\,dx = \int(x^{\frac{3}{2}} + 4x^{\frac{1}{2}})\,dx$

$$= \dfrac{x^{\frac{5}{2}}}{\frac{5}{2}} + \dfrac{4x^{\frac{3}{2}}}{\frac{3}{2}} + c = \dfrac{2}{5}x^{\frac{5}{2}} + \dfrac{8}{3}x^{\frac{3}{2}} + c$$

Finding the constant of integration

Each of the examples above contain an arbitrary constant c.
This arbitrary constant is generally called the **constant of integration**.
This constant of integration can be found if further information about the function is given.
This is illustrated in the following example.

Example 3

A curve with equation $y = f(x)$ passes through the point $(2, 0)$.
If $f'(x) = 3x^2 - \dfrac{1}{x^2}$, find $f(x)$.

$$f(x) = \int \left(3x^2 - \frac{1}{x^2}\right) dx = \int (3x^2 - x^{-2})\, dx$$

$$= \frac{3x^3}{3} - \frac{x^{-1}}{-1} = x^3 + \frac{1}{x} + c$$

$$f(x) = x^3 + \frac{1}{x} + c$$

Since the curve contains $(2, 0)$, then $(2, 0)$ satisfies the equation $y = f(x)$.

$$\Rightarrow 0 = 2^3 + \tfrac{1}{2} + c$$

$$\Rightarrow 0 = \frac{17}{2} + c \Rightarrow c = -\frac{17}{2}$$

$$\therefore \ f(x) = x^3 + \frac{1}{x} - \frac{17}{2}$$

Exercise 3.1

1. Find each of the following integrals:

   (i) $\int x\, dx$ $\dfrac{x^2}{2} + C$ (ii) $\int x^2\, dx$ (iii) $\int (3x^2 + 4x)\, dx$

   (iv) $\int -2x^2\, dx$ (v) $\int 3\, dx$ (vi) $\int (-x^2 + 3)\, dx$

   (vii) $\int (4x^3 + 6x)\, dx$ (viii) $\int (2x^2 - 3x - 1)\, dx$ (ix) $\int 12y^2\, dy$

2. Find each of these integrals:

   (i) $\int x^{-2}\, dx$ (ii) $\int 2x^{-3}\, dx$ (iii) $\int \dfrac{3}{x^2}\, dx$

   (iv) $\int -\dfrac{2}{x^3}\, dx$ (v) $\int \sqrt{x}\, dx$ (vi) $\int 3x^{\frac{1}{2}}\, dx$

   (vii) $\int \dfrac{1}{\sqrt{x}}\, dx$ (viii) $\int \sqrt[3]{x}\, dx$ (ix) $\int 4\pi r^2\, dr$

69

$+C$

3. Integrate each of these with respect to x:

   (i) $\int\left(2x^3 + \dfrac{3}{x^2}\right)dx$　　　(ii) $\int\left(\dfrac{4}{x^2} - 2 + x^3\right)dx$　　　(iii) $\int(4\sqrt{x} - 3)\,dx$

   (iv) $\int\left(\sqrt{x} + \dfrac{1}{\sqrt{x}}\right)dx$　　　(v) $\int\left(2\sqrt{x} - \dfrac{2}{x^2}\right)dx$　　　(vi) $\int\left(\dfrac{1}{x^2} - \dfrac{x}{\sqrt{x}}\right)dx$

4. Find y in terms of x for each of the following:

   (i) $\dfrac{dy}{dx} = x^2 + 3x$　　　(ii) $\dfrac{dy}{dx} = 6x^3 - 4x^2 + x - 5$

5. Find　(i) $\int(x - 3)^2\,dx$　　　(ii) $\int\left(x - \dfrac{1}{x}\right)^2 dx$　　　(iii) $\int\sqrt{x}(x - 3)\,dx$

6. Find　(i) $\displaystyle\int\dfrac{x^4 - 3x^3 + 4x}{x}\,dx$　　　(ii) $\displaystyle\int\dfrac{3x^3 - x^2 + 6}{x^2}\,dx$　　　(iii) $\displaystyle\int\dfrac{x^2 - 2x + 6}{\sqrt{x}}\,dx$

7. A curve with equation $y = f(x)$ contains the point $(-1, 4)$.
   If $f'(x) = 2x$, find the equation of the curve.

8. Find the function $y = f(x)$ given that $f'(x) = 2x - 5$ and the curve passes through the point $(1, 7)$.

9. If $\int(6x + 5)\,dx = 19$ when $x = 2$, find the constant of integration.

10. Find the constant of integration if $\int(6x^2 - 8x + 5)\,dx$ is 7 when $x = 2$.

11. Find y in terms of x in each of the following:

    (i) $\dfrac{dy}{dx} = x^2 + 2x$ and $y = 2$ when $x = 0$

    (ii) $\dfrac{dy}{dx} = 3 - x^2$ and $y = 2$ when $x = 3$

12. $\dfrac{dV}{dt} = t^2 - t$ when $t > 1$ and $V = 9$ when $t = 3$.

    (i) Find V in terms of t.　　　(ii) Calculate the value of V when $t = 10$.

13. The curve $y = f(x)$ for which $f'(x) = 4x + k$, where k is a constant, has a turning point at $(-2, -1)$.

    (i) Find the value of k.
    (ii) Find the coordinates of the point at which the curve meets the y-axis.

14. The curve for which $\dfrac{dy}{dx} = 2x + k$, where k is a constant, is such that the tangent at $(3, 6)$

    passes through the origin. Find the gradient of this tangent and hence determine:
    (i) the value of k　　　(ii) the equation of the curve.

Section 3.2 Integrating exponential and trigonometric functions

In chapter 7, T&T4 it was found that if

(i) $f(x) = e^x$, then $f'(x) = e^x$ $\Rightarrow$ $\int e^x \, dx = e^x + c$

(ii) $f(x) = e^{ax}$, then $f'(x) = ae^{ax}$ $\Rightarrow$ $\int e^{ax} \, dx = \dfrac{1}{a} e^{ax} + c$

(iii) $f(x) = a^x$, then $f'(x) = a^x \ln a$ $\Rightarrow$ $\int a^x \, dx = \dfrac{a^x}{\ln a} + c$

Example 1

Find each of the following:

(i) $\int e^{3x} \, dx$ (ii) $\int (e^{4x} + 6x) \, dx$ (iii) $\int (e^{5x} + 2) \, dx$ (iv) $\int (e^x + e^{-x}) \, dx$

(i) $\int e^{3x} \, dx = \dfrac{1}{3} e^{3x} + c$

(ii) $\int (e^{4x} + 6x) \, dx = \dfrac{1}{4} e^{4x} + \dfrac{6x^2}{2} + c$

$\qquad\qquad\qquad\quad = \dfrac{1}{4} e^{4x} + 3x^2 + c$

(iii) $\int (e^{5x} + 2) \, dx = \dfrac{1}{5} e^{5x} + 2x + c$

(iv) $\int (e^x + e^{-x}) \, dx = e^x + \dfrac{e^{-x}}{-1} + c$

$\qquad\qquad\qquad\quad = e^x - \dfrac{1}{e^x} + c$

Example 2

Given $y = 5^x$, show that $\int 5^x \, dx = \dfrac{5^x}{\ln 5} + c$.

We know that if $y = 5^x \Rightarrow \dfrac{dy}{dx} = 5^x \ln 5$ (check p25 formulae and tables)

$\therefore \quad dy = 5^x \ln 5 \, dx$

$\therefore \quad y = \int 5^x \ln 5 \, dx$

$\therefore \quad y = \ln 5 \int 5^x \, dx$

$\therefore \quad \int 5^x \, dx = \dfrac{y}{\ln 5} + c = \dfrac{5^x}{\ln 5} + c$

Integrals of the form $\int \sin ax$ and $\int \cos ax$

In our study of differential calculus, we found the derivatives of $\sin x$, $\sin ax$, $\cos x$ and $\cos ax$.

We will now use these results to write down the standard integrals of the basic trigonometric functions.

(i) $\dfrac{d}{dx}\sin x = \cos x$ $\qquad \Rightarrow \qquad$ $\int \cos x \, dx = \sin x + c$

(ii) $\dfrac{d}{dx}\sin ax = a \cos ax$ $\qquad \Rightarrow \qquad$ $\int \cos ax \, dx = \dfrac{\sin ax}{a} + c$

(iii) $\dfrac{d}{dx}\cos x = -\sin x$ $\qquad \Rightarrow \qquad$ $\int \sin x \, dx = -\cos x + c$

(iv) $\dfrac{d}{dx}\cos ax = -a \sin ax$ $\qquad \Rightarrow \qquad$ $\int \sin ax \, dx = -\dfrac{\cos ax}{a} + c$

Example 3

Find (i) $\int \cos 4x \, dx$ (ii) $\int \sin 3x \, dx$.

(i) $\int \cos 4x \, dx = \dfrac{\sin 4x}{4} + c = \tfrac{1}{4}\sin 4x + c$

(ii) $\int \sin 3x \, dx = -\dfrac{\cos 3x}{3} + c = -\tfrac{1}{3}\cos 3x + c$

Example 4

If $y = \sin 3x^2$, find $\dfrac{dy}{dx}$.

Hence, find $\int 6x \cos 3x^2 \, dx$.

$y = \sin 3x^2 \ \Rightarrow \ \dfrac{dy}{dx} = \cos 3x^2 \times \dfrac{d}{dx}(3x^2) \ \Rightarrow \ \dfrac{dy}{dx} = 6x \cos 3x^2$

Since $\dfrac{dy}{dx} = 6x \cos 3x^2 \ \Rightarrow \ \int 6x \cos 3x^2 \, dx = \sin 3x^2 + c$

Example 5

Let $h(x) = x \ln x$, $x \in R, x > 0$.
(i) Find $h'(x)$.
(ii) Hence, find $\int \ln x \, dx$.

(i) $h(x) = x \ln x$

$h'(x) = x \cdot \dfrac{1}{x} + \ln x \times 1$ ... 1st × derivative of 2nd + 2nd × derivative of 1st

$h'(x) = 1 + \ln x$

(ii) $\int (1 + \ln x)\, dx = x \ln x$ ... from (i) above

But $\int (1 + \ln x)\, dx = \int 1\, dx + \int \ln x\, dx$

$\therefore$ $\int 1\, dx + \int \ln x\, dx = x \ln x$

$\therefore$ $\int \ln x\, dx = x \ln x - \int 1\, dx$

$= x \ln x - x$

$\therefore$ $\int \ln x\, dx = x \ln x - x + c$

Exercise 3.2

1. Find the following integrals:

    (i) $\int e^{2x}\, dx$ (ii) $\int 3e^x\, dx$ (iii) $\int 2e^{4x}\, dx$ (iv) $\int e^{-3x}\, dx$

2. Integrate each of the following:

    (i) $\int (e^{3x} + 4)\, dx$ (ii) $\int 4e^{\frac{1}{2}x}\, dx$ (iii) $\int \left(e^{4x} + \dfrac{1}{e^{4x}} \right) dx$

3. If $y = e^{x^2}$, write down $\dfrac{dy}{dx}$.

    Hence, find $\int 2x\, e^{x^2}\, dx$.

4. Find each of the following integrals:

    (i) $\int \cos 3x\, dx$ (ii) $\int \sin 4x\, dx$ (iii) $\int -\sin 5x\, dx$ (iv) $\int \cos kx\, dx, \, k \in N$

5. Integrate each of the following:

    (i) $\int 3 \cos 6x\, dx$ (ii) $\int (\cos 2x - \sin 5x)\, dx$ (iii) $\int 3 \cos(-9x)\, dx$

6. Find $\int 3(e^x - 4 \sin 3x + 2)\, dx$.

7. Find the following integrals:

    (i) $\int (4e^{2x} + 4 \sin 3x)\, dx$ (ii) $\int (3 \cos x - 2 \cos 4x)\, dx$

8. Given $y = \cos 4x^2$, find $\dfrac{dy}{dx}$.

    Hence, find $\int -8x \sin 4x^2\, dx$.

$x^2 + 2x$

9. Given that $\dfrac{x+y}{z} = \dfrac{x}{z} + \dfrac{y}{z}$, use this identity to integrate each of the following:

(i) $\displaystyle\int \dfrac{e^{2x} + 4}{e^x}\, dx$ (ii) $\displaystyle\int \dfrac{e^{x+2} + 3}{e^x}\, dx$ (iii) $\displaystyle\int \dfrac{1 + 3e^x}{e^{2x}}\, dx$

10. Find (i) $\displaystyle\int (e^x - e^{-x})^2\, dx$ (ii) $\displaystyle\int (3 + e^x)(2 + e^{-x})\, dx$.

11. Given $y = 7^x$, use the rules of logs to find x in terms of y.

   (i) Hence, find $\dfrac{dx}{dy}$.

   (ii) Now find $\dfrac{dy}{dx}$ in terms of x.

   (iii) Use your result from (ii) to show that $\displaystyle\int 7^x\, dx = \dfrac{7^x}{\ln 7} + c$.

12. Given $\dfrac{dy}{dx} = ae^{-x} + 2,\ a \in R$ and $\dfrac{dy}{dx} = 5$ when $x = 0$.

   Find an expression for y, given that $y = -3$ when $x = 0$.

13. The curve for which $\dfrac{dy}{dx} = e^{kx}$, where k is a constant, is such that the tangent at $(1, e^2)$ passes through the origin. Find the gradient of this tangent and hence determine:

   (i) the value of k (ii) the equation of the curve.

14. Let $f(x) = 2x\,e^x$.
   (i) Find $f'(x)$.
   (ii) Hence, find $\displaystyle\int 2x\,e^x\, dx$.

15. Given $f(x) = x\sin x$, find $f'(x)$.
   Hence, find $\displaystyle\int x\cos x\, dx$.

16. Let $f(x) = 4xe^{2x}$.
   (i) Find $f'(x)$.
   (ii) Hence, find $\displaystyle\int 8x\,e^{2x}\, dx$.

17. Given $y = 2xe^{3x} + \cos x$, find $\dfrac{dy}{dx}$.

   Hence, find $\displaystyle\int 6x\,e^{3x}\, dx$.

Section 3.3 Applications of integration

In our study of differential calculus, we learned that in an equation of the type

$$s = 2t^2 - 3t + 4,$$

s represents the displacement of a body from some fixed origin after t seconds.

We also learned that $\dfrac{ds}{dt}$ represents the speed or velocity v.

The acceleration, a, of a body is defined as the rate of change of the velocity with respect to time,

that is, $\dfrac{dv}{dt} = a$ or $\dfrac{dv}{dt} = \dfrac{d^2s}{dt^2}$.

Accordingly displacement, velocity and acceleration are linked together by the process of differentiation with respect to time.

In reverse order, a, v and s are linked together by integration.
If we integrate an expression for the acceleration of a body with respect to time, we obtain an expression for the velocity of the body.

This is summarised diagramatically on the right.

Differentiate with respect to time

displacement – velocity – acceleration
s $\quad\quad\quad$ v $\quad\quad\quad$ a

Integrate with respect to time

Example 1

A body moves in a straight line.
At time t seconds, its acceleration is given by $a = 6t + 1$.
When $t = 0$, the velocity of the body is 2 m/sec and its displacement from a fixed point O is 1 metre.

(i) Find expressions for v and s in terms of t.
(ii) Find the velocity of the body after 4 seconds.

(i) Given $a = 6t + 1$, i.e. $\dfrac{dv}{dt} = 6t + 1$

   Velocity $(v) = \int (6t + 1)\, dt$

   $\therefore \quad v = \dfrac{6t^2}{2} + t + c$,   i.e. $v = 3t^2 + t + c$

   When $t = 0, v = 2$; thus, $2 = 0 + 0 + c \quad \therefore \quad c = 2$

   Thus, $v = 3t^2 + t + 2 \quad \ldots c = 2$

Using $\quad v = \dfrac{ds}{dt} = 3t^2 + t + 2$

$\Rightarrow \quad s = \int (3t^2 + t + 2)\,dt$

$s = \dfrac{3t^3}{3} + \dfrac{t^2}{2} + 2t + c$

$s = t^3 + \dfrac{t^2}{2} + 2t + c$

When $t = 0$, $s = 1 \Rightarrow 1 = 0 + c \Rightarrow c = 1$

Thus, $s = t^3 + \dfrac{t^2}{2} + 2t + 1$

(ii) Velocity $= v = 3t^2 + t + 2$

$\Rightarrow v = 3(4)^2 + (4) + 2 \quad$ ... when $t = 4$

$v = 54\,\text{m/sec}$ when $t = 4$

Therefore, the velocity $= 54\,\text{m/sec}$ after 4 seconds.

Exercise 3.3

In questions (1–5), s metres represents displacement relative to a fixed point O, v m/sec represents velocity, and a m/sec^2 represents acceleration.

1. A body starts from a fixed point O and moves in a straight line.
    Its velocity v is given by $v = 5t + 4$ after t seconds.

    (i) If s represents the distance from the origin, express s in terms of t, given
    that $s = 0$ when $t = 0$.
    (ii) Find the distance of the body from the origin after 4 seconds.

2. An object is travelling with a velocity of $v = \dfrac{ds}{dt} = t^2 - 4t + 3$.

    (i) Find the acceleration when $t = 5$.
    (ii) If s is the distance travelled, express s in terms of t, given that $s = 4$ when $t = 3$.
    (iii) Find the displacement when $t = 1$.

3. The acceleration of a body is given by $a = 6t - 12$.

    (i) Find the velocity v in terms of t, given that $v = 9$ when $t = 0$.
    (ii) Find the displacement s in terms of t, given that $s = 6$ when $t = 0$.
    (iii) Find the values of t when the body is at rest.

4. The acceleration of a particle can be modelled by the equation $a = (2t - 3)\,\text{cm/sec}^2$.
    If the particle starts 2 metres from the point O (moving away from O) and its speed
    when $t = 0$ is 3 m/sec, find

    (i) the velocity, v, and displacement, s, in terms of t
    (ii) the velocity and displacement when $t = 2$ seconds.

5. A body is projected vertically upwards with an initial velocity of 25 m/sec.
    Its acceleration is -10 m/sec^2. Find

    (i) the body's velocity at any time in terms of time t
    (ii) its height, s, above the point of projection at any time
    (iii) the time it takes to reach its maximum height
    (iv) the maximum height reached
    (v) the time taken to return to the point of projection.

6. $\dfrac{dN}{dt} = 4e^t + 10$ represents the rate at which a colony of bacteria increases, where N is
    the number of bacteria and t is measured in hours.

    (i) Find an expression for N in terms of t.
    (ii) If there were 10 bacteria in the colony initially, find the number in the colony
    after 5 hours, correct to the nearest whole number.

7. A train starts from rest at station A and $2\frac{1}{2}$ minutes later, passes through station B.
    Its velocity, t seconds after starting, is given by $v = 0.6t - 0.004t^2$, where v is expressed
    in metres per second.

    (i) Find an expression in t for the distance travelled from A.
    (ii) Find the distance between the two stations.

8. The rate at which water rises in a container is given

    by $\dfrac{dh}{dt} = 2t - 3$, where h is measured in cm and t is
    measured in seconds.

    (i) Find a formula for the height of the water in
    the container after t seconds, given that there
    was 4 cm of water in the container at the start.

    (ii) Find the time taken to fill the container if it is
    36 cm in height.

Section 3.4 Definite integrals

The diagram on the right shows the line $y = x$.
The shaded triangle is the area of the region
between the line $y = x$ and the x-axis between
the values $x = 0$ and $x = 3$.

Thus, the area is $\frac{1}{2}(3)(3) = 4\frac{1}{2}$ square units.

The equation of the line is $y = x$ or $f(x) = x$.

$$\int f(x)\,dx = \int x\,dx = \frac{x^2}{2} + c$$

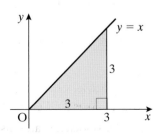

If we evaluate this integral at $x = 3$ and $x = 0$ and subtract the results, we get:

$$\left[\frac{9}{2} + c\right] - \left[\frac{0}{2} + c\right] = \frac{9}{2} + c - c = \frac{9}{2} = 4\frac{1}{2}$$

This result gives us the area of the shaded region already found by a different method on the previous page. It illustrates the use of integral calculus in finding the area between a line or curve and the x-axis.

$\int_{0}^{3} f(x)\, dx$ is the area between the curve $y = f(x)$ and the x-axis from $x = 0$ to $x = 3$.

The area is found by evaluating the integral at $x = 3$ and $x = 0$ and then subtracting the results.

The area enclosed between the curve $y = f(x)$, the x-axis and the lines $x = a$ and $x = b$ is given by

$$\text{Area} = \int_{a}^{b} y\, dx$$

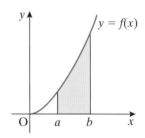

The area above may be written as

$$\int_{a}^{b} f'(x)\, dx = [f(x)]_{a}^{b} = f(b) - f(a)$$

Note: 1. $\int_{a}^{b} f(x)\, dx$ is called **a definite integral** since it gives a definite answer.

$\int (2x + 3)\, dx = x^2 + 3x + c$ is called **an indefinite integral** as it contains an unknown constant c.

2. The numbers a and b are called **the limits of integration**, a being the lower limit and b the upper limit.

3. The constant of integration may be ignored in definite integrals since the two c's cancel out when evaluating $f(b) - f(a)$.

Areas under a curve will be dealt with more fully in the next section.

Example 1

Evaluate   (i) $\int_{0}^{2} 3x^2\, dx$ (ii) $\int_{2}^{4} (x^2 - x + 3)\, dx$ (iii) $\int_{4}^{9} \frac{1}{\sqrt{x}}\, dx$

(i) $\int_{0}^{2} 3x^2\, dx = \left[\dfrac{3x^3}{3}\right]_{0}^{2} = [x^3]_{0}^{2}$

$\qquad\qquad = [2^3] - [0] = 8 - 0 = 8$

(ii) $\displaystyle\int_2^4 (x^2 - x + 3)\, dx = \left[\dfrac{x^3}{3} - \dfrac{x^2}{2} + 3x \right]_2^4$

$$= \left[\dfrac{64}{3} - \dfrac{16}{2} + 12 \right] - \left[\dfrac{8}{3} - \dfrac{4}{2} + 6 \right]$$

$$= \dfrac{152}{6} - \dfrac{40}{6} = 18\dfrac{2}{3}$$

(iii) $\displaystyle\int_4^9 \dfrac{1}{\sqrt{x}}\, dx = \int_4^9 x^{-\frac{1}{2}}\, dx = \left[\dfrac{x^{\frac{1}{2}}}{\frac{1}{2}} \right]_4^9 = \left[2\sqrt{x} \right]_4^9$

$$\left[2\sqrt{x} \right]_4^9 = \left[2\sqrt{9} \right] - \left[2\sqrt{4} \right]$$

$$= 6 - 4 = 2$$

Example 2

Evaluate   (i) $\displaystyle\int_{\frac{\pi}{4}}^{\frac{\pi}{2}} \cos 2x\, dx$ (ii) $\displaystyle\int_2^5 4e^x\, dx$ (iii) $\displaystyle\int_0^2 9^x\, dx$

(i) $\displaystyle\int_{\frac{\pi}{4}}^{\frac{\pi}{2}} \cos 2x\, dx = \left[\dfrac{\sin 2x}{2} \right]_{\frac{\pi}{4}}^{\frac{\pi}{2}}$

$$= \left[\dfrac{\sin 2\left(\frac{\pi}{2}\right)}{2} \right] - \left[\dfrac{\sin 2\left(\frac{\pi}{4}\right)}{2} \right] = \dfrac{\sin \pi}{2} - \dfrac{\sin \frac{\pi}{2}}{2}$$

$$= 0 - \dfrac{1}{2} = -\dfrac{1}{2}$$

(ii) $\displaystyle\int_2^5 4e^x\, dx = 4\int_2^5 e^x\, dx = 4[e^x]_2^5$

$$= 4[e^5 - e^2]$$

(iii) $\displaystyle\int_0^2 9^x\, dx = \left[\dfrac{9^x}{\ln 9} \right]_0^2 = \left[\dfrac{9^2}{\ln 9} \right] - \left[\dfrac{9^0}{\ln 9} \right]$

$$= \left[\dfrac{81}{\ln 9} \right] - \left[\dfrac{1}{\ln 9} \right] = \dfrac{81}{\ln 9} - \dfrac{1}{\ln 9} = \dfrac{80}{\ln 9}$$

Exercise 3.4

Evaluate the definite integrals in numbers (1–15):

1. $\displaystyle\int_1^2 6x\, dx$

2. $\displaystyle\int_1^3 (3x^2 - 2x)\, dx$

3. $\displaystyle\int_1^4 (3x^2 - 4)\, dx$

4. $\displaystyle\int_1^2 (x^3 + 2x)\, dx$

5. $\displaystyle\int_1^3 (x^2 - x + 1)\, dx$

6. $\displaystyle\int_{-1}^2 (2x - 5)\, dx$

$\dfrac{6x^2}{2}$

7. $\displaystyle\int_0^1 x^2(3-x)\,dx$

8. $\displaystyle\int_1^9 \sqrt{x}\,dx$

9. $\displaystyle\int_2^4 \frac{1}{x^2}\,dx$

10. $\displaystyle\int_4^9 \frac{dx}{\sqrt{x}}$

11. $\displaystyle\int_0^2 \frac{x^3 - 2x^2 + 4x}{x}\,dx$

12. $\displaystyle\int_1^4 (\sqrt{x} - 2)^2\,dx$

13. $\displaystyle\int_{-2}^{-1} \frac{2}{x^3}\,dx$

14. $\displaystyle\int_1^{16} \frac{\sqrt{x} - 4}{\sqrt{x}}\,dx$

15. $\displaystyle\int_1^4 \left(\sqrt{x} + \frac{1}{\sqrt{x}}\right)\,dx$

16. Show that $\displaystyle\int_1^2 (x-1)(x-2)\,dx = -\frac{1}{6}$.

17. Use factors to simplify the expression $\dfrac{x^2 - 16}{2x + 8}$.

    Hence, evaluate $\displaystyle\int_0^1 \frac{x^2 - 16}{2x + 8}\,dx$.

18. If $\displaystyle\int_0^k (2x - 4)\,dx = -3$, find the values of k if $k > 0$.

19. If $\displaystyle\int_0^k (x^2 - 3x)\,dx = 0$, find the value of k if $k > 0$.

20. Factorise $x^3 - 8$ and hence evaluate $\displaystyle\int_0^2 \frac{x^3 - 8}{x - 2}\,dx$.

21. Find the value of n such that $\displaystyle\int_0^1 nx^2\,dx = 1$.

22. Evaluate each of these definite integrals:

    (i) $\displaystyle\int_0^{\frac{\pi}{4}} \cos 2x\,dx$
    (ii) $\displaystyle\int_0^{\frac{\pi}{6}} \sin 3x\,dx$
    (iii) $\displaystyle\int_{\frac{\pi}{3}}^{\frac{\pi}{2}} 5 \sin x\,dx$
    (iv) $\displaystyle\int_0^{\frac{\pi}{2}} (2 \cos x + 1)\,dx$

23. Evaluate each of the following:

    (i) $\displaystyle\int_0^2 e^{4x}\,dx$
    (ii) $\displaystyle\int_{-1}^1 e^{x+3}\,dx$
    (iii) $\displaystyle\int_0^1 e^{\frac{x}{2}}\,dx$
    (iv) $\displaystyle\int_0^1 (e^{-2x} + 1)\,dx$

24. Find the value of each of these integrals:

    (i) $\displaystyle\int_0^1 \left(2e^{\frac{x}{3}} + 2\right)\,dx$
    (ii) $\displaystyle\int_{-2}^2 \frac{e^x + e^{-x}}{2}\,dx$
    (iii) $\displaystyle\int_1^3 5^x\,dx$
    (iv) $\displaystyle\int_0^e 7^x\,dx$

25. If $f(x) = \dfrac{\cos x}{\sin x}$, show that $f'(x) = \dfrac{-1}{\sin^2 x}$.

    Hence, find $\displaystyle\int_{\frac{\pi}{4}}^{\frac{\pi}{2}} \frac{1}{\sin^2 x}\,dx$.

26. Find $\dfrac{d}{dx}(x \sin 3x)$.

    Hence, evaluate $\displaystyle\int_0^{\frac{\pi}{6}} 3x \cos 3x\,dx$.

Section 3.5 Finding areas by integration

In this section, we will show how integration can be used to find the area, A, between a curve $y = f(x)$ and the x-axis from $x = a$ to $x = b$, as represented by the shaded area in the diagram on the right.

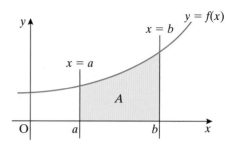

One way to estimate the area would be to divide it into a large number of rectangular strips, as shown below. Since each of these strips approximates to a rectangle, the sum of the areas of those rectangles gives an approximate value for A.

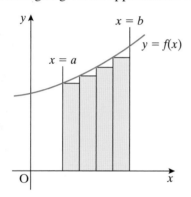
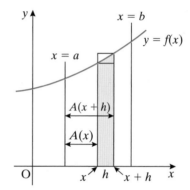

We will now consider one such rectangle, as shown on the right above.
Let the area under the curve from $x = a$ to $x = x$ be $A(x)$, and the area from $x = a$ to $x = x + h$ be $A(x + h)$.
The area of the narrow (shaded) strip is approximately equal to $h.f(x)$

$$\Rightarrow A(x + h) - A(x) \approx f(x).h$$

$$\Rightarrow \frac{A(x + h) - A(x)}{h} \approx f(x)$$

As $h \to 0 \Rightarrow \lim_{h \to 0} \frac{A(x + h) - A(x)}{h} = f(x)$

$$\Rightarrow \frac{dA}{dx} = f(x)$$

$$\Rightarrow dA = f(x)\,dx$$

$$\Rightarrow A = \int f(x)\,dx$$

Thus the integral of the function $y = f(x)$ gives the area function $A(x)$.
If we substitute b and a for x, we get the area between the curve, the x-axis and the lines $x = b$ and $x = a$.

Area under
a Curve

The area, A, of the region between the curve $y = f(x)$ and the x-axis between the lines $x = a$ and $x = b$ is given by

$$A = \int_a^b f(x)\,dx$$

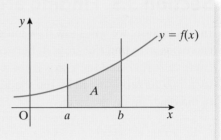

When using $\int_a^b y\,dx$ to find the area between a curve and the x-axis, the areas of the regions above and below the x-axis must be found separately.

If $b > a$, the value of $\int_a^b y\,dx$ will be positive if the area enclosed is above the x-axis, and negative if the area is below the x-axis.

If an area is -16, we take the absolute value, 16, to be the area.

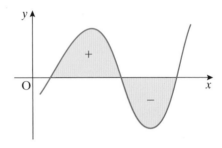

Area between a curve and the y-axis

If we require the area between a curve and the y-axis, the function must be written in the form $x = f(y)$.

The area of the shaded region between the curve and the y-axis between the lines $y = b$ and $y = a$ is given by:

Area between a curve
and the y-axis

$$\text{Area } A = \int_a^b x\,dy$$

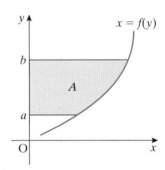

If the region is to the right of the y-axis, the area is positive; if the region is to the left of the y-axis, the area is negative.

Areas to the right and to the left of the y-axis must be found separately and then added.

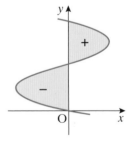

Example 1

Find the area of the shaded region shown
in the given diagram.

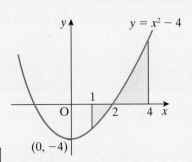

$$\text{Area} = \int_2^4 (x^2 - 4)\,dx + \int_1^2 (x^2 - 4)\,dx$$

$$= \left[\frac{x^3}{3} - 4x\right]_2^4 + \left[\frac{x^3}{3} - 4x\right]_1^2$$

$$= \frac{64}{3} - 16 - \left(\frac{8}{3} - 8\right) + \left[\left(\frac{8}{3} - 8\right) - \left(\frac{1}{3} - 4\right)\right]$$

$$= \frac{64}{3} - 16 - \left(-\frac{16}{3}\right) + \left[-\frac{16}{3} - \left(-\frac{11}{3}\right)\right]$$

$$= \frac{64}{3} - 16 + \frac{16}{3} + \left[-\frac{16}{3} + \frac{11}{3}\right]$$

$$= \frac{80}{3} - 16 + \left[-\frac{5}{3}\right] \quad \text{... since area below the } x\text{-axis is negative, we take the absolute}$$
$$\text{value of } \left[-\frac{5}{3}\right]$$

$$= \frac{32}{3} + \left|-\frac{5}{3}\right| = \frac{32}{3} + \frac{5}{3} = \frac{37}{3} \text{ square units.}$$

Area between two curves

The given figure shows two curves $y = f(x)$ and
$y = g(x)$ intersecting at the points where $x = a$
and $x = b$.

The shaded area $= \int_a^b g(x)\,dx - \int_a^b f(x)\,dx$

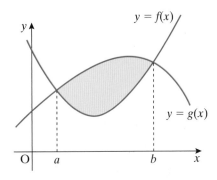

Example 2

Find the area of the region bounded by the curve $y = -x^2 + 5x - 4$ and the line $y = x - 1$.

The curve $y = -x^2 + 5x - 4$ represents a quadratic curve with a maximum turning point as the coefficient of x^2 is negative.

$y = 0 \Rightarrow -x^2 + 5x - 4 = 0$
$\qquad \Rightarrow x^2 - 5x + 4 = 0$
$\qquad \Rightarrow (x - 4)(x - 1) = 0$
$\qquad \Rightarrow x = 4 \text{ or } x = 1$

$\therefore$ The curve intersects the x-axis at
$\quad x = 4$ and at $x = 1$.
A rough sketch of the curve is shown.

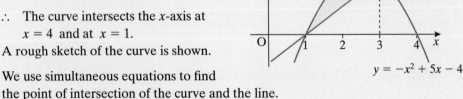

We use simultaneous equations to find the point of intersection of the curve and the line.

$\qquad y = -x^2 + 5x - 4 \quad \text{and} \quad y = x - 1$
$\qquad \Rightarrow -x^2 + 5x - 4 = x - 1$
$\qquad \Rightarrow x^2 - 4x + 3 = 0$
$\qquad \Rightarrow (x - 3)(x - 1) = 0 \Rightarrow x = 3 \text{ or } x = 1$

Thus, the curve intersects the line at the points where $x = 1$ and $x = 3$.
(There is no need to find the corresponding y-values.)

The required shaded area is the area between the curve and the x-axis between $x = 3$ and $x = 1$ less the area between the line and the x-axis between $x = 3$ and $x = 1$.

$\text{Area} = \int_1^3 (-x^2 + 5x - 4)\, dx - \int_1^3 (x - 1)\, dx$

$\qquad = \left[-\dfrac{x^3}{3} + \dfrac{5x^2}{2} - 4x \right]_1^3 - \left[\dfrac{x^2}{2} - x \right]_1^3$

$\qquad = \left[\left(-9 + \dfrac{45}{2} - 12 \right) - \left(-\dfrac{1}{3} + \dfrac{5}{2} - 4 \right) \right] - \left[\left(\dfrac{9}{2} - 3 \right) - \left(\dfrac{1}{2} - 1 \right) \right]$

$\qquad = \left[\dfrac{3}{2} + \dfrac{11}{6} \right] - \left[\dfrac{3}{2} + \dfrac{1}{2} \right]$

$\qquad = \dfrac{4}{3} \text{ sq. units}$

Example 3

The diagram on the right shows a sketch
of the function $y = \dfrac{2}{x^2}$.

The shaded region represents the area bounded
by the curve and the x-axis between the lines
$x = 3$ and $x = 1$.

If the line $x = k$ divides this area into two
equal portions, find the value of k.

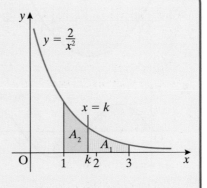

$$A_1 = A_2$$

$$\Rightarrow \int_k^3 \frac{2}{x^2}\,dx = \int_1^k \frac{2}{x^2}\,dx$$

$$\Rightarrow \int_k^3 2x^{-2}\,dx = \int_1^k 2x^{-2}\,dx$$

$$\Rightarrow \left[\frac{2x^{-1}}{-1}\right]_k^3 = \left[\frac{2x^{-1}}{-1}\right]_1^k$$

$$\Rightarrow \left[-\frac{2}{x}\right]_k^3 = \left[-\frac{2}{x}\right]_1^k$$

$$\Rightarrow \left(-\frac{2}{3}\right) - \left(-\frac{2}{k}\right) = \left(-\frac{2}{k}\right) - \left(-\frac{2}{1}\right)$$

$$\Rightarrow -\frac{2}{3} + \frac{2}{k} = -\frac{2}{k} + 2$$

$$\Rightarrow \frac{4}{k} = 2\frac{2}{3} \ \Rightarrow\ \frac{4}{k} = \frac{8}{3} \ \Rightarrow\ 8k = 12 \ \Rightarrow\ k = \frac{3}{2}$$

Exercise 3.5

Find the area of the shaded region in numbers (1–8):

1.

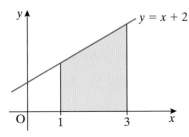

$y = x + 2$

2.

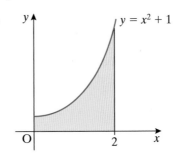

$y = x^2 + 1$

$$\int_0^2 (x^2 + 1)\,dx$$

$$\left[\frac{x^3}{3} + x\right]_0^2$$

area
ll

$$\frac{14}{3}$$

$$\left(\frac{8}{3} + 2\right)$$

$$4\frac{2}{3}$$

3.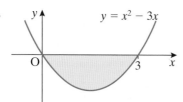

$y = x^2 - 3x$

4.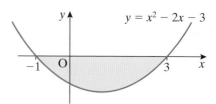

$y = x^2 - 2x - 3$

5.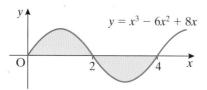

$y = x^3 - 6x^2 + 8x$

6.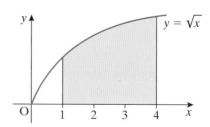

$y = \sqrt{x}$

7.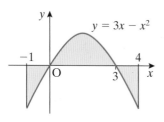

$y = 3x - x^2$

8.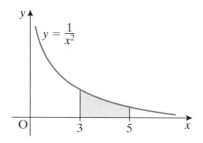

$y = \dfrac{1}{x^2}$

9. The curve $y = x^2 - 3x - 4$ intersects the x-axis at the points A and B.

Find the coordinates of A and B and hence find the area of the shaded region.

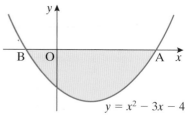

$y = x^2 - 3x - 4$

10. Find the coordinates of the points where the curve $x = 9 - y^2$ intersects the y-axis.

Hence, find the area of the shaded region.

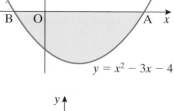

$x = 9 - y^2$

11. Find the total area enclosed between the curve $y = (x + 1)(x - 2)$, the x-axis and the lines $x = 0$ and $x = 3$.

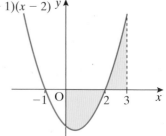

$y = (x + 1)(x - 2)$

12. Use integration to find the area enclosed between the curve $x = (y - 2)(y - 1)$ and the y-axis.

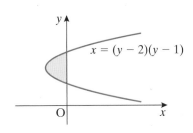

13. The given diagram shows the curve $y = x^2$ and the line $y = 2x$ intersecting at the point P.

   (i) Find the coordinates of P.
   (ii) Hence, find the area bounded by the curve and the line.

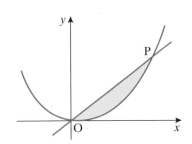

14. Find the area of the region enclosed by the given curve $y = 5x - x^2$ and the line $\ell: x + y - 8 = 0$.

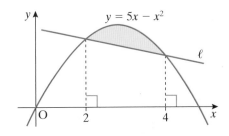

15. The given diagram shows the curve $y = -x^2 - x + 2$ and the line $x + y - 1 = 0$. The line intersects the curve at the points A and B.

   (i) Find the coordinates of A and B.
   (ii) Find the area of the shaded region.

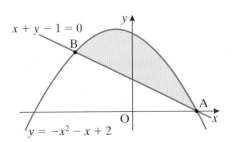

16. The diagram shows the curve $y^2 = 8x$ and the line $y = 2x$.

   Find the points of intersection of the line and the curve and hence find the area enclosed by the line and curve.

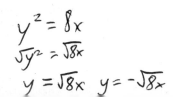

$y^2 = 8x$

$\sqrt{y^2} = \sqrt{8x}$

$y = \sqrt{8x} \quad y = -\sqrt{8x}$

not function as 2 y's for one x

87

17. The sketch on the right shows the curves

$$y^2 = 4x \text{ and } x^2 = 4y.$$

   (i) Find the coordinates of the point A.
   (ii) Find the area of the shaded region enclosed by the two curves.

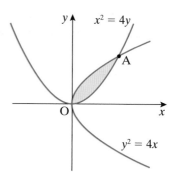

18. The diagram on the right shows the curve $y = 2x - x^2$ and the line $y = -2x$ intersecting at the origin and at the point P.

   (i) Find the coordinates of P and Q.
   (ii) By finding the areas of A_1 and A_2, find the area of the shaded region.

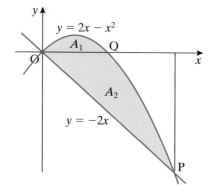

19. The diagram shows part of the curve $y = x^2 + 2$ and the line $y = 6$.
The line intersects the curve at the points C and D.

   (i) Find the coordinates of C and D.
   (ii) Find the area of the region bounded by the curve and the line [CD].

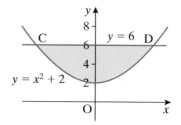

20. The point P is the maximum point of the graph of the curve $y = x(4 - x)$.

   (i) Find the coordinates of P.
   (ii) By finding an appropriate area between the curve and the x-axis, find the area of the shaded region.

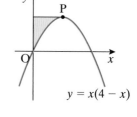

21. Part of the curve $y = x^2 + 4x + 4$ is shown on the right. If the area bounded by the curve, the x-axis and the lines $x = 0$ and $x = 2k$ is four times the area bounded by the curve, the x-axis and the lines $x = 0$ and $x = k$, find the value of k in surd form.

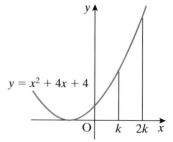

22. The diagram shows the vertical section through a tunnel 14 m long. The roof is an arc modelled by the equation $y = 6 - 0.08x^2 - 0.0006x^4$.

    (i) Find the area of the cross-section.
    (ii) Find the volume of the tunnel.

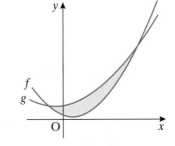

23. The functions f and g are defined for $x \in R$ as,
    $$f(x) = 2x^2 - 3x + 2 \text{ and}$$
    $$g(x) = x^2 + x + 7.$$

    (i) Find the coordinates of the two points where the curves $y = f(x)$ and $y = g(x)$ intersect.
    (ii) Find the area of the region enclosed between the two curves.

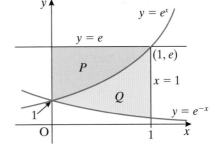

24. The given figure shows parts of the graphs of $y = e^x$ and $y = e^{-x}$.

    The figure also shows two enclosed regions P and Q.

    (i) Find the area of region P.
    (ii) Find the area of region Q in terms of e.

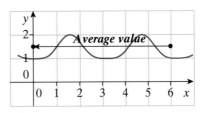

Section 3.6 Average value of a function

In some cases it is useful to know the **average value** of a function, especially if the function is periodic.

The average value of a continuous function over a given interval (e.g. $f(x) = 6 + 6x^2 - x^3$ from $x = 1$ to $x = 5$) is defined as the height of a rectangle standing on the same interval $(5 - 1 = 4)$ which has the same area as the area trapped between the function and the x-axis.

i.e. Average value $\times 4 = \displaystyle\int_1^5 (6 + 6x^2 - x^3)dx = 116$

$\Rightarrow$ average value of $f(x)$, from $x = 1$ to $x = 5$,
$$= 116 \div 4 = 29$$

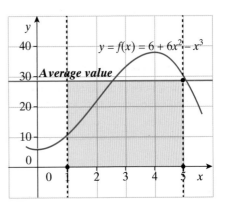

In general terms the average value of $y = f(x)$, over an interval of $[a, b]$ is defined as the height of the rectangle that has the same area as the area between the x-axis and the curve for the interval $[a, b]$.
The **exact average value** can be found using integration.

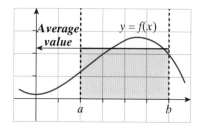

The average value of a function $f(x)$ over an interval $[a, b]$ is

$$\text{Average value} = \frac{1}{b - a} \int_a^b f(x)\, dx.$$

Example 1

The graph of the function, $f(x) = x^2 - 4x + 5$ is shown. Find the average value of the function for $1 \leq x \leq 4$.
Draw a horizontal line to represent this average value and explain its meaning.

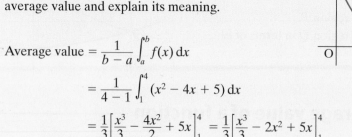

$$\text{Average value} = \frac{1}{b - a} \int_a^b f(x)\, dx$$

$$= \frac{1}{4 - 1} \int_1^4 (x^2 - 4x + 5)\, dx$$

$$= \frac{1}{3} \left[\frac{x^3}{3} - \frac{4x^2}{2} + 5x \right]_1^4 = \frac{1}{3} \left[\frac{x^3}{3} - 2x^2 + 5x \right]_1^4$$

$$= \frac{1}{3} \left[\left(\frac{64}{3} - 32 + 20 \right) - \left(\frac{1}{3} - 2 + 5 \right) \right]$$

$$= \frac{1}{3} \left[\left(9\tfrac{1}{3} \right) - \left(3\tfrac{1}{3} \right) \right]$$

$$= \frac{1}{3} [6] = 2$$

∴   The average value = 2

The line $y = 2$ represents the average value. The shaded rectangle is equal in area to the area between the curve and the x-axis from $x = 1$ to $x = 4$.

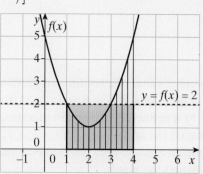

Example 2

A body starts from rest and moves in a straight line.
After t seconds its velocity (v cm/s) is given by $v = 2t - 4, t \geqslant 0$.

(i) By completing the table on the right, estimate the average velocity over the first 3 seconds.

$t =$	0	1	2	3
$v =$				

(ii) Use integration to test the accuracy of your answer.

(i)

$t =$	0	1	2	3
$v =$	−4	−2	0	2

Average velocity $= \dfrac{-4 - 2 + 0 + 2}{4} = -1$ cm/sec   ... although $t = 3$ seconds, four readings were taken.

(ii) The average value of a function $f(x)$ is $\dfrac{1}{b-a}\displaystyle\int_a^b f(x)\,dx$.

Average velocity $= \dfrac{1}{3-0}\displaystyle\int_0^3 (2t - 4)\,dt$

$\qquad = \dfrac{1}{3}\left[\dfrac{2t^2}{2} - 4t\right]_0^3 = \dfrac{1}{3}[t^2 - 4t]_0^3$

$\qquad = \dfrac{1}{3}\left[(3^2 - 4(3)) - (0 - 0)\right]$

$\qquad = \dfrac{1}{3}[9 - 12] = \dfrac{1}{3}[-3] = -1$ cm/s

In this case, the average velocity is also -1 cm/s.
This is the true average velocity; the first method only gives an estimate.
The estimate in (i) obtained by sampling was accurate in this example but for most functions is not.

Example 3

The average value of the function $f(x) = 2x + 3$ for $1 \leqslant x \leqslant k$ is 11.
Find the value of k.

$$\text{Average value} = \frac{1}{b - a} \int_a^b f(x)\, dx$$

$$= \frac{1}{k - 1} \int_a^b (2x + 3)\, dx$$

$$= \frac{1}{k - 1} \left[\frac{2x^2}{2} + 3x \right]_1^k$$

$$= \frac{1}{k - 1} [(k^2 + 3k) - (1 + 3)]$$

$$= \frac{1}{k - 1} [k^2 + 3k - 4]$$

$\therefore \quad \frac{1}{k - 1}(k^2 + 3k - 4) = 11 \quad$ … the average value, 11, is given.

$\therefore \quad k^2 + 3k - 4 = 11(k - 1)$
$k^2 - 8k + 7 = 0$
$(k - 7)(k - 1) = 0$
$k = 7 \text{ or } k = 1$

$\therefore \quad k = 7 \quad$ … $k = 1$ is the second limit, already given.

Exercise 3.6

1. On the right is the graph of the function
   $f(x) = -x^2 + 4x + 12$.

   (i) By reading the values of $f(0), f(1), \ldots f(6)$,
   estimate the average value of the function in
   the interval $0 \leqslant x \leqslant 6$.

   (ii) Now use integration to find the exact average
   value of $f(x)$ in the interval $[0, 6]$.

   (iii) Find the percentage error in using
   the estimate.

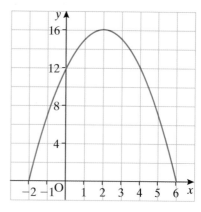

2. Find the average value of each of these functions in the given interval:

   (i) $f(x) = 2x - 4$ in the interval $2 \leqslant x \leqslant 5$.
   (ii) $f(x) = x^2 - x$ in the interval $0 \leqslant x \leqslant 2$.
   (iii) $f(x) = 2x - x^2$ in the interval $0 \leqslant x \leqslant 2$.

3. Find the average value of the function $f(x) = x^3$ for $0 \leqslant x \leqslant 4$.

4. Find the average value of the function $f(x) = x^2 + 4$ for $-2 \leqslant x \leqslant 3$.

5. Find the average value of each of the following functions for the stated intervals:

   (i) $f(x) = \sin x, x \in \left[0, \frac{\pi}{2}\right]$ (ii) $f(x) = \cos x, x \in [0, 2\pi]$

   (iii) $f(x) = e^x, x \in [0, 3]$ (iv) $f(x) = e^{4x}, x \in [0, 2]$

6. The average value of the function $f(x) = x + 1$ for $2 \leqslant x \leqslant k$ is 8.
   Find the value of k.

7. The average value of the function $f(x) = x^3$ for $0 \leqslant x \leqslant k$ is 16.
   Find the value of k.

8. Find the average value of each of these functions in the given interval:

   (i) $f(x) = \dfrac{1}{x^2}$, for $1 \leqslant x \leqslant 5$ (ii) $f(x) = 5\cos\left(\dfrac{x}{2}\right)$, for $0 \leqslant x \leqslant 2\pi$

9. The volume, $V\,\text{cm}^3$, of water in a conical vessel is given by $V = \dfrac{\pi h^3}{12}$, where $h\,\text{cm}$
   is the depth of the water.
   Find the average volume of water in the vessel as the depth increases from $2\,\text{cm}$ to $8\,\text{cm}$.

10. A body falls from rest. Its velocity in metres per second at time t seconds is given by
    $v = 9.8t$. Find the average velocity of the body over the first 3 seconds of its motion.

11. The velocity v in m/s of a body t seconds after timing commences is given by $v = 3t^2 - 4$.

    (i) Find the average velocity during the interval $t = 1$ to $t = 3$.
    (ii) Find the average acceleration during the interval $t = 1$ to $t = 3$.

12. A particle moves with velocity
    $v = 5 - (t - 3)^2$, where v is measured
    in metres/sec.

    (i) Find the average velocity of the
    particle in the first six seconds.
    (ii) At what time(s) will it have
    this average velocity?

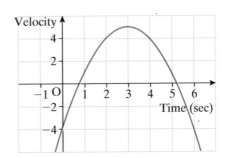

13. The tension T newtons in a particular spring depends on the extension x metres of the
    spring from its natural length in accordance with the rule $T = 30x$.
    Find the average tension in the spring as x increases from $0.1\,\text{m}$ to $0.2\,\text{m}$.

14. Given the curve whose equation is $y = x^{-\frac{1}{2}}$, find

    (i) the average value of $\dfrac{1}{y}$, with respect to x, in the interval $1 \leqslant x \leqslant 4$

    (ii) the area of the region R bounded by the curve, the x-axis and the lines $x = 1$ and $x = 4$.

15. A mass of gas of volume v at pressure p expands according to the law $pv^{\frac{3}{4}} = 30$. Find the average pressure as the gas expands from $v = 1$ to $v = 16$.

16. An object is fired vertically upwards so that after time t, its velocity is given by $v = 40 - 10t$, where v is in metres per second. Find the average velocity between $t = 1$ and $t = 3$.

Revision Exercise 3 (Core)

1. Find each of the following integrals:

    (i) $\int (2x + 5)\, dx$ (ii) $\int (3x^2 - 2x + 4)\, dx$ (iii) $\int \left(x^2 + \dfrac{1}{x^2}\right) dx$

2. Integrate each of these:

    (i) $\int \sin 3x\, dx$ (ii) $\int \cos 5x\, dx$ (iii) $\int (2\sin x + 3\cos 2x)\, dx$

3. Find each of these integrals:

    (i) $\int e^{5x}\, dx$ (ii) $\int (e^{2x} + e^{-x})\, dx$ (iii) $\int (4 + e^{3x})\, dx$

4. If $\dfrac{dy}{dx} = x^2 - 3x + 2$, find y.

5. Find each of these:

    (i) $\int \left(\dfrac{x^3 - 2}{x^2}\right) dx$ (ii) $\int (\sqrt{x} - 3)\, dx$ (iii) $\int (\sqrt{x} + 3)^2\, dx$

6. Evaluate each of the following integrals:

    (i) $\displaystyle\int_0^3 (2x^2 - 4x + 1)\, dx$ (ii) $\displaystyle\int_0^{\frac{\pi}{4}} \cos 2x\, dx$ (iii) $\displaystyle\int_0^{\frac{\pi}{3}} (\cos 3\theta + \sin 3\theta)\, d\theta$

7. Show that $\displaystyle\int_0^1 \left(x^{\frac{1}{2}} + x^{\frac{3}{2}}\right) dx = \dfrac{16}{15}$.

8. Evaluate each of these definite integrals:

    (i) $\displaystyle\int_0^3 (e^{2x} + 1)\, dx$ (ii) $\displaystyle\int_0^2 2e^{-2x}\, dx$ (iii) $\displaystyle\int_1^2 \left(e^{2x} + \dfrac{4}{x^2}\right) dx$

9. Find the exact area of the regions enclosed by
   the graph of $y = x(2 - x)(x - 3)$ and the x-axis.

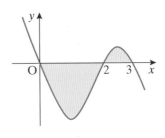

10. The curve $y = f(x)$ passes through the point $(1, 3)$.
    If $\dfrac{dy}{dx} = 15x^2 - 12x$, find $f(x)$.

11. Find the average value of the function $f(x) = 2x^2 - x$ over the interval $[0, 4]$.

12. $\dfrac{dy}{dx} = e^{2x} - x$ and $y = 5$ when $x = 0$.
    Find an expression for y in terms of x.

13. The given figure shows the curve $y = x^2 - 5x + 4$
    crossing the x-axis at A and B.
    (i) Find the coordinates of A and B.
    (ii) Find the total area of the shaded regions.

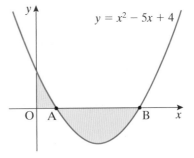

14. A particle is moving in a straight line such that after t seconds, its velocity is v m/sec,
    where $v = 6t + 12t^2$.
    Find (i) the average velocity during the first two seconds of motion
         (ii) the average acceleration between $t = 1$ and $t = 5$.

15. If $f(x) = x \sin 2x$, find $f'(x)$.
    Use your result to find $\int 2x \cos 2x \, dx$.

Revision Exercise 3 (Advanced)

1. (i) Evaluate $\displaystyle\int_1^3 (9x^2 - 4x) \, dx$.

   (ii) If $\displaystyle\int_0^a (9x^2 - 4x) \, dx = 0$, find the possible value of a when $a > 0$.

2. Find the average value of the function $f(x) = (x + 3)(2x - 5)$ in the
   interval $[1, 5]$.

3. The figure shows the curve $y = x^2$ and the straight line $2x + y = 15$.

   (i) Find the coordinates of P and Q.

   (ii) Find the area of the shaded region.

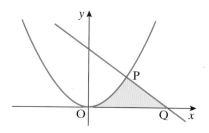

4. The volume, $V\,\text{cm}^3$, of water in a hemispherical bowl is given by $V = \frac{1}{3}\pi(30h^2 - h^3)$, where h cm is the depth of the water.

   Find the average volume of water in the bowl as the depth increases from 0 to 4 cm.

5. Part of the curve $y = x^3 - 3x^2 + 5$ is given. The point A is a local maximum point of the curve and ℓ is a tangent to the curve at A. Find the coordinates of A and hence find the area between the line ℓ and the curve.

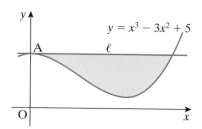

6. Given $\dfrac{dy}{dx} = ae^{-x} + 1$ and also $\dfrac{dy}{dx} = 3$ when $x = 0$.

   If $y = 5$ when $x = 0$, find the value of y when $x = 2$.

7. The figure shows part of the curve $y = \dfrac{10}{x^2}$.

   (i) Find the area of region A.

   (ii) Find the value of P for which the regions B and C are of equal area.

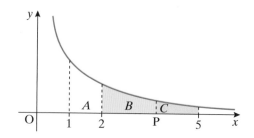

8. The roof of an exhibition hall has the shape of the function

   $$f(x) = 25 - 0.02x^2, \text{ for } -20 \leqslant x \leqslant 20.$$

   The hall is 80 metres long.
   A cross-section of the hall is shown.
   An air conditioning company wishes to find the volume of the hall so that a suitable system may be installed.
   Find this volume.

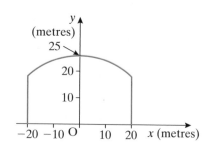

9. Let $f(x) = x^2 \ln 3x$, for $x \in R, x > 0$.

   (i) Find $f'(x)$.

   (ii) Hence, find $\int 2x \ln 3x\, dx$.

10. The figure shows the shaded region R which is bounded by the curve $y = -2x^2 + 5x$ and the line $y = 2$. The points A and B are the points of intersection of the line and the curve.

   (i) Find the coordinates of the points A and B.

   (ii) Find the exact area of R.

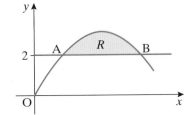

11. The kinetic energy k joules of a 10 kg body depends on the velocity v m/sec in accordance with the rule $k = 5v^2$.
Find the average kinetic energy possessed by the body as v increases from 1 m/sec to 7 m/sec.

12. A particle starts from rest 3 metres from a fixed point O and moves in a straight line with an acceleration a given by $a = 6t + 10$, where t is the time in seconds.

   (i) Find the velocity v after 5 seconds.

   (ii) Express its position, s, from the fixed point O in terms of t.

   (iii) How many metres is the particle from O after 3 seconds?

   (iv) Find the average speed from $t = 1$ to $t = 4$.

13. In the figure, the graph of $y^2 = 9(1 - x)$ is shown.

   (i) Find the coordinates of A and B.

   (ii) Find the exact area of the shaded region by

      evaluating $\int_0^b \left(1 - \dfrac{y^2}{9}\right) dy$ for a suitable choice of b.

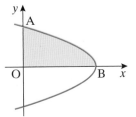

14. The diagram shows the graphs of a cubic function $y = f(x)$ and its slope function $y = f'(x)$.
Both graphs contain the point $(0, 6)$.
The graph of $y = f'(x)$ also passes through the points $(2, 0)$ and $(4, 0)$.

   (i) Given that $f'(x)$ is of the form

      $f'(x) = k(x - a)(x - b)$,

      (a) write down the values of a and b

      (b) find the value of k.

   (ii) Find the equation of the function $y = f(x)$.

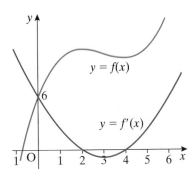

15. The gradient of a curve is given by $\dfrac{dy}{dx} = ax + \dfrac{b}{x^2}$.

If the curve passes through the point $(-1, -4)$ and has a turning point at $(1, 0)$, find the equation of the curve.

Revision Exercise 3 (Extended Response Questions)

1. The diagram shows part of the curve with equation

$$y = x - \dfrac{1}{x^2}.$$

C is the point $(2, 0)$.
Find:

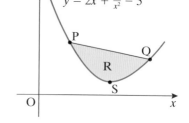

(a) the equation of the tangent to the curve at point A
(b) the coordinates of the point T where this tangent meets the x-axis
(c) the coordinates of the point B where the curve meets the x-axis
(d) the area of the region enclosed by the curve and the lines AT and BT
(e) the ratio of the area found in part (d) to the area of the triangle ATC.

2. The figure shows part of the curve, C, with equation

$$y = 2x + \dfrac{8}{x^2} - 5, x > 0.$$

The points P and Q lie on C and have x-coordinates 1 and 4 respectively.
The region R, shaded in the figure, is bounded by C and the straight line joining P and Q.

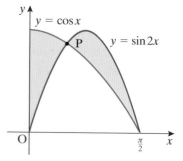

(a) Find the exact area of R.
(b) Use calculus to show that y is increasing for $x > 2$.
(c) Find the coordinates of the turning point S of the curve.
(d) Horizontal lines are drawn through the points P and S.
Find the area enclosed by the curve, the y-axis and these two lines by combining appropriate areas between the curve, these two horizontal lines and the x-axis.

3. The diagram shows the graphs of the functions $y = \cos x$ and $y = \sin 2x$.

(a) Find the x-coordinate of the point P where the two curves intersect.
(b) Hence, find the area of the shaded region.

4. During a storm, water flows into a 7000-litre tank at a rate of $\dfrac{dV}{dt}$ litres per minute, where $\dfrac{dV}{dt} = 120 + 26t - t^2$ and t is the time in minutes since the storm began.

   (a) At what times is the tank filling at twice the initial rate?

   (b) Find the volume of water that has flowed into the tank since the start of the storm as a function of t given $V = 0$ when $t = 0$.

   (c) Initially, the tank contains 1500 litres of water. When the storm finishes, 30 minutes after it began, the tank is overflowing.
   How many litres of water have been lost?

5. (a) In the figure, P is a point on the curve $y = x^2$.
   Prove that the curve divides the rectangle OMPN into two regions whose areas are in the ratio $2 : 1$.

   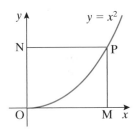

   (b) In the figure, P is a point on the curve $y = x^{\frac{1}{2}}$.
   Prove that the area of the shaded region is two-thirds of the area of the rectangle OMPN.

   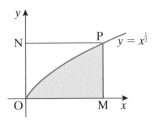

   (c) For the curve $y = x^n$, P is a point on the curve with PM and PN the perpendiculars from P to the x-axis and the y-axis respectively. Prove that the area of the region enclosed between PM, the x-axis and the curve is equal to $\dfrac{1}{n + 1}$ of the area of the rectangle OMPN.

6. A large mound of earth has a constant cross-sectional area. The cross-section is given by the equation $y = \dfrac{x^2}{1000}(50 - x)$, where y is the height of the mound in metres at a distance x metres from the edge.

   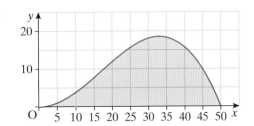

   (a) Find the height of the mound when:
       (i) $x = 10\,\text{m}$ (ii) $x = 40\,\text{m}$.

   (b) Find the slope of the boundary curve $y = \dfrac{x^2}{1000}(50 - x)$ when:
       (i) $x = 10\,\text{m}$ (ii) $x = 40\,\text{m}$.

(c) (i) Find the value of x for which the height of the mound is a maximum.

(ii) Find the maximum height of the mound.

(d) Find the cross-sectional area of the mound.

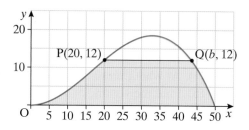

(e) The top of the mound is to be removed as shown.

(i) Point P has coordinates $(20, 12)$.
Find the coordinates of Q.

(ii) Find the values of a, b and R so that the area of the top of the mound to be removed is given by $\int_a^b \dfrac{x^2}{1000}(50 - x)\,dx - R$.

7. (a) Let $f(x) = 1 + e^x$.

Show that $f(x) \times f(-x) = f(x) + f(-x)$.

(b) Find y in terms of x given that $\dfrac{dy}{dx} = \dfrac{3 - e^{2x}}{e^x}$ and $y = 4$ when $x = 0$. (c) The curves $y = e^{2x}$ and $y = e^{-x}$ intersect at the point $(0, 1)$ as shown in the diagram:

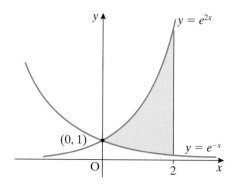

Find the exact area enclosed by the curves and the line $x = 2$.

Applications of Differential Calculus

chapter 4

Key words

increasing function   decreasing function   stationary points   local maximum
local minimum   point of inflection   slope function   rate of change   velocity
acceleration   related rates of change

Section 4.1 Tangents – Increasing and decreasing functions

In chapter 7 book 4, it was stated that for any function $y = f(x)$, the derived function $\dfrac{dy}{dx}$ can be interpreted geometrically as the slope of the tangent to the curve at any point on the curve.

If $y = f(x)$, then $f'(a)$ gives the slope of the tangent to the curve at the point where $x = a$.

Thus, to find the equation of the tangent to a curve at the point (x_1, y_1):

(i)   Find $\dfrac{dy}{dx}$.

(ii)   Evaluate $\dfrac{dy}{dx}$ at (x_1, y_1).

(iii)   Use the equation
$$y - y_1 = m(x - x_1)$$
to find the equation of the tangent at the point (x_1, y_1).

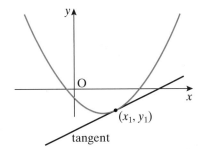

Example 1

Find the equation of the tangent to the curve $y = \dfrac{x^2}{3} - x + 1$ at the point $(4, \tfrac{7}{3})$.

To find the slope of the tangent to the curve, we first find $\dfrac{dy}{dx}$.

$$y = \frac{x^2}{3} - x + 1 \;\Rightarrow\; \frac{dy}{dx} = \frac{2x}{3} - 1$$

$$= \frac{2(4)}{3} - 1 = \frac{5}{3} \quad \text{... at } x = 4$$

Equation of tangent at $(4, \frac{7}{3})$:

$$y - y_1 = m(x - x_1)$$

$$y - \tfrac{7}{3} = \tfrac{5}{3}(x - 4)$$

$$\Rightarrow 3y - 7 = 5x - 20$$

$$\Rightarrow 5x - 3y - 13 = 0 \text{ is the required equation.}$$

Example 2

At what points on the curve $y = x^3 - 9x^2 + 20x - 8$ is the tangent parallel to the line $4x + y - 3 = 0$?

The slope of the line $4x + y - 3 = 0$ is -4. ... $y = -4x + 3$
Any line parallel to $4x + y - 3 = 0$ will have slope -4.

We find $\dfrac{dy}{dx}$ to find the slope of any tangent to $y = x^3 - 9x^2 + 20x - 8$.

$$\frac{dy}{dx} = 3x^2 - 18x + 20$$

For slope -4, $\quad 3x^2 - 18x + 20 = -4$

$$\Rightarrow \quad 3x^2 - 18x + 24 = 0$$

$$\Rightarrow \quad x^2 - 6x + 8 = 0$$

$$\Rightarrow \quad (x - 2)(x - 4) = 0 \Rightarrow x = 2 \text{ or } x = 4$$

We now find the corresponding y-values for $x = 2$ and $x = 4$.

$x = 2 \Rightarrow y = (2)^3 - 9(2)^2 + 20(2) - 8 \Rightarrow y = 4$

$\quad \therefore (2, 4)$ is one point where the slope is -4.

$x = 4 \Rightarrow y = (4)^3 - 9(4)^2 + 20(4) - 8 \Rightarrow y = -8$.

$\quad \therefore (4, -8)$ is a second point where the slope is -4

$\quad \therefore$ The two required points are $(2, 4)$ and $(4, -8)$.

Increasing and decreasing functions

Examining the given curve from left to right, we can see that it is rising (or increasing) from A to B, and decreasing from B to C.

From A to B, the slope of the tangent $\left(\text{i.e. } \dfrac{dy}{dx}\right)$ is positive.

From B to C, the slope of the tangent is negative.

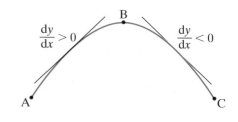

Example 3

Find the interval for which the function $f(x) = x^3 - 3x^2 - 9x + 9$ is

(i) increasing (ii) decreasing

(i) When $f(x)$ is increasing, $f'(x) > 0$.

$f'(x) = 3x^2 - 6x - 9 \Rightarrow 3x^2 - 6x - 9 > 0$
$$\Rightarrow x^2 - 2x - 3 > 0$$
$$\Rightarrow (x - 3)(x + 1) > 0$$

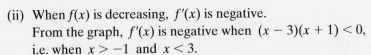

Using a rough sketch of the quadratic function $y = x^2 - 2x - 3$, we can see that:

$(x - 3)(x + 1) > 0 \Rightarrow x > 3$ and $x < -1$.
Therefore, $f(x)$ is increasing when $x > 3$ and $x < -1$.

(ii) When $f(x)$ is decreasing, $f'(x)$ is negative.
From the graph, $f'(x)$ is negative when $(x - 3)(x + 1) < 0$,
i.e. when $x > -1$ and $x < 3$.

$\therefore$ $f(x)$ is decreasing in the interval $-1 < x < 3$.

Example 4

Show that the curve $y = x^3 + 3x^2 + 6x$ is increasing for all values of $x \in R$.

If a curve is increasing, then $\dfrac{dy}{dx}$ is positive.

$y = x^3 + 3x^2 + 6x \Rightarrow \dfrac{dy}{dx} = 3x^2 + 6x + 6$

$$= 3(x^2 + 2x + 2)$$
$$= 3(x^2 + 2x + 1 + 1)$$
$$= 3[(x + 1)^2 + 1]$$

Since $(x + 1)^2, x \in R$ is always positive, then $3[(x + 1)^2 + 1]$ is positive.
Therefore, the curve is increasing for all $x \in R$ as $3[(x + 1)^2 + 1]$ is positive
for all $x \in R$.

Exercise 4.1

1. Find the slope of the tangent to the curve at the given point in each of the following functions:

   (i) $y = x^2 - 3x + 2$ at $(1, 0)$

   (ii) $y = x + \dfrac{1}{x}$ at $\left(\dfrac{1}{2}, \dfrac{5}{2}\right)$

2. Find the equation of the tangent to the curve $f(x) = 2x^2 - 4x - 5$ at the point $(3, 1)$.

3. Find the equation of the tangent to the curve $f(x) = x^2 - 6x$ at the point where $x = 2$.

4. Find the equation of the tangent to the curve $y = x^3 + \dfrac{1}{2x^2}$ at the point where $x = 1$.

5. Find the value of k if the slope of the tangent to the curve $y = x^2 + kx$ is 3 at the point where $x = -1$.

6. Find the coordinates of the point on the curve $y = x^2 + 3x - 1$ at which the slope of the tangent to the curve is 5.

7. Find the coordinates of the point on the curve $y = x^2 + 4x + 6$ at which the slope is -2.

8. Find the equation of the tangent to the curve $y = \dfrac{5x^2}{1 + x^2}$ at the point $(2, 4)$.

9. Find the coordinates of the points on the curve $y = x^3 - 12x + 4$ at which the slope of the tangent is zero.

10. Given that the curve with equation $y = ax^2 + bx + 5$ has slope 4 at the point $(5, 0)$, find the values of the constants a and b.

11. A curve is defined by the equation $y = ax^2 + b$, where a, b are constants. If the gradient of the curve at the point $(2, -2)$ is 3, find the values of a and b.

12. Find the equation of the tangent to the curve $y = \ln x + x - 2$ at the point where $x = 1$.

13. Find the equation of the tangent to the curve $y = e^{3x}$ at the point $(0, 1)$.

14. Find the coordinates of the two points on the curve $y = x^3 - 3x^2 - 5x + 10$ where the tangents to the curve are parallel to the line $y = 4x - 7$.

15. Sarah throws a stone horizontally from a point on top of a 500 m cliff.

    The equation of the path of the stone is $y = \dfrac{-x^2}{125}$.

    (Axes are taken from the point of projection.)

    (i) How far out to sea does the stone reach?

    (ii) If $\tan \theta$ is the slope of the curve at this point, find the angle at which the stone enters the water.

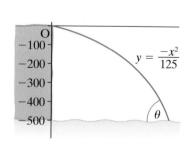

16. What is the sign of $\dfrac{dy}{dx}$ when a curve is (i) increasing (ii) decreasing?

Now find the interval for which each of the following functions is decreasing.

(a) $y = x^2 - x - 6$

(b) $y = x^3 + 6x^2 - 2$

17. Given $f(x) = 4x^2 + 4x + 7$.
    (i) Find $f'(x)$.
    (ii) Hence, find the range of values of x for which
        (a) $f(x)$ is increasing
        (b) $f(x)$ is decreasing.

18. Find the range of values of x for which $f(x)$ is an increasing function in each of the following:
    (i) $f(x) = 4x - 3x^2$
    (ii) $f(x) = 3x^2 + 8x + 2$
    (iii) $f(x) = 2x^3 - 15x^2 + 36x$

19. Find the range of values of x for which $f(x)$ is a decreasing function in each of the following:
    (i) $f(x) = 3x - 5x^2$
    (ii) $f(x) = 4 - 2x - x^2$
    (iii) $f(x) = 2x^3 - 3x^2 - 12x$

20. Show that $f(x) = x^3 - 6x^2 + 18x + 4$ is an increasing function for all values of $x \in R$.

21. Show that the curve $y = \dfrac{2x + 1}{3x + 6}$ is increasing for all $x \neq -2$.

22. The parabola with equation $y = x^2 - 14x + 53$ has a tangent at the point P(8, 5).

    (i) Find the equation of this tangent.

    (ii) Show that the tangent found in (i) is also a tangent to the parabola with equation $y = -x^2 + 10x - 27$ and find the coordinates of the point of contact, Q.

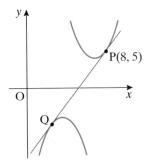

23. A trail over a mountain pass can be modelled by the curve with equation $y = 2 + 0.12x - 0.01x^3$, where x and y are, respectively, the horizontal and vertical distances measured in kilometres, $0 \leqslant x \leqslant 3$.
    (i) Find the gradients at the beginning and the end of the trail.
    (ii) Calculate the point where the gradient is zero, and calculate also the height of the pass.

24. The curve with equation $y = \sqrt{x+2}$ meets the x-axis at A and the y-axis at B.

(a) Find the coordinates of A and B.

(b) By using the chain rule, find $\dfrac{dy}{dx}$.

(c) (i) Find the gradient of the curve where $x = -1$.
   (ii) Find the equation of the tangent at the point where $x = -1$.
   (iii) If the tangent meets the x-axis at C and the y-axis at D, find the distance $|CD|$.

(d) Find the values of x for which $\dfrac{dy}{dx} < 1$.

Section 4.2 Stationary points

In the diagram below, the tangents to the curve at the points A and B are parallel to the x-axis, and so the slope of each tangent is zero.

Points on a curve at which $\dfrac{dy}{dx}$ is zero are called **stationary points**.

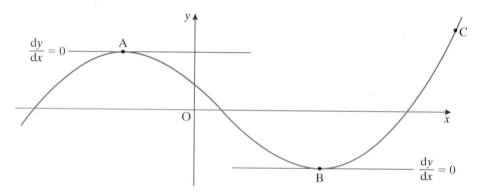

In the curve above, A and B are stationary points and they are also **turning points**.

The turning point at A is called a **local maximum point**, since the value of the function at this point exceeds all values of the function immediately to the right or left of A.

A maximum value of a function is not necessarily the greatest value of the function. This is illustrated in the curve above where the value of the function at C is greater than the value of the function at A.

The turning point at B above is called a **minimum turning point** or simply a **local minimum**.

The following steps should be used to find the turning points of a curve:

(i) find $\dfrac{dy}{dx}$ of the function

(ii) let $\dfrac{dy}{dx} = 0$ and solve the equation

(iii) for each value of x, find the corresponding value for y.

Example 1

Find the turning points of the curve $y = x + \frac{1}{x}$.

To find the turning points, we solve the equation $\frac{dy}{dx} = 0$.

$$y = x + \frac{1}{x} \Rightarrow y = x + x^{-1}$$

$$\frac{dy}{dx} = 1 - \frac{1}{x^2}$$

$$\frac{dy}{dx} = 0 \Rightarrow 1 - \frac{1}{x^2} = 0 \Rightarrow x^2 - 1 = 0$$

$$\Rightarrow x^2 = 1 \Rightarrow x = \pm 1$$

$$x = 1 \Rightarrow y = 2 \quad \text{and} \quad x = -1 \Rightarrow y = -2$$

$\therefore$ The turning points of the curve are $(1, 2)$ and $(-1, -2)$.

Determining the nature of a turning point

In the diagram below, the positive signs $(+)$ indicate where the slope of the curve is positive $\left(\text{i.e. } \frac{dy}{dx} > 0\right)$, and the negative signs indicate where the slope of the curve is negative $\left(\text{i.e. } \frac{dy}{dx} < 0\right)$.

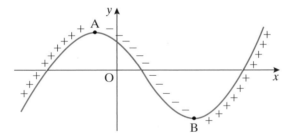

As the point A is approached from the left, the slope of the curve is positive but decreasing; at A, the slope is zero, and to the right of A, the slope is negative. Thus, as we go through the point A, the slope of the curve changes from positive to negative (i.e. is decreasing).

Thus, the rate of change of $\frac{dy}{dx}$ $\left(\text{i.e. } \frac{d^2y}{dx^2}\right)$ is negative.

$\Rightarrow \frac{d^2y}{dx^2}$ is negative at a maximum turning point.

Similarly, at the point B, the slope of the curve changes from negative to positive, that is, it is increasing.

Thus, the rate of change of $\frac{dy}{dx}$ $\left(\text{i.e. } \frac{d^2y}{dx^2}\right)$ is positive at the point B.

$\Rightarrow \frac{d^2y}{dx^2}$ is positive at a minimum turning point.

If, $\dfrac{dy}{dx} = 0$ and $\dfrac{d^2y}{dx^2} < 0$, i.e. is negative, at a point, then the point is a local maximum point.

If, $\dfrac{dy}{dx} = 0$ and $\dfrac{d^2y}{dx^2} > 0$, i.e. is positive, at a point, then the point is a local minimum point.

Example 2

Find the turning points of the curve $y = x^3 - 9x^2 + 15x$ and determine the nature of these turning points.

To find the turning points, we solve the equation $\dfrac{dy}{dx} = 0$.

$y = x^3 - 9x^2 + 15x \Rightarrow \dfrac{dy}{dx} = 3x^2 - 18x + 15$

$\begin{aligned}\dfrac{dy}{dx} = 0 \Rightarrow\ & 3x^2 - 18x + 15 = 0 \\ \Rightarrow\ & x^2 - 6x + 5 = 0 \\ \Rightarrow\ & (x - 5)(x - 1) = 0 \\ \Rightarrow\ & x = 5 \text{ or } x = 1\end{aligned}$

When $x = 5$, $y = (5)^3 - 9(5)^2 + 15(5) \Rightarrow y = -25$
$\therefore\ (5, -25)$ is a turning point.

When $x = 1$, $y = (1)^3 - 9(1)^2 + 15(1) = 7$
$\therefore\ (1, 7)$ is also a turning point.

To determine the nature of these turning points, we find $\dfrac{d^2y}{dx^2}$.

$\dfrac{dy}{dx} = 3x^2 - 18x + 15 \Rightarrow \dfrac{d^2y}{dx^2} = 6x - 18$

At $x = 5$, $\dfrac{d^2y}{dx^2} = 6(5) - 18 = 12$, which is **positive.**

$\Rightarrow (5, -25)$ is a minimum turning point.

At $x = 1$, $\dfrac{d^2y}{dx^2} = 6(1) - 18 = -12$, which is **negative.**

$\Rightarrow (1, 7)$ is a maximum turning point.

Points of Inflection

The curve traced in the diagram below is said to be **concave upwards** from the point A to the point B, and **concave downwards** from the point B to the point C.

The point B, where the curve changes from being concave upwards to concave downwards, is called a **point of inflection**.

At a point of inflection, the tangent to the curve crosses the curve.

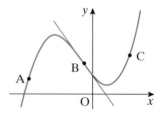

At a point of inflection, B, of a curve $y = f(x)$, $\dfrac{d^2y}{dx^2} = 0$ and changes sign as the curve passes through B.

At a point of inflection, the slope of the tangent to the curve need not be zero as shown in the diagram on the previous page.

Point of Inflection	At a point of inflection, B, on the curve $y = f(x)$, $\dfrac{d^2y}{dx^2} = 0$ and changes sign as the curve passes through B.

Thus, to find the point(s) of inflection of a curve:

(i)   find $\dfrac{d^2y}{dx^2}$

(ii) solve the equation $\dfrac{d^2y}{dx^2} = 0$

(iii) for each value of x, find the corresponding value of y.

Note: The point B on the given curve is a point of inflection. The tangent to the curve at B is also parallel to the x-axis.

The point B is called a **saddle point** or a **horizontal point of inflection** and is another example of a stationary point.

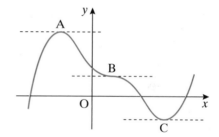

Example 3

Find the point of inflection of the curve $y = x^3 - 3x^2 - 2$.

$y = x^3 - 3x^2 - 2$

$\Rightarrow \dfrac{dy}{dx} = 3x^2 - 6x \;\Rightarrow\; \dfrac{d^2y}{dx^2} = 6x - 6$

$\dfrac{d^2y}{dx^2} = 0 \;\Rightarrow\; 6x - 6 = 0 \;\Rightarrow\; x = 1$

When $x = 1$, $y = (1)^3 - 3(1)^2 - 2 = -4$

$\therefore (1, -4)$ is the point of inflection.

Example 4

Verify that the curve $y = \dfrac{x+2}{2x-3}$ has no turning points or points of inflection.

Verify also that the curve is decreasing for all values of $x \in R$.

To find the turning points, we solve the equation $\dfrac{dy}{dx} = 0$.

$$y = \frac{x+2}{2x-3} \Rightarrow \frac{dy}{dx} = \frac{(2x-3)(1) - (x+2)(2)}{(2x-3)^2}$$

$$= \frac{2x - 3 - 2x - 4}{(2x-3)^2} = \frac{-7}{(2x-3)^2}$$

The expression $\dfrac{-7}{(2x-3)^2}$ can never be zero, **as a fraction is zero only if the numerator is zero.**

Since $\dfrac{-7}{(2x-3)^2} \neq 0$, the curve has no turning points.

To find the point of inflection, we solve the equation $\dfrac{d^2y}{dx^2} = 0$.

$$\frac{dy}{dx} = \frac{-7}{(2x-3)^2} = -7(2x-3)^{-2}$$

$$\Rightarrow \frac{d^2y}{dx^2} = 14(2x-3)^{-3}(2) = \frac{28}{(2x-3)^3}$$

Since $\dfrac{d^2y}{dx^2} = \dfrac{28}{(2x-3)^3} \neq 0$, the curve has no point of inflection.

A curve is decreasing if $\dfrac{dy}{dx}$ is negative.

$\dfrac{dy}{dx} = \dfrac{-7}{(2x-3)^2}$, which is always negative as $(2x-3)^2$ is always positive.

$\Rightarrow$ The curve is decreasing for all $x \in R$.

Exercise 4.2

1. Find the turning point of the function $y = x^2 - 4x + 9$ and show that it is a local minimum.

2. Find the turning point of the curve $y = 4 - 8x - 2x^2$ and show that it is a local maximum.

3. Find the turning point of the function $y = 3x^2 - 6x + 4$ and determine if it is a local maximum or a local minimum.

4. Find the maximum and minimum turning points of the curve $y = x^3 - 9x^2 + 15x + 2$.

5. Find the coordinates of the turning points of each of the following curves and determine the nature of each turning point:

    (i) $y = 2x^3 - 3x^2 - 12x + 5$ (ii) $y = \dfrac{x^2}{x + 2}$

6. Find the coordinates of the maximum and minimum turning points of the function $f(x) = 4x + \dfrac{4}{x}$.

7. Find the turning point of the function $y = x^2 + \dfrac{250}{x}$ and determine if it is a maximum or a minimum turning point.

8. Find the turning point of the function $y = x - \sqrt{x}$ $(x \geqslant 0)$ and determine the nature of this turning point.

9. By solving the equation $\dfrac{d^2y}{dx^2} = 0$, find the coordinates of the point of inflection of each of these curves:

    (i) $y = x^3 + 3x^2 + 1$ (ii) $y = x^3 - 6x^2 + 9x + 2$.

10. Show that the curve $y = \cos x$ has a point of inflection at $x = \dfrac{\pi}{2}$.

11. The function $y = ax^3 + bx^2 + c$ has turning points at $(0, 4)$ and $(-1, 5)$. Find the values of a, b and c.

12. Given that $f(x) = \dfrac{x + 1}{x - 3}, x \in R$ and $x \neq 3$.

    Show that the graph of $y = f(x)$ has no turning points.

13. A curve has equation $y = 2x^2 - \ln x, x > 0$.

    (i) Show that the slope of the curve is 3 at the point where $x = 1$.
    (ii) Find the coordinates of the turning point of the curve and investigate if this point is a local maximum or local minimum.

14. The equation of a function is $y = e^x - x$.

    (i) Find the coordinates of the stationary point of this function.
    (ii) Determine the nature of the stationary point.

15. (a) Find the stationary points on the curve with equation $y = x^3 - 9x^2 + 24x - 20$ and justify their nature.

    (b) (i) Show that $(x - 2)^2(x - 5) = x^3 - 9x^2 + 24x - 20$.
        (ii) Hence, sketch the graph of $y = x^3 - 9x^2 + 24x - 20$.

16. The function $f(x) = (1 + x)\log_e(1 + x)$ is defined for $x > -1$.

    (i) Show that the curve $y = f(x)$ has a turning point at $\left(\dfrac{1 - e}{e}, \dfrac{-1}{e}\right)$.

    (ii) Determine whether the turning point is a local maximum or a local minimum.

17. The function $f(x) = ax^3 + bx^2 + cx + d$ has a maximum point at $(0, 4)$ and a point of inflection at $(1, 0)$.
    Find the values of a, b, c and d.

18. Given that $f(x) = \dfrac{x}{x + 2}, x \in R$ and $x \neq -2$.
    Show that the graph of $f(x)$ has no turning points or points of inflection.
    (Use GeoGebra to illustrate this.)

19. Let $g(x) = x^2 + \dfrac{a}{x^2}$, where a is a real number and $x \in R$, $x \neq 0$.
    Given that $g(x)$ has a turning point at $x = 2$,
    (i) find the value of a
    (ii) show that $g(x)$ has no local maximum point.

20. A diesel lorry is driven from Limerick to Galway at a steady speed of v kilometres per hour.
    The total cost of the journey, $€C$, is given by $C = \dfrac{1400}{v} + \dfrac{2v}{7}$.
    (i) Find the value of v for which C is a minimum.
    (ii) Find $\dfrac{d^2C}{dv^2}$ and hence verify that C is a minimum for this value of v.
    (iii) Calculate the minimum total cost of the journey.

Section 4.3 Graphs of the derived (or slope) function ——

The curve on the right is the graph of the function
$$y = x^2 - 2x - 3.$$

$\dfrac{dy}{dx}$ for this function is $2x - 2$.

$\dfrac{dy}{dx} = 2x - 2$ is the **derived** or **slope function**.

The blue line represents this slope function.

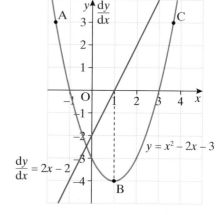

From the two graphs, the following can be observed:

(i) From A to B on the curve, the slope is negative. For this x-interval, the slope function (blue line) is also negative, i.e. the blue line is below the x-axis.

(ii) From B to C on the curve, the slope is positive. For this x-interval, the slope function (blue line) is also positive, i.e. the blue line is above the x-axis.

(iii) The slope of the curve at the point B is zero, i.e. $\dfrac{dy}{dx} = 0$.
    At the point B, $x = 1$.
    Notice that the slope function is also zero at the point where $x = 1$.
    This illustrates that $\dfrac{dy}{dx}$ (the slope function) is zero at a turning point.

The slope function of a cubic function

The red curve on the right is the graph
of a cubic function, $y = f(x)$.
The blue curve is the graph of its
slope function, $y = g(x)$.

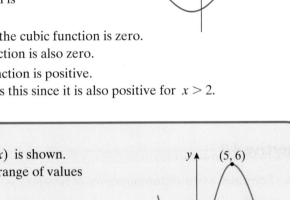

Some of the features of these curves are:

> In the function $y = f(x)$, for $x < -3$,
  the slope is positive.
  This is represented in the slope function
  $y = g(x)$, where $g(x)$ is positive for $x < -3$.

> From A to B, the slope of the curve is negative.
  That is, from $x > -3$ and $x < 2$, the slope
  is negative.
  It can be seen that the slope function is
  negative from $-3 < x < 2$.

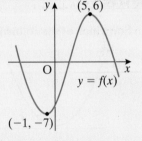

> At $x = -3$ and $x = 2$, the slope of the cubic function is zero.
  At these two x-values, the slope function is also zero.

> For $x > 2$, the slope of the cubic function is positive.
  For $x > 2$, the slope function reflects this since it is also positive for $x > 2$.

Example 1

The graph of the function $y = f(x)$ is shown.
Use the graph to write down the range of values
of x for which

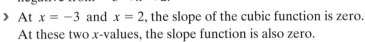

(i) $f'(x) > 0$ (ii) $f'(x) < 0$ (iii) $f'(x) = 0$.

(i) $f'(x)$ represents the slope of the curve at any point.
  $\therefore$ $f'(x) > 0$ for $-1 < x < 5$

(ii) $f'(x) < 0$ for $x < -1$ and $x > 5$

(iii) $f'(x) = 0$ at $x = -1$ and at $x = 5$

Example 2

Draw a rough sketch of $y = f'(x)$ for each of the following graphed functions.

(i) 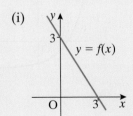   (ii) 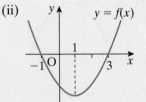   (iii)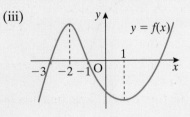

(i) $f'(x) = -1$ ... the slope for all x.

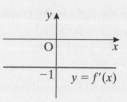

(ii) $f'(x) > 0$ for $x > 1$
$f'(x) < 0$ for $x < 1$
$f'(x) = 0$ for $x = 1$

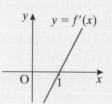

(iii) $f'(x) > 0$ for $x < -2$ and $x > 1$
$f'(x) < 0$ for $-2 < x < 1$
$f'(x) = 0$ for $x = -2$ and $x = 1$

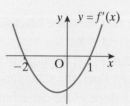

Exercise 4.3

1. For which of the following curves of $y = f(x)$ is $\dfrac{dy}{dx}$ positive for all values of x?

(i)
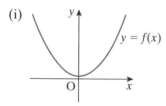

(ii)
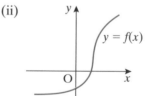

(iii)
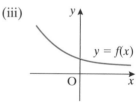

2. For which of the following curves is $\dfrac{dy}{dx}$ negative for all values of x?

(i)
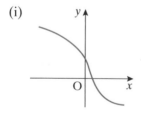

(ii)
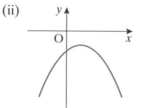

(iii)
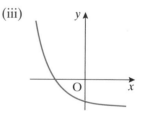

3. The graph of the function $y = f(x)$ is shown on the right.

   (i) Explain what is meant by '$f'(x) > 0$' ?

   (ii) For what range of values of x is $f'(x) > 0$?

   (iii) For what range of values of x is $f'(x) < 0$?

   (iv) For what values of x is $f'(x) = 0$?

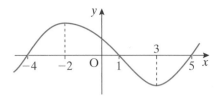

4. Give three reasons why the given line represents the slope function of the given curve.

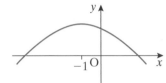 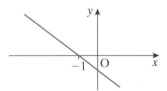

5. The diagram on the right is the graph of a function $y = f(x)$.

Which one of the three graphs below represents the graph of the slope function $y = f'(x)$? Explain your answer.

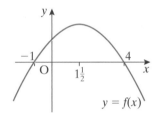

Ⓐ 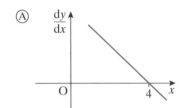   Ⓑ 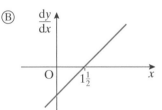   Ⓒ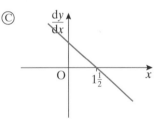

6. The graph of the function $y = f(x)$ is shown on the right.

Which one of the three graphs below represents the slope function of the given curve?

Explain your answer.

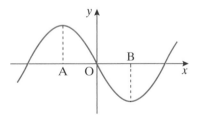

Ⓐ 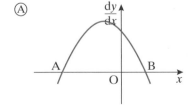   Ⓑ 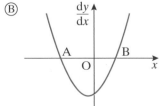   Ⓒ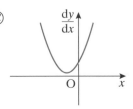

7. For the graph of $y = f(x)$, find:

    (i) $\{x : f'(x) > 0\}$

    (ii) $\{x : f'(x) < 0\}$

    (iii) $\{x : f'(x) = 0\}$

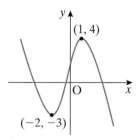

8. Draw a rough sketch of the graph of $y = f'(x)$ for each of the following:

    (i)
    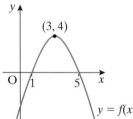

    (ii)
    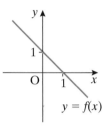

    (iii)
    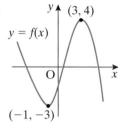

9. The slope function for each of two curves $y = f(x)$ is given below:

    Find (i) the x-coordinate of the turning point of each curve

    (ii) the range of values for x for which each curve is decreasing.

    (a)
    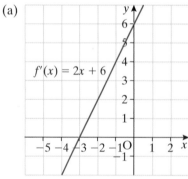

    (b)
    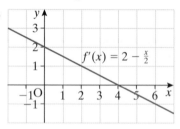

10. The graphs of the slope functions of two curves are given below.

    Find (i) the x-coordinate of the stationary points of each curve

    (ii) the range of values of x for which each curve is increasing.

    (a)
    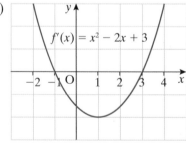

    (b)
    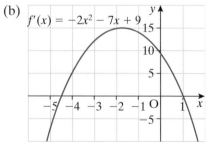

11. The derivative of a function f is given by $f'(x) = x^2 - 9$.
Here are two statements about f:

1. f is increasing at $x = 1$.
2. f has a stationary point at $x = -3$.

Which of the following is true?

A. Neither statement is correct.
B. Only statement **1** is correct.
C. Only statement **2** is correct.
D. Both statements are correct.

12. The graph of the cubic function $y = f(x)$ is
shown in the diagram. There are turning points
at $(1, 1)$ and $(3, 5)$.

Draw a rough sketch of the graph of

   (i) $y = f'(x)$
   (ii) $y = f''(x)$

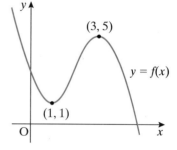

13. The diagram shows the graphs of a
cubic function $y = f(x)$ and its derived
function $y = f'(x)$.

Both graphs pass through the point $(0, 6)$.

The graph of $y = f'(x)$ also passes through
the points $(2, 0)$ and $(4, 0)$.

Given that $y = f'(x)$ is of the form $k(x - a)(x - b)$,

   (i) write down the values of a and b
   (ii) find the value of k.

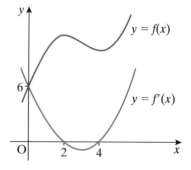

Section 4.4 Maximum and minimum problems

In section 4.2, it was shown that differential calculus can
be used in a very effective way to show that the maximum
value of the given function is 10, and that this occurs
when $x = 2$, as seen from the graph over.

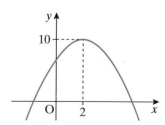

In this section, we will show how differential calculus can
also be used to maximise or minimise the value of any
function, such as €C to represent cost, Area (A) to represent
area, or V to represent volume.

The solutions of the more basic problems involving maxima and minima will consist
of the following steps:

1. Draw a diagram, where necessary, and mark on it the given dimensions.

2. Write down an expression in one variable for the quantity to be maximised or minimised. If the quantity is in two variables, use the given information to express one of the variables in terms of the other so that the quantity may then be expressed in terms of one variable.

3. Differentiate the function and equate it to zero.

4. Solve this equation to find the value(s) of x at which the maximum or minimum value occurs.

5. Substitute this value for x in the given equation to find the maximum or minimum value.

6. Use the second derivative test $\left(\text{i.e. } \dfrac{d^2y}{dx^2}\right)$ to determine if the value(s) for x gives a maximum or minimum value of the function.

Example 1

A factory produces n items per hour.

The overhead costs, $C(n) = €\left(400 - 16n + \dfrac{n^2}{4}\right)$.

How many items should be produced to keep the overhead costs to a minimum?

$C = €\left(400 - 16n + \dfrac{n^2}{4}\right)$

$\dfrac{dC}{dn} = -16 + \dfrac{n}{2}$

$\dfrac{dC}{dn} = 0 \ \Rightarrow \ -16 + \dfrac{n}{2} = 0$

$\Rightarrow n = 32$

$\dfrac{d^2C}{dn^2} = \dfrac{1}{2}$ which is > 0

Since $\dfrac{d^2C}{dn^2} > 0$, $n = 32$ is the number that should be produced to keep the overheads costs to a *minimum*.

Example 2

A closed rectangular box is made of thin metal. The length of the box is three times its width. The volume of the box is $36\,\text{cm}^3$ and its width is x cm.

Show that the surface area is $\left(6x^2 + \dfrac{96}{x}\right)\text{cm}^2$.

Find the dimensions of the box with least surface area.

Volume $= 36\,\text{cm}^3$

$\Rightarrow 3x^2h = 36$

$\Rightarrow x^2h = 12$

$\Rightarrow h = \dfrac{12}{x^2}$

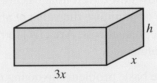

Surface area $= 2(3xh) + 2(xh) + 2(3x^2)$
$$= 6xh + 2xh + 6x^2$$
$$= 8xh + 6x^2$$
$$= 8x\left(\frac{12}{x^2}\right) + 6x^2 = \left(\frac{96}{x} + 6x^2\right) \text{cm}^2 \quad \dots \left(h = \frac{12}{x^2}\right)$$

$\Rightarrow$ Surface area $(S) = \left(6x^2 + \frac{96}{x}\right) \text{cm}^2$

$\dfrac{dS}{dx} = 12x - \dfrac{96}{x^2} \quad \dots \left(\dfrac{96}{x} = 96x^{-1}\right)$

$\dfrac{dS}{dx} = 0 \Rightarrow 12x - \dfrac{96}{x^2} = 0$

$\qquad \Rightarrow 12x^3 - 96 = 0 \Rightarrow x^3 = 8 \Rightarrow x = 2$

To investigate if this value of x gives a maximum or a minimum value, we find $\dfrac{d^2S}{dx^2}$.

$\dfrac{dS}{dx} = 12x - \dfrac{96}{x^2} = 12x - 96x^{-2}$

$\qquad \Rightarrow \dfrac{d^2S}{dx^2} = 12 + 192x^{-3}$

$\qquad\qquad = 12 + \dfrac{192}{x^3} = 12 + \dfrac{192}{8}$ when $x = 2$

$\qquad\qquad = 36 > 0 \Rightarrow$ minimum value

When $x = 2$, the dimensions of the box are:

length $= 3x = 6$; breadth $= x = 2$; height $= \dfrac{12}{x^2} = 3$

$\therefore$ The dimensions are 6 cm by 2 cm by 3 cm.

Example 3

A rectangle is formed by using the positive x-axis and y-axis and a point B(x, y) on the line $2x + y = 6$, as shown.

(i) Find an expression for the area, A square units, of this rectangle in terms of x.

(ii) What is the domain set of values of x?

(iii) Use differentiation to find the maximum possible area of this rectangle.

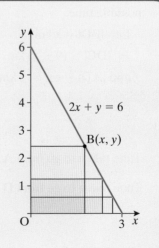

(i) Area = length × breadth
$$A = x(y) = xy$$
We now express the area in terms of one variable.
Since $2x + y = 6 \Rightarrow y = 6 - 2x$
Area $(A) = x(6 - 2x) = 6x - 2x^2$

(ii) Since the line intersects the x-axis at $(3, 0) \Rightarrow 0 < x < 3$.

(iii) $A = 6x - 2x^2$

$$\frac{dA}{dx} = 6 - 4x$$

$\Rightarrow 6 - 4x = 0 \Rightarrow x = 1.5$ ... for a maximum or minimum to occur, $\frac{dA}{dx} = 0$

$\frac{d^2A}{dx^2} = -4$, which is less than zero.

When $x = 1.5$, a maximum occurs since $\frac{d^2A}{dx^2} < 0$.

Maximum area $= 6(1.5) - 2(1.5)^2 = 4.5$ square units.

Example 4

A man wishes to get from a point A on one side of a river to a point C on the opposite side, as shown. The point C is 9 km from the point B which is 3 km directly across the river from A.

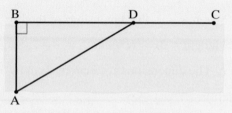

The man can row at 4 km/hr and walk at 5 km/hr. If the man rows from A to D, and walks from D to C, find $|BD|$ such that the man gets from A to C in the least possible time.

Let $|BD| = x$ km
$\Rightarrow |DC| = (9 - x)$ km
and $|AD| = \sqrt{x^2 + 9}$ km

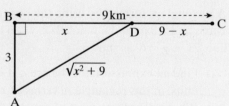

Time taken to go from A to D = $\dfrac{\sqrt{x^2 + 9}}{4}$ hours   ... $\left(Time = \dfrac{Distance}{Speed} \right)$

Time taken to go from D to C = $\dfrac{9 - x}{5}$ hours

$\Rightarrow$ Total time, $T = \left(\dfrac{\sqrt{x^2 + 9}}{4} + \dfrac{9 - x}{5}\right)$ hours

$$= \tfrac{1}{4}(x^2 + 9)^{\frac{1}{2}} + \tfrac{1}{5}(9 - x)$$

$$\frac{dT}{dx} = \frac{1}{4} \cdot \frac{1}{2} \cdot \frac{2x}{\sqrt{x^2 + 9}} - \frac{1}{5}$$

$$= \frac{x}{4\sqrt{x^2 + 9}} - \frac{1}{5}$$

$\dfrac{dT}{dx} = 0 \Rightarrow \dfrac{x}{4\sqrt{x^2 + 9}} - \dfrac{1}{5} = 0$

$$\Rightarrow \frac{x}{4\sqrt{x^2 + 9}} = \frac{1}{5}$$

$$\Rightarrow \frac{x^2}{16(x^2 + 9)} = \frac{1}{25}$$

$$\Rightarrow 25x^2 = 16x^2 + 144$$

$$\Rightarrow 9x^2 = 144$$

$$\Rightarrow x^2 = 16 \Rightarrow x = \pm 4$$

$\Rightarrow x = 4\,\text{km}$ ... disregard the negative answer

$\Rightarrow |BD| = 4\,\text{km}$

Exercise 4.4

1. If $x + y = 6$ and $A = x^2 y$, find the maximum value of A.

2. The perimeter P cm of a certain shape of side x cm is given by $P(x) = \dfrac{1152}{x} + 8x + 20$.
   (i) Calculate the value of x which gives P a minimum value.
   (ii) Determine this minimum value of P.

3. A rectangular piece of ground is enclosed by
   100 metres of fencing. If the length of the enclosure
   is x m, express y in terms of x.
   Hence, find the maximum area that can be enclosed.

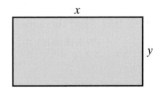

4. In the given right-angled triangle ABC, the lengths of [AB]
   and [BC] vary such that their sum is always 8 cm.
   (i) If $|AB| = x$, express $|BC|$ in terms of x.
   (ii) Find the maximum area of the triangle ABC.

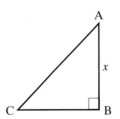

5. A storage tank in the shape of a cuboid has a capacity of $108 \, \text{m}^3$. It has a square base of side x metres with vertical sides and open at the top.

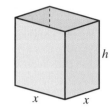

   (i) Express the height, h, in terms of x.

   (ii) Show that the surface area, S, is given by $S = x^2 + \dfrac{432}{x}$.

   (iii) Find the dimensions of the tank if the surface area is to be a minimum.

6. A square sheet of card of side $12 \, \text{cm}$ has four equal squares of side $x \, \text{cm}$ cut from the corners, as shown. The sides are then turned up to make an open rectangle box.

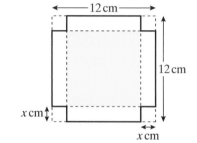

   (i) Express the volume of the box in terms of x.

   (ii) Show that the volume of the box is a maximum when x is 2.

7. A closed rectangular box with a square base of side $x \, \text{cm}$ and height $h \, \text{cm}$ has a total surface area of $54 \, \text{cm}^2$.

   (i) Express h in terms of x.

   (ii) Express the volume of the box in terms of x.

   (iii) For what value of x is the volume at a maximum? Hence, find this volume.

8. The given diagram shows the line $3x + 4y = 12$ containing the point $P(x, y)$. OAPB is a rectangle.

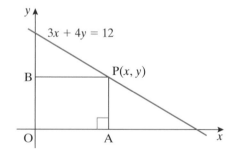

   (i) Express the coordinates of P in terms of x only.

   (ii) Express the area of the rectangle OAPB in terms of x.

   (iii) Find the value of x if the area of OAPB is a maximum and hence find this area.

9. A closed cylindrical can has height $h \, \text{cm}$ and radius $r \, \text{cm}$. If the total surface area is $24\pi \, \text{cm}^2$, find an expression for the volume, $V \, \text{cm}^3$, in terms of r. Hence, find the value of r which will make the volume a maximum.

   [**Note:** The surface area of a closed cylinder is $2\pi r^2 + 2\pi rh$.]

10. The sum of the height and the base radius of a right circular cone is $20 \, \text{cm}$.

   (i) Express the height, h, in terms of the radius, r.

   (ii) For what value of r is the volume a maximum?

11. The perimeter of a sector of a circle of radius r is 8 metres.

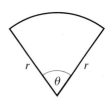

    (i) Express θ in terms of r, where θ is the angle of the sector in radians, as shown.

    (ii) Hence, show that the area of the sector, in square metres, is $4r - r^2$.

    (iii) Find the maximum possible area of the sector.

12. A householder has a garden in the shape of a right-angled isosceles triangle. It is intended to put down a section of rectangular wooden decking at the side of the house, as shown in the diagram.

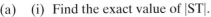

    (a) (i) Find the exact value of $|ST|$.

       (ii) Given that the breadth of the decking is x metres, show that the area of decking, A square metres, is given by
$$A = (10\sqrt{2})x - 2x^2.$$

    (b) Find the dimensions of the decking which maximise its area.

13. The given diagram shows a cylinder cut from a solid sphere of radius 3 cm.

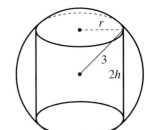

Given that the cylinder has a height of $2h$, find its radius in terms of h.

Hence, show that the volume, V, of the cylinder is given by $V = 2\pi h(9 - h^2)$.

Now find the maximum volume of the cylinder.

14. PQRS is a rectangle formed according to the following conditions:

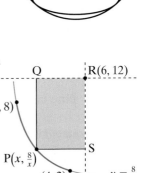

    ❯ it is bounded by the lines $x = 6$ and $y = 12$

    ❯ P lies on the curve with equation $y = \dfrac{8}{x}$ between $(1, 8)$ and $(4, 2)$

    ❯ R is the point $(6, 12)$.

    (a) (i) Express the lengths of [PS] and [RS] in terms of x, the x-coordinates of P.

       (ii) Hence, show that the area, A square units, of PQRS is given by
$$A = 80 - 12x - \frac{48}{x}.$$

    (b) Find the greatest and least possible values of A, and the corresponding values of x for which they occur.

15. The diagram shows part of the curve
    $y = -x^2 + 6x$ crossing the x-axis at the
    origin and at the point B.
    P (x, y) is a point of the curve and PA $\perp$ AB.

    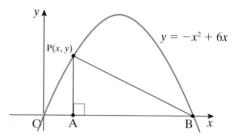

    (i) Express the coordinates of P in terms
        of x only.
    (ii) Express the area of the triangle ABP
        in terms of x.
    (iii) Find the maximum area of the triangle ABP.

16. A beam has a rectangular cross-section of depth x cm and width y cm.
    The strength, S, of the beam is given by $S = 5x^2y$.
    The perimeter of a cross-section of the beam is 120 cm.

    (i) Find y in terms of x.
    (ii) Express S in terms of x.
    (iii) What are the possible values for x?
    (iv) Find the values of x and y which give the strongest beam.
    (v) If the cross-sectional depth of the beam must be less than 19 cm, find the maximum
        strength of the beam.

Section 4.5 Rates of change

In our study of calculus so far, we have seen that $\dfrac{dy}{dx}$ represents the rate of change of y with
respect to x.

Similarly, if V represents volume and t represents time, then $\dfrac{dV}{dt}$ is the rate of change of
volume with respect to time.

It is clear that the process of differentiation may be used to tackle many kinds of problems
involving rates of change.

One of the more important applications of the rate of change concerns the movement of a
particle which starts at a fixed point O.
The **displacement** is defined as the change in position of the particle relative to O.

In this study of motion in a straight line, equations of the type $s = 2t^2 - 3t + 4$
occur frequently.
In this equation, s represents the distance travelled (displacement) and t represents time.

The rate of change of s with respect to t (i.e. velocity) is given by $\dfrac{\mathbf{ds}}{\mathbf{dt}}$.

Velocity may be positive, negative or zero.
If the velocity is positive, the particle is moving to the right.
If the velocity is negative, the direction of the motion is to the left.
A velocity of zero means the particle is instantaneously at rest.

The rate of change of velocity with respect to time is called the **acceleration**, a, of the object in motion.

$\therefore$ acceleration $(a) = \dfrac{dv}{dt}$ or $\dfrac{d^2s}{dt^2}$.

Speed and Acceleration

If s represents the distance travelled in time t, then

(i) $\dfrac{ds}{dt}$ is the velocity of the object at any given time

(ii) $\dfrac{d^2s}{dt^2}$ represents the acceleration of the object.

Note: In the vast majority of the questions in the next exercise, 'velocity' and speed are interchangeable.

Example 1

A body moves in a straight line so that its distance s, in metres, from a fixed point after t secs is given by the equation

$$s = 10 + 27t - t^3.$$

Find   (i)   the speed after 2 seconds
           (ii)   after how many seconds is the body at rest
           (iii)   the acceleration after 2 seconds.

(i) $s = 10 + 27t - t^3$

     Speed $= \dfrac{ds}{dt} = 27 - 3t^2$

               $= 27 - 3(2)^2$

               $= 15$ metres/sec, after 2 seconds

(ii)   If the body is at rest, the speed is zero.

     $\dfrac{ds}{dt} = 0 \Rightarrow 27 - 3t^2 = 0$

              $\Rightarrow 3t^2 = 27 \Rightarrow t^2 = 9 \Rightarrow t = 3$ ... $(t > 0)$

     $\therefore$ the body is at rest after 3 seconds

(iii)   Acceleration is $\dfrac{d^2s}{dt^2}$

     $\dfrac{ds}{dt} = 27 - 3t^2 \Rightarrow \dfrac{d^2s}{dt^2} = -6t$

     $\Rightarrow$ acceleration $= -12$ metres/sec^2, when $t = 2$

Note: metres/sec^2 represents "metres per second per second".

Example 2

A marketing director of a company found that the revenue, €R, from selling a fixed number of produced items at €P each is given by the formula

$$R = 30P - 2P^2.$$

(i) Find $\dfrac{dR}{dP}$ and explain what this means.

(ii) Calculate $\dfrac{dR}{dP}$ when $P = 10$.

(iii) For what selling prices is revenue rising?

(i) $R = 30P - 2P^2$

$$\frac{dR}{dP} = 30 - 4P$$

$\dfrac{dR}{dP}$ is the rate at which the revenue is changing relative to the price, P.

(ii) $\dfrac{dR}{dP} = 30 - 4P = 30 - 4(10) = -10$, when $P = 10$

(iii) The revenue is rising when $\dfrac{dR}{dP}$ is positive.

$$\frac{dR}{dP} > 0 \text{ when } 30 - 4P > 0$$
$$30 > 4P$$
$$4P < 30$$
$$P < 7.5$$

For $P < €7.50$, the revenue increases as P increases.

Note: In general, the phrase "the rate of change of ..." is taken to mean the rate of change with respect to **time**.

However, each question must be read carefully to identify the relevant variables and rates.

Exercise 4.5

1. The relationship between p and q is given by $p = 2q^3 + q$.
   Find the rate of change of p with respect to q when $q = 4$.

2. The variables x and y are linked by the equation $y = 2x^2 + x$.
   (i) Find the rate of change of y with respect to x when $x = 4$.
   (ii) Find the value of x when the rate of change of y with respect to x is 9.

3. The area of a circle of radius r is given by $A = \pi r^2$.
   Find the rate of change of the area of the circle with respect to the radius when the radius is   (i) 5 cm   (ii) 10 cm.

4. Write down the volume of a cube of side x cm. Find the rate of change of the volume with respect to x when

(i) $x = 10$ cm   (ii) the volume $= 125$ cm^3.

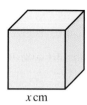

x cm

5. The population, P, of a new housing estate t years after a certain date is given by the formula $P = 100(5 + t - 0.25t^2)$.

Find the rate of change of the population after 3 years.
Explain your answer.

6. The expected assets, €M, of a proposed new company will be given by $M = 200\,000 + 600t^2 - \dfrac{200}{3}t^3$, where t is the number of months after the business is set up.

   (i) Find the rate of growth of assets at time t months.
   (ii) Find the rate of growth of assets when $t = 3$.
   (iii) Will the rate of growth of assets be zero at any time?

7. The distance, in metres, travelled by an object in t seconds is given by the formula

$$s = t^3 - 2t^2 + 3t - 4.$$

Find   (i) the speed and   (ii) the acceleration when $t = 4$.

8. A body moves in a straight line so that the distance, s metres, travelled after t seconds is given by the formula

$$s = t^3 - 4t^2 + 4t.$$

   (i) Find the speed of the body after 3 seconds.
   (ii) Find the acceleration of the body after 1 second.
   (iii) After how many seconds is the body momentarily at rest?

9. An object is projected upwards and its height in metres above its point of projection after t seconds is

$$h = 600t - 5t^2.$$

   (i) After how many seconds is the object momentarily at rest?
   (ii) Find the greatest height, in km, the object reaches.

10. A particle P moves in a straight line. After t seconds, the displacement, in metres, of P from a fixed point O on the line is given by $s = t^3 - 2t^2 + 4t$. Calculate

   (i) the distance between P and O at time $t = 2$
   (ii) the times at which the velocity of P equals 4 metres per second.

11. A particle moves in a straight line so that its position, s cm, relative to O at time t seconds $(t \geqslant 0)$ is given by

$$s = 2t^3 - 5t^2 + 4t - 5.$$

   (i) When is its velocity zero, and what is its acceleration at these points?
   (ii) When is its acceleration zero, and what is its velocity at that time?

12. A particle moving in a straight line is x cm from the point O at time t seconds $(t \geqslant 0)$, where $x = t^3 - 11t^2 + 24t - 3$.

   (i) Find its initial position and velocity.
   (ii) Find its velocity at any time.
   (iii) At what times is the particle stationary?
   (iv) What are the positions of the particle when it is stationary?
   (v) For how long is the particle's velocity negative?
   (vi) Find its acceleration at any time.
   (vii) When is the particle's acceleration zero, and what is its velocity and position at that time?

13. A number of cells, n, grows over time t such that $n = n_0 e^{0.2t}$ where $n_0 = 5$.

   (i) Find the number of cells when $t = 0$ and when $t = 10$.
   (ii) Find the average rate of growth over the period $t = 0$ to $t = 10$.
   (iii) Find the instantaneous rate of growth when $t = 5$.

Section 4.6 Related rates of change

In the previous section, we dealt with the use of the derivative as a measure of the rate of change of a function with respect to the variable.

If $A = \pi r^2$ represents the area of a circle of radius r, then $\dfrac{dA}{dr}$ is the rate of change of the area with respect to r.

However, in practical cases, most rates of change are measured with respect to time. For example, if V represents volume,

$\dfrac{dV}{dt}$ is the rate of change of volume with respect to time.

In many situations, we are given one rate of change and asked to find another rate of change. In these situations, the *Chain Rule* is particularly useful when finding the required rate of change.

The Chain Rule states that $\dfrac{dy}{dx} = \dfrac{dy}{du} \cdot \dfrac{du}{dx}$.

This can be extended to $\dfrac{dy}{dx} = \dfrac{dy}{d\bullet} \cdot \dfrac{d\bullet}{dx}$, where $\bullet$ stands for any variable.

For example, $\dfrac{dA}{dr} = \dfrac{dA}{dt} \cdot \dfrac{dt}{dr}$

If we are given that $\dfrac{dA}{dr} = 8$, then $\dfrac{dr}{dA} = \dfrac{1}{8}$.

Similarly, if $\dfrac{dV}{dt} = 6\pi$, then $\dfrac{dt}{dV} = \dfrac{1}{6\pi}$.

$$\dfrac{dt}{dr} = \dfrac{1}{\dfrac{dr}{dt}}$$

The method of solving problems involving 'related rates' is illustrated in the following examples.

Example 1

The radius of a circle is increasing at the rate of 2 cm/sec.
Find the rate at which the area is increasing when the radius is 3 cm.

We are given $\dfrac{dr}{dt} = 2$ and we require $\dfrac{dA}{dt}$.

$\dfrac{dA}{dt} = \dfrac{dr}{dt} \cdot \dfrac{dA}{dr}$

$\quad = 2.2\pi r$

$\quad = 2.2\pi(3) \quad \dots r = 3$

$\quad = 12\pi$

$\therefore \quad \dfrac{dA}{dt} = 12\pi \, \text{cm}^2/\text{sec}$

To find $\dfrac{dA}{dr}$, we use the

formula $A = \pi r^2$

$\Rightarrow \dfrac{dA}{dr} = 2\pi r$

When solving problems with related rates of change, these steps should prove useful.

1. Write down the rate you require, e.g. $\dfrac{dA}{dt}$.

2. Write down the rate you are given, e.g. $\dfrac{dr}{dt}$.

3. Use the Chain Rule to link these rates: $\dfrac{dA}{dt} = \dfrac{dA}{?} \cdot \dfrac{?}{dt} = \dfrac{dA}{dr} \cdot \dfrac{dr}{dt}$

4. Find an equation connecting the variables of the missing rate, i.e. $A = \pi r^2$.

Example 2

The volume, $V \, \text{cm}^3$, of water in a container is given by the expression $V = 12h^2$, where $h \, \text{cm}$ is the depth of the water.
Water is flowing into the container at a steady rate of 90 cm³/sec.
Find the rate, in cm/sec, at which the depth of the water is increasing when $h = 3$.

We require $\dfrac{dh}{dt}$ and we are given $\dfrac{dV}{dt} = 90$.

Now, $\dfrac{dh}{dt} = \dfrac{dV}{dt} \cdot \dfrac{dh}{dV}$

We need to find $\dfrac{dh}{dV}$

$V = 12h^2 \text{ (given)} \Rightarrow \dfrac{dV}{dh} = 24h \Rightarrow \dfrac{dh}{dV} = \dfrac{1}{24h}$

$\dfrac{dh}{dt} = \dfrac{dV}{dt} \cdot \dfrac{dh}{dV}$

$\qquad = 90 \times \dfrac{1}{24h} = \dfrac{90}{24(3)} = \dfrac{90}{72} = \dfrac{5}{4} \text{ when } h = 3$

$\therefore \quad \dfrac{dh}{dt} = \dfrac{5}{4} \text{ cm/sec}$

Exercise 4.6

1. In each of the following, fill in the missing rate:

   (i) $\dfrac{dA}{dt} = \dfrac{dA}{dr} \cdot \underline{\quad}$

   (ii) $\dfrac{dV}{dr} = \dfrac{dV}{dt} \cdot \underline{\quad}$

   (iii) $\dfrac{dM}{dt} = \dfrac{dM}{ds} \cdot \underline{\quad}$

2. In each of the following, find the indicated rate.

   (i) $\dfrac{dA}{dt} = 8, \dfrac{dA}{dr} = 4, \dfrac{dr}{dt} = ?$

   (ii) $\dfrac{dV}{dt} = 8, \dfrac{dr}{dt} = 2, \dfrac{dV}{dr} = ?$

3. If $\dfrac{dy}{dx} = 10$ and $\dfrac{dx}{dt} = 2$, find $\dfrac{dy}{dt}$.

4. If $A = \pi r^2$ and $\dfrac{dr}{dt} = 1$, find $\dfrac{dA}{dt}$ when $r = 5$.

5. The radius of a circle is increasing at the rate of $3\,$cm/second. Find the rate of increase of the area when $r = 9\,$cm.

6. The side, $x\,$cm, of a square is increasing at the rate of $5\,$cm/sec. Find the rate of increase of the area when the side is $10\,$cm in length.

7. If $M = (2p + 3)^4$, find $\dfrac{dM}{dt}$ when $p = 1$, given that $\dfrac{dp}{dt} = 2$.

8. If $V = \frac{4}{3}\pi r^3$ and $\dfrac{dV}{dt} = 6\,$cm³/sec, find $\dfrac{dr}{dt}$ when $r = 3\,$cm.

9. The volume of a sphere is increasing at the rate of $24\pi\,\mathrm{cm^3/sec}$. Find the rate of increase of the radius when it is 6 cm in length.

10. The perimeter of a rectangle has a constant value of 40 cm. One side, of length x cm, is increasing at the rate of 0.5 cm/sec.

 (i) Find, in terms of x, an expression for the area of the rectangle.
 (ii) Find the rate at which the area is increasing when $x = 3$ cm.

11. The path of a football is given by the equation $y = x - \dfrac{x^2}{40}, x \geqslant 0$.

 If $\dfrac{\mathrm{d}x}{\mathrm{d}t} = 10\sqrt{2}$ for all t, find $\dfrac{\mathrm{d}y}{\mathrm{d}t}$ when $x = 10$.

12. A pump is inflating a spherical balloon. The radius of the balloon is increasing at a rate of 1 cm/sec when the length of the radius is 2 metres.

 (i) Find the rate at which the pump is working (i.e. the rate of change of the volume).
 (ii) If the air continues to be pumped at this rate, find the rate of change of the radius when it is 5 metres in length.
 (iii) At what rate is the surface area of the balloon increasing when $r = 5$ m?

13. A 10m ladder leans against a vertical wall. The top of the ladder is at a height of 8m up the wall and is slipping down the wall at a rate of 1m/sec.

 At what rate is the foot of the ladder sliding along the ground when the top of the ladder is 8m up the wall?

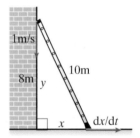

14. A circular cylinder has a radius of r cm, height $4r$ cm and a volume $V\,\mathrm{cm^3}$.

 Express V in terms of r, and hence find an expression for $\dfrac{\mathrm{d}V}{\mathrm{d}r}$.

 The radius is increasing at the rate of 0.5 cm/sec when the radius is 6 cm.

 Find the rate at which the volume is increasing at this instant.

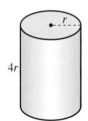

15. A circle has radius r cm, circumference C cm and area $A\,\mathrm{cm^2}$.

 Show that $\dfrac{\mathrm{d}C}{\mathrm{d}A} = \dfrac{1}{r}$.

 The area of a circle is increasing at the rate of $2\,\mathrm{cm^2/sec}$. Find the rate of increase of the circumference when the radius is 3 cm.

Revision Exercise 4 (Core)

1. Find the equation of the tangent to the curve $y = x^2 - \dfrac{9}{x}$ at the point where $x = 3$.

2. Find the stationary points of the curve $y = x^3 - 12x + 5$ and determine if each point is a maximum or a minimum.

3. The curve $f(x) = x^3 - bx^2 - 9x + 7$ has a stationary point when $x = -1$.
   Find the value of b.

4. Find the range of values of x for which the function $f(x) = x^3 + 3x^2 - 9x$ is decreasing.

5. The point $P(x, y)$ lies on the curve with equation $y = 6x^2 - x^3$.
   (i) Find the value of x for which the gradient of the tangent at P is 12.
   (ii) Hence, find the equation of the tangent at P.

6. A particle moves in a straight line so that, after a time of t seconds, its distance s metres from a fixed point O is given by $s = 2t^3 - 24t$.
   (i) Find the speed of the particle after 4 seconds.
   (ii) After how many seconds is the particle at rest?

7. The equation of a curve is $y = x \sin 2x$.
   Find the slope of the curve at the point where $x = \dfrac{\pi}{3}$.

8. For $x + y = 100$, prove that product $P = xy$ is a maximum when $x = y$, and find the maximum value of P.

9. The number of salmon swimming upstream in a river in order to spawn is approximated by $s(x) = -x^3 + 3x^2 + 360x + 5000$, with x representing the temperature of the water in degrees (°C). (This function is valid only if $6 \leqslant x \leqslant 20$.)
   Find the water temperature that results in the maximum number of salmon swimming upstream.

10. The volume of a cube, of edge x cm, is increasing at the rate of 12 cm³/second. Find the rate of increase of the length of the edge of the cube when the volume of the cube is 125 cm³.

11. The equation of a curve is $y = x + \dfrac{4}{x}$.
    Show that $(2, 4)$ is a minimum turning point and find the coordinates of the maximum turning point.
    Find also the set of values of $x > 0$ at which the curve is increasing.

12. The curve of $f(x) = ax^2 + bx + c$ passes through the point $(2, 24)$ and the gradient of the curve at this point is 22.
The value of $f''(x)$ is 6.

  (i) Find the values of a, b and c.
  (ii) Find the coordinates of the points where the curve crosses the x-axis.
  (iii) Find the coordinates of the minimum turning point.

13. Gas is escaping from a spherical balloon at the rate of $10\pi\,\text{cm}^3$ per minute. How fast is the radius decreasing when the radius is 5 cm?

14. A projectile is fired vertically upwards from the ground and the distance, s metres, above the ground is given by $s = 196t - 4.9t^2$, where t seconds is the time measured from the time of projection.
Find the time taken to reach the maximum height and the maximum height attained by the projectile.

15. The graph of a cubic function $y = f(x)$ is shown on the right.

  One of the four diagrams A, B, C, D below shows the graph of the derivative of f.

  State which one it is, and justify your answer.

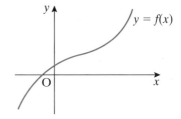

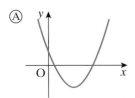 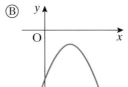 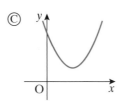 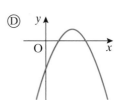

Revision Exercise 4 (Advanced)

1. Find the equation of the tangent to the curve $f(x) = \sqrt{x^2 - 3}$ at the point $(2, 1)$.

2. Find the coordinates of the two points on the curve $y = x^2 + \ln x$ where the slope of the tangent is 3.

3. A spherical hot-air balloon is being blown up so that its volume increases at a constant rate of $2\,\mathrm{m}^3$ per minute.

2 m³/min

   (i) Find the rate of increase of the radius when $r = 2.5\,\mathrm{m}$.
   (ii) Find the rate of increase of its surface area when $r = 2.5\,\mathrm{m}$.

4. The diagram shows a sketch of the curve with equation $y = x^3 - 6x^2 + 8x$.

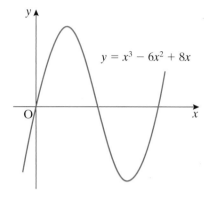

$y = x^3 - 6x^2 + 8x$

   (a) Find the coordinates of the points on the curve where the gradient of the tangent is -1.
   (b) The line $y = 4 - x$ is a tangent to this curve at a point A. Find the coordinates of A.
   (c) Draw a rough sketch of the graph of $\dfrac{dy}{dx}$.

5. The diagram shows a rectangular cake-box, with no top, which is made from thin card. The volume of the box is $500\,\mathrm{cm}^3$. The base of the box is a square with sides of length x cm.

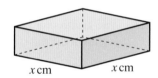

x cm x cm

   (i) Show that the area, $A\,\mathrm{cm}^2$, of card used to make the box is given by $A = x^2 + \dfrac{2000}{x}$.
   (ii) Find the minimum area of card used.

6. The cost of manufacturing an object depends on the time, t hours, spent working on it. The cost $\text{€}C$ can be modelled by the equation $\text{€}C = \dfrac{16}{t^3} + \dfrac{3t^2}{4}$.

   (i) Find the rate of change of the cost when $t = 4$ hours.
   (ii) Find the minimum cost of manufacturing the object.

7. If $y = xe^x$, find $\dfrac{dy}{dx}$.

   Hence, find the coordinates of the turning point of the curve $y = xe^x$ and determine if it is a maximum or a minimum turning point.

8. The graphs of four functions A, B, C and D are given below:

Ⓐ 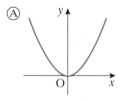   Ⓑ 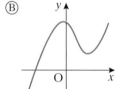   Ⓒ 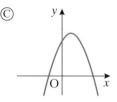   Ⓓ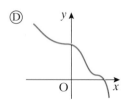

134

The graphs of the slope functions of these four functions are shown below.
Match each graph to the graph of its slope function.

① 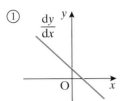 ② 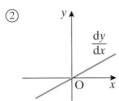 ③ 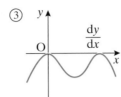 ④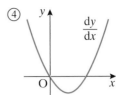

9. The curve $y = x^3 + ax^2 + bx + c$ passes through the point $(1, 1)$ and has turning points at $x = -1$ and $x = 3$.
   Find the values of a, b and c.

10. A drawing for a window has a perimeter of 40 cm.
    It has a semicircular top on a rectangular base, as shown.
    Show that the area of the window, A cm², is given by the

    formula $A = 40r - 2r^2 - \dfrac{\pi r^2}{2}$, where r is the radius of

    the semicircle.
    Find the maximum value for the area, giving your

    answer in the form $\dfrac{a}{b + \pi}$, $a, b \in N$.

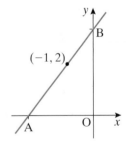

11. A straight line with a positive slope m passes through the
    point $(-1, 2)$ and cuts the x-axis at A, and the y-axis at B.
    Find, in terms of m, the coordinates of A and B.

    (i) Show that the area, A, of the triangle AOB

    is given by $A = \dfrac{(m + 2)^2}{2m}$.

    (ii) Hence, find the minimum value of A.

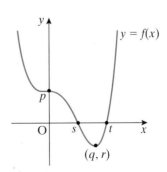

12. The graph of $y = f(x)$ shown has stationary
    points at $(0, p)$ and (q, r).

    Here are two statements about $f(x)$:

    (1) $f(x) < 0$ for $s < x < t$
    (2) $f'(x) \leqslant 0$ for $x < q$

    Which of the following is true?

    A Neither statement is correct.
    B Only statement (1) is correct.
    C Only statement (2) is correct.
    D Both statements are correct.

13. The equation of a curve is $f(x) = x^3 + 3kx^2 + 32, k \in R$.
Find the coordinates of the two turning points of the curve, giving the coordinates of one of these points in terms of k.
Hence, find the value of k for which the equation $f(x) = 0$ has three real roots, two of which are equal.

14. A house is to be connected to a mains gas supply at S, a distance of 4m horizontally away and 3m below the surface.
It costs €25 per metre to lay the pipeline underground and €10 per metre along the ground.

Find the length of pipe used on the surface to minimise the total cost.

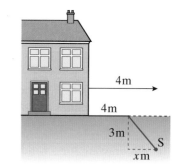

15. The graph of the function $y = f(x)$ is shown on the right.
   (i) Draw the graph of $y = f'(x)$, indicating where the graph intersects the x-axis.
   (ii) Draw a sketch of the graph of $y = f''(x)$. Explain the connection between the point where this graph intersects the x-axis and a significant point on the graph of $y = f(x)$.

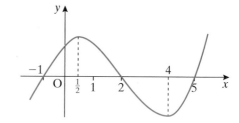

Revision Exercise 4 (Extended Response Questions)

1. This diagram shows a right circular cylindrical metal rod which is expanding as it is heated. After t seconds, the radius of the rod is x cm and the length of the rod is $5x$ cm.

   The cross-sectional area of the rod is increasing at the constant rate of 0.032 cm²/sec.

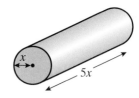

   (a) Find $\dfrac{dx}{dt}$ when the radius of the rod is 2 cm, giving your answer to 3 significant figures.
   (b) Find the rate of increase of the volume of the rod when $x = 2$.

2. A rectangular block is such that the sides of its base are of length x cm and $3x$ cm. The sum of the lengths of all its edges is 20 cm.

   (a) Find an expression, in terms of x, for the height of the block.
   (b) Show that the volume, V cm³, is given by $V = 15x^2 - 12x^3$.

(c) What values of x should be considered, i.e. find the domain of the function with the rule $V = 15x^2 - 12x^3$?

(d) Find $\dfrac{dV}{dx}$.

(e) Find $\left\{ x: \dfrac{dV}{dx} = 0 \right\}$ and hence find the maximum volume possible.

3. The height, h metres, above level ground of a ball thrown vertically upwards is given by $h = 2 + 40t - 5t^2$, where t is measured in seconds and $t > 0$.

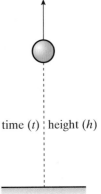

time (t) ⋮ height (h)

  (i) Find the rate of change of the height when
     (a) $t = 2$ (b) $t = 2.5$

 (ii) Find when the rate of change of height is zero. Describe the motion of the ball near this value of t.

(iii) Find the height of the ball when the rate of change of height is zero.

(iv) Find the rate of change of the height when $t = 6$ and interpret the result.

 (v) If the rate of change of height measures the speed of the ball, find the speed with which the ball leaves the hand.

(vi) By finding the value of t, correct to 2 places of decimals, estimate the speed of the ball as it hits the ground.

4. A right circular cone lies inside a sphere of radius 1m, as shown. The centre of the sphere, O, lies x m from the base of the cone.

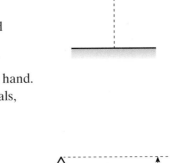

(a) The volume of a cone is given by the formula $V = \tfrac{1}{3}\pi r^2 h$.
   Find: (i) r in terms of x
          (ii) h in terms of x

(b) Show that $V = \dfrac{\pi}{3}(1 + x - x^2 - x^3)$.

(c) State a suitable domain for the function with rule $V = \dfrac{\pi}{3}(1 + x - x^2 - x^3)$.

(d) (i) Find $\dfrac{dV}{dx}$.

     (ii) Find $\left\{ x: \dfrac{dV}{dx} = 0 \right\}$.

   (iii) State the maximum possible volume of the cone.

5. A boatman at the point A is 6 km from the nearest point C on a straight shoreline. He wishes to get to the point B, 10 km from C, where $|\angle ACB| = 90°$.
He can row the boat at 5 km/hr and travel along the shoreline at 13 km/hr.
He rows to the point P where $|PC| = x$ km and then travels by road along the shoreline to B.

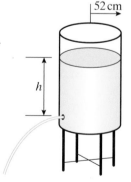

(i) Express $|AP|$ and $|PB|$ in terms of x.
(ii) Find x if the time taken to go from A to B is a minimum.
(iii) Calculate this minimum time, correct to the nearest minute.

6. The population density, P, of a city depends on the radius chosen from the centre of the city.
For a particular city, $P = 10 + 40r - 20r^2$, where P is measured in thousands and r is measured in kilometres from the centre of the city.

(a) What is the population density at the centre of the city?
(b) What are the possible values of r? (i.e. find the domain of values of r.)
(c) Sketch a graph of P against r.
(d) Find $\dfrac{dP}{dr}$.

(e) Evaluate $\dfrac{dP}{dr}$ at $r = 0.5, 1$ and 2.

(f) Find the value of r (the distance from the centre of the city), where the population density is greatest. Hence, find the population density for this value of r.

7. An open cylindrical tank of water has a hole near the bottom. The radius of the tank is 52 cm. The hole is a circle of radius 1 cm. The water level gradually drops as water escapes through the hole.

Over a certain 20-minute period, the height of the surface of the water is given by the formula

$$h = \left(10 - \frac{t}{200}\right)^2$$

where h is the height of the surface of the water in cm, as measured from the centre of the hole, and t is the time in seconds from a particular instant $t = 0$.

(a) What is the height of the surface at time $t = 0$?
(b) After how many seconds will the height of the surface be 64 cm?
(c) Find the rate at which the **volume** of water in the tank is decreasing at the instant when the height is 64 cm.
Give your answer correct to the nearest cm^3 per second.

(d) The rate at which the volume of water in the tank is decreasing is equal to the speed of the water coming out of the hole, multiplied by the area of the hole. Find the speed at which the water is coming out of the hole at the instant when the height is 64 cm.

(e) Show that, as t varies, the speed of the water coming out of the hole is a constant multiple of $\sqrt{h}$.

(f) The speed, in centimetres per second, of water coming out of a hole like this is known to be given by the formula

$$v = c\sqrt{1962h}$$

where c is a constant that depends on certain features of the hole. Find, correct to one decimal place, the value of c for this hole.

8. A container in the shape of a right circular cone of height 10 cm and base radius 1 cm is used to catch water leaking from a tap.
The tap is leaking at a rate of 0.1 cm³/sec.

   (a) Write an equation for the volume of water in the cone in terms of r and h.

   (b) Using similar triangles, find a relationship between r and h.

   (c) Express the volume in terms of h.

   (d) Write the rate 0.1 cm³/sec as a differential.

   (e) Using the chain rule, find the rate at which the water is rising when the water is half-way up the cone.

   (f) Use the result in (e) above to find the rate at which the surface area is increasing at this point.

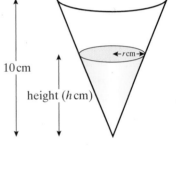

9. A company uses waterproof paper to make disposable conical drinking cups.
To make each cup, a sector AOB is cut from a circular piece of paper of radius 9 cm.
The edges AO and OB are then joined to form the cup, as shown.

The radius of the rim of the cup is r, and the height of the cup is h.

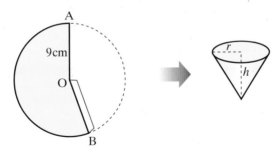

   (a) By expressing r^2 in terms of h, show that the capacity of the cup, in cm³, is given by the formula

$$V = \frac{\pi}{3}h(81 - h^2).$$

(b) There are two positive values of h for which the capacity of the cup is $\dfrac{154\pi}{3}$.

One of these values is an integer.

Find the two values.

Give the non-integer value correct to two decimal places.

(c) Find the maximum possible volume of the cup, correct to the nearest cm³.

(d) Complete the table below to show the radius, height, and capacity of each of the cups involved in parts (b) and (c) above.

In each case, give the radius and height correct to two decimal places.

	cups in part (b)		cup in part (c)
radius (r)			
height (h)			
capacity (V)	$\dfrac{154\pi}{3} \approx 161$ cm³	$\dfrac{154\pi}{3} \approx 161$ cm³	

(e) In practice, which one of the three cups above is the most reasonable shape for a conical cup?

Give a reason for your answer.

(f) For the cup you have chosen in part (e), find the measure of the angle AOB that must be cut from the circular disc in order to make the cup.

Give your answer in degrees, correct to the nearest degree.

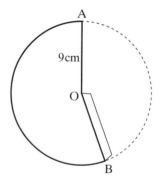

10. A rare species of bird lives only on a remote island. A mathematical model predicts that the bird population, P, is given by

$$P = 150 + 300e^{-0.05t}$$

where t is the number of years after observations began.

(a) According to the model, how many birds were there when observations began?

(b) According to the model, what will be the rate of change in the bird population ten years after observations began?

(c) What does the model predict will be the limiting value (i.e. as t approaches infinity) of the bird population?

(d) The species will become eligible for inclusion in the *WWF endangered species list* when the population falls below 200. When does the model predict that this will occur?

Financial Maths

Key words

future value   present value   compound interest   depreciation   annuity

instalment savings   instalment payments   loans   mortgage

Geometric series are very important in the world of economics where we meet such terms as
(i) Compound Interest   (ii) Future Value   (iii) Present Value   (iv) Pensions   (v) Annuity
(vi) Mortgage repayments   (vii) Instalment savings, etc.

Section 5.1 Compound interest

When the interest earned by a sum of money on
deposit in a bank is not withdrawn, it is added to
the **principal** for the second year.

The interest grows year by year and is said to
be *compounded*.

At a rate of 5% per annum, the increase in the
interest earned by €10 000 can be seen year-on-
year from the table.

Year	Principal	Interest
One	€10 000	€500
Two	€10 500	€525
Three	€11 025	€551
Four	€11 576	€579
Five	€12 155	€608
	€12 763	

If the interest is withdrawn and not reinvested each year, a total of 5 × €500 = €2500 is earned.

Compounding the interest, a total of €2763 is earned.

Generally, if i (per cent, expressed as a decimal) is the interest rate, then $i \times P$ is the interest
earned, where €P is the principal or investment at the beginning of the year.

At the start of the second year, there is $P + iP = \mathbf{P(1 + i)^1}$ on deposit in the bank.

The change in the principal, year-by-year, can be seen from the following table:

Year (end)	Principal	Interest
	P	$i \times P$
one	$P + iP = \mathbf{P(1 + i)^1}$	$i \times P(1 + i)$
two	$P(1+ i) + iP(1 + i) = P(1+ i)(1 + i) = \mathbf{P(1 + i)^2}$	$i \times P(1 + i)^2$
three	$P(1 + i)^2 + iP(1 + i)^2 = P(1 + i)^2(1 + i) = \mathbf{P(1 + i)^3}$	
year t	$= \mathbf{P(1 + i)^t}$	

At the end of year t, there is $€P(1 + i)^t$ on deposit.

For example, €10 000, invested for 5 years at 5% compounded annually, amounts to
€10 000 $(1 + 0.05)^5 = $ €12,763. $\therefore$ the interest gained $= $ €2763.

> **APR** ("Annual Percentage Rate") is the "true" annual rate of interest charged for borrowing money.
>
> **AER** ("Annual Equivalent Rate") is the rate of interest paid on **investments**.

1. Final value

If the interest is fixed for a period of time t, then the principal €P added to the compound interest is called the **final value** of €P.

> The final value of a sum of money €P, invested now at i% for t years, is
> $$\textbf{Final value (F)} = €P(1 + i)^t$$
> $$\textbf{Interest earned} = €P(1 + i)^t - €P$$

Example 1

Find the final value of €5000 invested at 4% (AER) per annum, compounded annually, for 6 years. Find also the interest earned over the period.

Future value $= €P(1 + i)^t = $ €5000 $(1 + 0.04)^6 = $ €6326.60

Interest earned $= $ €6326.60 $- $ €5000 $= $ €1326.60

Example 2

An investment bond offers a return of 15% if invested for 4 years.
Calculate the AER (annual equivalent rate) for this bond, as a percentage, correct to two places of decimals.

A return of 15% after 4 years means that the amount (future value) is 1.15 times the sum invested, €P.

$\therefore \quad €P(1 + i)^4 = €P(1.15)$
$\therefore \quad (1 + i)^4 = 1.15$
$(1 + i) = 1.15^{\frac{1}{4}} = 1.03555$ ... taking the fourth root of both sides
$\therefore \quad i(\text{annual equivalent rate}) = .03555 = 3.555\%$
$$= 3.56\%$$

It is now common practice to have interest "added monthly" to a savings account. In this case a monthly interest rate is applied that is equivalent to the annual rate.

If r is the monthly rate and $i = 5\%$ is the annual equivalent rate (AER), then for 12 payments

$$(1 + r)^{12} = (1 + i) = (1 + 0.05) = 1.05$$
$$\therefore \quad (1 + r) = (1.05)^{\frac{1}{12}} = 1.004074$$
$$\therefore \quad r = 1.004074 - 1 = 0.004074 = 0.4074\%$$

$$\therefore \quad 5\% \text{ per year is equivalent to } 0.4074\% \text{ per month.}$$

Note: i is always expressed as a decimal, e.g. $5\% = 0.05$

To calculate monthly interest rates, $r\%$:
$$(1 + r)^{12} = (1 + i) \qquad r\% \text{ per month}, \quad i\% \text{ per year}$$

Example 3

€5000 is invested at 4% AER. If the interest is added monthly, find the final value of this investment after (i) $3\frac{1}{2}$ years (ii) 5 years 2 months.

The monthly effective rate r is found by solving the equation $(1 + r)^{12} = 1.04$.
$$\therefore \quad (1 + r) = 1.04^{\frac{1}{12}} = 1.003274$$
$$\therefore \quad r = 0.003274 = 0.3274\% \text{ per month.}$$

The final value after
(i) $3\frac{1}{2}$ years $= 3\frac{1}{2} \times 12 = 42$ months
$$\Rightarrow F = 5000(1.003274)^{42} = €5735.77$$

(ii) 5 years 2 months $= 62$ months
$$\Rightarrow F = 5000(1.003274)^{62} = €6123.26.$$

2. Present value

To find the present value of €10 000 due in three years time, we must calculate what sum of money, invested at $i\%$ (e.g. $5\% = 0.05$) compounded annually, would have a final value of €10 000.

$$\text{Final value} = \text{Present value} \times (1 + i)^t$$

$$\Rightarrow \text{Present value} = \frac{\text{Future value}}{(1 + i)^t}$$

$$\text{Present value} = \frac{\text{Final value}}{(1 + i)^t}$$

$$\Rightarrow \text{Present value} = \frac{10\,000}{(1.05)^3} = €8638.38$$

Therefore, at an annual equivalent rate of 5%, the present value of €10 000 (in 3 years time) is €8638.38.

143

Example 4

The local GAA club runs a draw.
You win first prize and you are offered

(a) €15 000 now **or**

(b) €18 000 in four years time.

Which prize should you choose
to have the greatest value? Assume a discount rate of 4%.

> When calculating present value, the rate i% is often referred to as the "*discount rate*".

The present value of €18 000 based on a discount rate of 4% is

$$\text{Present value} = \frac{\text{Final value}}{(1 + i)^t} = \frac{18\,000}{(1.04)^3} = €15\,386.48$$

Therefore, the best value prize, based on a discount rate of 4%, is option (b) €18 000 in four years time.

Summary

Final value: $F = P(1 + i)^t$	Present value: $P = \dfrac{F}{(1 + i)^t}$

Example 5

In how many years would €5000 increase in value to €6500 if invested at an AER of 3.5%?

$$F = P(1 + i)^t$$
$$\therefore \quad €6500 = €5000\,(1.035)^t$$

Method 1 (Logs)(See chapter 12 book 4)

$\Rightarrow \quad (1.035)^t = \dfrac{€6500}{€5000} = 1.3$

$\Rightarrow \quad ln(1.035)^t = ln\,1.3$ ... taking the log of both sides

$\Rightarrow \quad t\,ln(1.035) = ln\,1.3$ ... $ln\,A^n = n\,ln\,A$

$\Rightarrow \quad t = \dfrac{ln\,1.3}{ln(1.035)} = 7.63$ years

Method 2 (Calculator)

$\Rightarrow \quad (1.035)^t = 1.3$

$\Rightarrow \quad t = \log_{1.035}(1.3) = 7.63$ ...

using the [log■□] key on the calculator.

Exercise 5.1

1. Find the final value, correct to 2 places of decimals, of €3000 invested for 10 years at an annual equivalent rate (AER) of 3%.

2. Given an AER of 2.5%, find the final value, correct to 2 places of decimals, of €5000 invested for 8 years. What interest would be paid on this investment?

3. Given $(1 + r)^{12} = (1 + i)$, where r is the interest rate per month and i the interest rate per year, find r in terms of i.

4. What monthly rate of interest, correct to 2 places of decimals, is equivalent to an annual rate of   (i) 6%   (ii) 2.5%   (iii) 4% ?

5. Sean invested €4500 for five years in EUROBANK.
   His investment amounted to €5607.82 at the end of its term.
   Find the AER that applied to his investment.

6. Sandra wins €15 000 in a draw and invests it in a credit union where the AER is 3.5%.

   Copy and complete this chart, showing how the value of her money changes over the five years of the investment.

Year	Principal	Interest
One	€15 000	
Two		
Three		
Four		
Five		

7. Kamil asks for interest to be added half-yearly to his account.
   If the bank offers an AER of 4%, find, correct to four significant figures, the equivalent half-yearly rate.

8. Find the final value of €6500 invested for 6 years 4 months if the monthly equivalent rate is 1.932%.

9. €12 000 is invested at an AER of 3.5%.
   Find the value of the investment after
      (i) 5 years 3 months   (ii) 8 years 2 months   (iii) 10 years 6 months.

10. If a bank offers a discount rate of 4.2%, find the present value of €10 000 due to be paid in 10 years time.

11. Jonathan is 12 years old. When he is 21, he is due to inherit €25 000.
    What is the present value of his inheritance assuming a discount rate of 4.5%?

12. €50000 is invested in a bank offering an AER of 3.5%.
    How long will it take this investment to double in value?

13. I plan to borrow €175 000 to buy a house.
    If the bank charges an AER of 4.5%, what would this loan amount to in 20 years, assuming no repayments?

14. Using logs, find how many years it will take €1130 to have a final value of €3000 if invested at 5% per annum compound interest.

15. The formula $(1 + r)^{12} = (1 + i)$, where r is the interest rate per month and i the interest rate per annum, is used to calculate the effective monthly interest rate.
       (i) If 6% interest is offered per year, calculate the effective monthly rate correct to four places of decimals.

(ii) If *r* was simply calculated by dividing the yearly interest by 12, calculate using both methods, the difference in final values of €10 000 in 3 years at 6% per annum, if the interest is compounded monthly.

(iii) What is the minimum number of places of decimals that need to be taken in calculating *r* before a difference is noted in final values?

16. Anna invests €15 000 at an AER of 3%. After two years, she withdraws €2000 but leaves the remainder of her investment for a further three years.

What is the value of her investment at the end of this period?

Section 5.2 Depreciation

In the previous section, money lodged into a savings account appreciated in value. The final value was greater than the present value.

Depreciation occurs when the final value of an asset is less than the present value. Cars, computers and household appliances generally depreciate in value over time. Houses in Ireland appreciated in value up to 2007 but have since greatly depreciated in value relative to this "peak" value. Two types of depreciation can be considered.

1. **Straight line depreciation** occurs when the value of an object reduces by a constant amount each year.
   For example, take a car costing €20 000 that loses 10% of its original value each year. This car loses €2000 in value each year and so the car has no value after 10 years.

2. **Reducing balance depreciation** occurs when the value of an object reduces by a fixed percentage of its value each year.
   Consider a car costing €20 000 that loses 10% of its value each year on a reducing balance.
   The value of the car after 10 years = €20 000 $(1 - 0.1)^{10}$ = €6973.57.

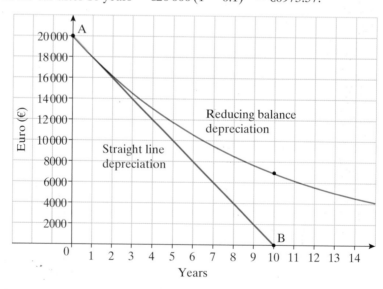

(**Note:** Our course emphasises the reducing balance method for calculating depreciation.)

Similar to compound interest when $F = P(1 + i)^t$, the final value of an item based on a reducing balance is given by the formula $\mathbf{F = P(1 - i)^t}$.

Depreciation: $F = P(1 - i)^t$

F = final value
i = the percentage depreciation of €P per year
t = number of years
P = initial value

Example 1

A company buys a new machine priced at €35 000.
The machine depreciates by 20% on a reducing balance basis each year.

(i) What will the value of the machine be in 4 years time?
(ii) By how much has the machine depreciated in value during this time?

(i) Final value: $F = P(1 - i)^t = €35\,000 \times (1 - 0.2)^4$
$$= €35\,000 \times (0.8)^4 = €14\,336.$$

(ii) Depreciation $= €35\,000 - €14\,336 = €20\,664.$

Example 2

A garage has a petrol stock of 100 000 litres.
If the manager estimates (a) that he will sell 4000 litres a day
                          (b) that he will sell 5% of his stock per day,
calculate the difference in his estimates after 20 days.

After 20 days: $4000 \times 20 = 80\,000$ litres sold
$\Rightarrow$ $100\,000 - 80\,000 = 20\,000$ litres left.

After 20 days the future (depleted) stock, $F = P(1 - i)^t$
$$= 100\,000\,(1 - 0.05)^{20} = 35\,849 \text{ litres}$$

Therefore the difference in his estimates is 15 849 litres.

Exercise 5.2

(In the following exercise, depreciation is used on a reducing balance basis unless otherwise stated.)

1. How much will a car, costing €30 000, be worth in

    (i) five years   (ii) ten years time   based on a depreciation of 15% per annum?

2. A new television costs €1400. Assuming a depreciation rate of 8% per month, find the value of the television after 15 months.

3. A car costing €44 000 depreciates in value by 20% in the first year, and by 15% per year on a reducing balance basis for each subsequent year.
   Find the value of the car after   (i) 3 years   (ii) 6 years.

4. A company buys a machine costing €140 000.
   In order to facilitate its replacement, the company invests €25 000 in a bank offering a return of 3.5% per annum compound interest.
   If the machine depreciates at a rate of 20% per annum, find

   (a)   (i) the value of the machine in 4 years time
         (ii) the value of their savings investment in 4 years time.

   (b)   If inflation over the 4 years averages 2% per annum, find
         (i) the cost of buying a new machine in 4 years time
         (ii) how much money the company will need to add to their savings in order to replace the machine, taking the second-hand value of the machine in 4 years time into account.

   (**Note:** Inflation is a rise in the *general level of prices* of goods and services in an economy.)

5. A company asset reduces in value from €175 000 to €73 187.09, at a depreciation rate of 16% per annum over t years. Find the value of t.

6. A creamery has a stock of 60 000 kg of dried milk powder at the end of January 2004. If the stock is reduced at a rate of 15% per month, find the dried milk stock, to the nearest kg, at the beginning of April 2005.

7. A farmer buys a tractor for €180 000.
   He assumes that the tractor will have a trade-in value of €80 000 in 10 years time.

   (i) Calculate the rate of depreciation per annum, correct to one place of decimals, based on these figures.
   (ii) At this rate, when will the value of the tractor fall below €60 000?

8. A computer is bought for €2500.
   Compare the trade-in value of the computer after 4 years based on

   (a) a net loss in value of €550 per year   or   (b) a loss of 35% per year.

9. A computer system is bought for €23 500. It depreciates at a rate of 28% per annum.

   Find the value of the computer after

   (i) 2 years   (ii) 5 years   (iii) 7 years.

10. An air-conditioning system cost €8000. A straight line depreciation and a reducing balance curve for this system are shown below.

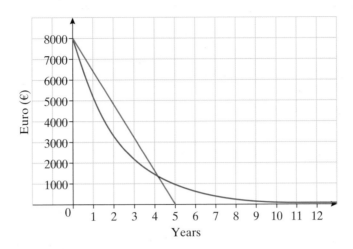

(i)   Using the graph, estimate the rate of depreciation.
      (Let the value after 20 years be €1.)
(ii) Explain why the reducing balance curve can never have a zero value.
(iii) Find the slope of the straight line representing depreciation.
(iv) Estimate the point of intersection of the two graphs.
(v)   After 5 years, what is the value of the system on a reducing balance basis?
(vi) In your opinion, which method of depreciation gives a more realistic value for the system? Explain your answer.

Section 5.3 Instalment savings (annuities)

1. Instalment saving

If a constant amount of money is saved each month for 3 years in total, then each instalment earns different (compound) interest, since it is invested for a different length of time. The first instalment is in the bank for 3 years = 36 months ; the last instalment is in the bank for only one month.

Let €P be invested at the beginning of each month for 3 years at a monthly rate of $i\%$.

The first payment has a value of $P(1 + i)^{36}$ after 36 months.
The second payment has a value of $P(1 + i)^{35}$ after 35 months, etc ...

The total value of the investment is the sum of these 36 individual amounts.

This sum is calculated as follows:

$$P(1 + i)^{36} + P(1 + i)^{35} + P(1 + i)^{34} + \ldots\ldots P(1 + i)^2 + P(1 + i)^1.$$

If we reverse the order, we get

$$P(1 + i)^1 + P(1 + i)^2 + P(1 + i)^3 \ldots\ldots + P(1 + i)^{35} + P(1 + i)^{36}$$

which is the sum of the geometric series where

the first term, $\quad a = P(1 + i)^1$
the common ratio, $\quad r = (1 + i)$
the number of terms, $\quad n = 36$

Using the formula for the sum of n terms of a geometric sequence, $S_n = \dfrac{a(1 - r^n)}{(1 - r)}$, we get

$$\text{final value} = \frac{P(1 + i)[1 - (1 + i)^{36}]}{1 - (1 + i)} = \frac{P(1 + i)[1 - (1 + i)^{36}]}{-i}$$

$$= \frac{P(1 + i)[(1 + i)^{36} - 1]}{i}$$

In general, the **Final value, F, of instalment savings over t instalments is:**

$$F = €P(1 + i)^1 + €P(1 + i)^2 + €P(1 + i)^3 + \ldots €P(1 + i)^t = \frac{€P(1 + i)[(1 + i)^t - 1]}{i}$$

$€P$ = the amount saved at the start of each month/year
t = the number of payments (months/years)
i = the interest rate, expressed as a decimal

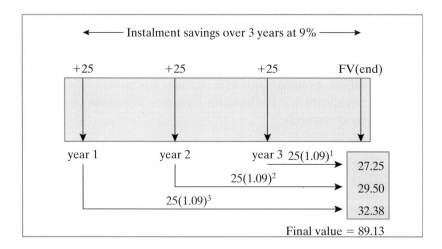

For example, if I save €25 every year for 3 years, the accumulated total (final value) of my savings would be €89.13 at the end of the third year.

Example 1

Catríona saves €400 every three months for five years at an effective quarterly rate of 0.9%.

(i) Represent her savings by a geometric series
(ii) Find the value of her investment at the end of the period.

$i = 0.9\% = 0.009$

5 years $= (5 \times 4)$ quarters $= 20$ payments

(i) Catríona's savings are represented by

$400(1.009) + 400(1.009)^2 + 400(1.009)^3 + \dots + 400(1.009)^{20}$

(ii) $a = 400(1.009)$

$r = (1 + i) = 1.009$

$n = 20$

$S_n = \dfrac{a(1 - r^n)}{(1 - r)}$

$a = $ first term

$S_n = \dfrac{400(1.009)[1 - (1.009)^{20}]}{1 - 1.009}$

$= €8800.89$

Note: In all calculations, the rate "i" is converted from a percentage to a decimal.

E.g. $i = 5\% = 0.05$.

Example 2

Find the sum of money, €P, that needs to be saved per month to cover the cost of a €1500 holiday in 18 months time. The interest rate on offer is 0.4% per month.

The final value (FV) needed $= €1500$

$$F = €P(1 + i) + €P(1 + i)^2 \dots = \dfrac{€P(1 + i)[(1 + i)^n - 1]}{i}$$

$i = 0.4\%$
$n = 18$ $\bigg\}$ $1 + i = 1.004$

$\therefore$ FV $= €1500 = €P(1.004) + €P(1.004)^2 \dots €P(1.004)^{18}$

$\therefore$ $€1500 = \dfrac{€P(1.004)[(1.004)^{18} - 1]}{0.004} = \dfrac{€P \times 0.0748}{0.004} = €P \times 18.70$

$\therefore$ P $= €1500 \div 18.7$

$= €80.21$ per month

2. Pensions

Similar to instalment savings, we can calculate the sum of money needed to be invested now to guarantee a **fixed pension** payable over a number of years.

For example, if I want a pension of €P per year for the next 20 years, I will need to calculate the present value of each of the payments, €P, I will receive.

The total of these "present value" amounts is the sum of money that needs to be invested.

The sum of €P, paid to you at the end of the first year, has a present value now of $\dfrac{€P}{(1 + i)}$.

The sum of €P, paid at the end of the second year, has a present value now of $\dfrac{€P}{(1 + i)^2}$.

The sum to be invested is obtained by summing all these amounts.

$$\frac{€P}{(1 + i)} + \frac{€P}{(1 + i)^2} + \frac{€P}{(1 + i)^3} + \ldots + \frac{€P}{(1 + i)^{20}}$$

This is the sum of a geometric series containing 20 terms, where

$$\therefore\ S_n = \frac{a(1 - r^n)}{(1 - r)} = \frac{P}{(1 + i)} \times \frac{\left(1 - \left(\frac{1}{1 + i}\right)^{20}\right)}{\left(1 - \left(\frac{1}{1 + i}\right)\right)}$$

$$\begin{cases} a = \dfrac{€P}{(1 + i)} \\[2mm] r = \dfrac{1}{(1 + i)} \\[2mm] n = 20 \end{cases}$$

In general, the **Present value (cost), PV, of a pension fund is given by:**

$$PV = \frac{€P}{(1 + i)} + \frac{€P}{(1 + i)^2} + \frac{€P}{(1 + i)^3} + \ldots\ldots \frac{€P}{(1 + i)^t} = \frac{P}{(1 + i)} \times \frac{\left(1 - \left(\frac{1}{1 + i}\right)^t\right)}{\left(1 - \left(\frac{1}{1 + i}\right)\right)}$$

€P = yearly pension
n = number of years (lifetime of pension)
i = fixed rate of interest over the term of the pension

$$= \frac{P}{(1 + i)^t}\left(\frac{(1 + i)^t - 1}{i}\right)$$

Note: Most pensions operate on a guaranteed rate of interest.

However, some may depend on market performance and gain or lose compared to the fixed (guaranteed) rate.

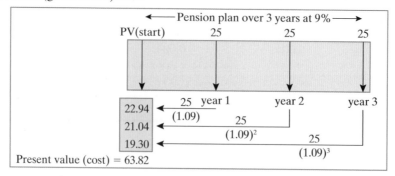

That is, if I want a pension of €25 every year for 3 years, I need to invest €63.82 now.

Example 3

What amount of money is needed now to provide a pension of €25 000 a year for 20 years, assuming an AER of 4%?

$$i = 4\% = 0.04 \quad \Rightarrow \quad 1 + i = 1.04$$

The amount required, or present value (P) of this pension, is represented by the geometric series:

$$P = \frac{25\,000}{1.04} + \frac{25\,000}{(1.04)^2} + \frac{25\,000}{(1.04)^3} + \cdots\cdots\frac{25\,000}{(1.04)^{20}}$$

$$\left.\begin{array}{l} a = \dfrac{€25\,000}{(1.04)} \\[3mm] n = 20 \\[3mm] r = \dfrac{1}{1+i} = \dfrac{1}{1.04} \end{array}\right\} \quad S_n = \dfrac{a(1-r^n)}{(1-r)} = \dfrac{25\,000}{(1.04)} \times \dfrac{\left(1 - \left(\frac{1}{1.04}\right)^{20}\right)}{\left(1 - \left(\frac{1}{1.04}\right)\right)}$$

$$= €339\,758.16$$

Thus, a pension fund of €339 758.16 invested now will provide 20 yearly payments of €25 000.

Note 1: In answering questions on instalment savings and pensions it is best practice to set up the geometric series underpinning each question.
It is important to identify the first term, the common ratio and the number of terms in the series for each particular question.

Note 2: It is also important to have a clear understanding of the time-line of series i.e when the first/last payment is to be made/received.

Example 4

Calculate the final value of an instalment savings plan based on saving €600 at the **start** of each year @ 4% per annum for 5 years.

(i) Calculate the present value of these payments.
(ii) Hence show that if the present value was put on deposit at the same rate for the same length of time, it would have the same final value.

Savings plan: $FV = 600(1.04) + 600(1.04)^2 + 600(1.04)^3 + 600(1.04)^4 + 600(1.04)^5$

$$= €600(1.04)\left(\frac{(1.04)^5 - 1}{0.04}\right) = €3\,379.79 \text{ (at the end of 5 years)}$$

(i) Present value $(PV) = €600 + \dfrac{€600}{(1.04)^1} + \dfrac{€600}{(1.04)^2} + \dfrac{€600}{(1.04)^3} + \dfrac{€600}{(1.04)^4}$

$$= €600 \times \dfrac{\left(1 - \left(\dfrac{1}{1.04}\right)^5\right)}{\left(1 - \left(\dfrac{1}{1.04}\right)\right)} = \dfrac{600}{(1.04)^4}\left(\dfrac{(1.04)^5 - 1}{0.04}\right)$$

$$= €2777.94 \text{ (\textbf{at the start of the 5 years})}$$

(ii) If €2777.94 is invested @ 4% for 5 years its final
value is $€2777.94(1.04)^5 = €3379.79$ (**at the end of the 5th year**).

ICT: Using a graphics calculator or computer software, a comparison between instalment savings and the final value (amount) of a sum of money left on deposit can easily be made.

Saving €600 per year @ 4%: $FV(y) = 600*(1.04)(1.04^x - 1)/(0.04)$
€2778 on deposit @ 4%: $FV(y) = 2778(1.04)^x$ y: the FV in euro
    x: the number of years

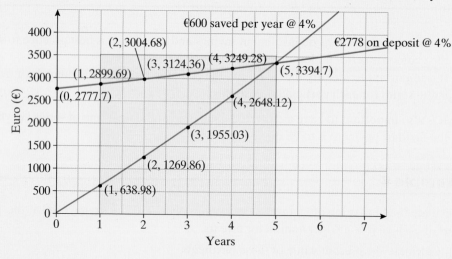

Exercise 5.3

1. Calculate the final value (1 month after the final payment) of 36 monthly instalments of €20.00 at an interest rate of 0.5% per month. What is the total interest earned on these savings?

2. Marie has saved €30.00 per month since her 18th birthday.
    If her bank has guaranteed her an interest rate of 4% per annum, find
    (i) the equivalent monthly rate of interest, correct to two places of decimals
    (ii) the value of her savings on her 21st birthday.

3. A special savings account offers an AER of 4% per annum. If I invest €2000 at the beginning of each year for 5 years into this account, how much will my investment be worth at the end of the 5th year?

4. Show that the final value of a series of n payments of €P, earning an interest rate of i% per annum, can be written as:
$$\text{Final value} = P(1 + i)\left(\frac{(1 + i)^n - 1}{i}\right)$$

5. Show that the present value of a series of n payments of €P, earning an interest rate of i% per annum, can be written as:
$$\text{Present value} = \frac{P}{(1 + i)^n}\left(\frac{(1 + i)^n - 1}{i}\right)$$

6. Anne received a cheque in the post for €6523.33 after saving €A at the start of each year for 5 years with her bank in a scheme offering 9% per annum.
   (i) write down a geometric series representing the value of her investment at the end of the 5th year.
   (ii) find the value of A.

7. (i) If a bank advertises an interest rate of 9% per annum find the equivalent monthly rate.
   (ii) Find the final value (1 month after the final payment) of €200 invested every month for 2 years in this bank.

8. George wants to make regular payments into an account that pays 8.5% per annum compound interest in order to have €10 000 at the end of the 7th year. Find how much he must invest at the beginning of each year.

9. Ella wants to have €5000 in 3 years time.
   She invests in an annuity that pays 7.2% per annum, compounded quarterly.
   How much does she need to deposit each quarter to achieve her target of €5000?

10. Prove that the present value of an annuity (instalments paid at the beginning of each period) is given by:
   Final value (calculated at the end of each period) $\div (1 + i)^n$.

11. Show how the present value of an annuity involving depositing €3000 per year in an account for 6 years can be written as a geometric series, given that the interest rate is 8% per annum. (Assuming each payment is made at the start of each year)
   (i) Calculate the present value.
   (ii) Calculate the future value of the annuity.
   (iii) If the present value of the annuity in (i) was put on deposit as a single investment at 8% per annum, show that it will amount to the same future value of the annuity after 6 years.

Section 5.4 Loans – Mortgages

If we wish to calculate the repayments needed for a car loan or a mortgage on a house, we use the same procedure for finding the present value as was used in the previous section.

The sum of the present values of each repayment over the given period of time must be equal to the value of the car loan or mortgage.

$$€ \text{ Mortgage } (P) = \frac{€ \text{ Payment (A)}}{1 + i} + \frac{€ \text{ Payment (A)}}{(1 + i)^2} + \frac{€ \text{ Payment (A)}}{(1 + i)^3} + \dots \frac{€ \text{ Payment (A)}}{(1 + i)^t}$$

$$€ \text{ Mortgage } (P) = \frac{€ \text{ Payment (A)}}{1 + i} \left[\frac{1 - \left(\frac{1}{1 + i}\right)^t}{1 - \left(\frac{1}{1 + i}\right)} \right] = \left(\frac{€ \text{ Payment (A)}}{1 + i} \right) \left[\frac{\frac{(1 + i)^t - 1}{(1 + i)^t}}{\left(\frac{i}{1 + i}\right)} \right]$$

$$= \left(\frac{€ \text{ Payment (A)}}{i} \right) \left[\frac{(1 + i)^t - 1}{(1 + i)^t} \right]$$

$$\therefore \quad € \text{ Payment (A)} = € \text{ Mortgage } (P) \frac{(i)(1 + i)^t}{(1 + i)^t - 1}$$

i = the effective monthly rate of interest (expressed as a decimal)
t = the number of payments
€ Mortgage (P) = the amount of the mortgage or loan
€ Payment (A) = the repayment per month

(formulae and tables, p.31)

Example 1

Calculate the size of the monthly repayments needed for a car loan of €10 000 if the loan is to be repaid over a 5-year term at an effective monthly rate of 0.72%.

$i = 0.72\% = 0.0072 \implies 1 + i = 1.0072$

$n = 5 \times 12 = 60$ repayments

$$\therefore \quad € \text{ A (Repayment)} = € P \,(\textit{Loan}) \, \frac{(i)(1 + i)^t}{(1 + i)^t - 1} = \frac{€10\,000(0.0072)(1.0072)^{60}}{(1.0072)^{60} - 1}$$

$$= €206 \quad \dots \text{ correct to the nearest euro}$$

Note: When using the mortgage/loan formula, each (re)payment is paid at the end of each accounting period, i.e. at the end of a month or at the end of a year.

Example 2

Find the monthly repayments required for a mortgage of €150 000, based on an annual rate of 4.5% over 20 years.

We first find the effective monthly rate:

$(1 + r)^{12} = (1 + i)$, where $r\%$ = rate per month and $i\%$ = rate per year.

$\Rightarrow (1 + r)^{12} = 1.045$

$\Rightarrow (1 + r) = (1.045)^{\frac{1}{12}} = 1.00367$

$\Rightarrow r = 0.00367$ per month = 0.367% per month

$n = 20 \times 12 = 240$ payments

$$\therefore \text{€}A = \text{€}P\frac{(i)(1 + i)^t}{(1 + i)^t - 1} = \frac{\text{€}150\,000\,(0.00367)(1.00367)^{240}}{(1.00367)^{240} - 1} = \text{€}941.22$$

Therefore the monthly repayment is €941.22.

Exercise 5.4

1. Calculate the monthly repayments required for a mortgage of €200 000, paid over a 30-year period at an annual interest rate of 6%.

2. Alice wants to take out a 20-year mortgage.
   The interest rate over the lifetime of the mortgage is 8% per annum.
   Alice can afford repayments of €850 per month.
   What is the largest mortgage she can afford?
   Give your answer to the nearest €100.

3. What is the monthly payment, correct to the nearest euro, on a mortgage of €75 000, assuming an interest rate of 8%, for
   (a) 20 years   (b) 25 years   (c) 30 years?
   How much interest is paid under each option?

4. Your local car dealer offers you two different payment plans to buy a €15 000 car.
   Plan A: A 10% discount on the price of the car and a loan on the balance at an annual rate of 9% for 5 years.
   Plan B: No discount but a loan for the total price €15 000 at an annual rate of 3% for 5 years.
   Which plan should you opt for?

5. A woman has saved €250 000 to fund a pension and she now plans to retire.
   She wishes to draw down equal annual instalments from these savings for the next 25 years.
   Assuming a 5% interest rate, calculate the value of each yearly instalment.

6. Two people want to buy your house. The first person offers you €200 000 now. The second person offers you 25 annual payments of €15 000 each.
   Assuming you can get an annual rate of 5% on your money, which offer should you accept?

7. Malcolm needs €400 per month, for 3 years, while he studies at college.
   What amount of money do his parents need to invest, at 6.6% p.a. compounded monthly, to provide the money that Malcolm needs?

Revision Exercise 5 (Core)

1. A woman invests €1000 each year at 8% per annum, compound interest.
   Find the value of her investment after 5 years.

2. €300 is invested each month for eight years.
   Find the total value of the investment after eight years, assuming a constant rate of 6% per annum.

3. A car loan of €20 000 is to be repaid in 25 equal instalments.
   If the effective interest rate is 2%, calculate the amount of each instalment, correct to the nearest euro.

4. Silvia is planning an overseas trip lasting 3 years and she estimates that she will need €600 per month for expenses.
   How much money does she need to have saved to fund this trip?
   Assume a rate of interest of 4% per annum over the period of the trip.

5. A credit card company offers clients an introductory interest rate on outstanding balances of 1.25% per month, and a regular rate of 2.5% per month after 1 year.
   Find the equivalent interest rates (AER) per annum.

6. John makes savings of €200 at the beginning of each month for 5 months at an effective monthly rate of 0.75%.
   Express these savings as a geometric series.
   Write down the first term, the common ratio and an expression for the sum of the five terms.

7. Find what €1600 would amount to if invested at the beginning of each year for 5 years at 6% p.a. compound interest.

8. Kris is investing in an annuity by saving €3000 per year at 7.3% p.a. for 8 years.

   (i) Find the final value of the annuity if the investment is made at the start of each year.

   (ii) By finding the present value of all his payments, calculate the single amount of money which could be invested at the same rate and for the same amount of time to give the same final payment.

   (iii) Find the final value of the sum of money from (ii) if it is invested at 7.3% for 8 years.

Revision Exercise 5 (Advanced)

1. Your company has an expected pension liability of €500 000 in 10 years time.

   (i) What amount of money would you now require to cover this expected liability. Assume an annual rate of 9%.

   (ii) How much would you need to set aside at the end of each year for the next 10 years to cover the liability (assume the same rate applies)?

2. Which is the better result at the end of 20 years?

   (i) An investment of €100 000 at 12% per annum compounded monthly **or**

   (ii) €1000 invested monthly at 12% per annum compounded monthly.

3. The graphs of two different bank accounts, C and D, are shown below.
   The interest rate applying to each account is the same.
   Use the data in the graphs to calculate the rate of interest applying to both accounts.
   Describe the difference between the accounts.
   Calculate the value of account C after 5 years.

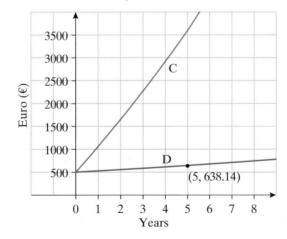

4. A bank offers you a rate of 10% on a 20-year mortgage to be paid in monthly repayments.
   If the most you can afford to pay in monthly repayments is €700, find the value of the biggest mortgage you can afford.

5. Assume that you are going to retire in 25 years time.
   You want a mortgage of €100 000 now to extend and renovate your house but want to have it paid in full before you retire. The maximum repayment per month your budget will allow is €800. What is the rate of interest you need from your bank to have the loan repaid in 300 monthly payments (i.e. 25 years)?

6. A ten-year pension fund of €127 953 is to be drawn down at the rate of €15 000 per year.

   If a 3% annual rate applies to the fund, copy and complete this chart which indicates the value of the fund at the start of each year.

Year	Pension fund	Interest	Payment
One	€127 953	€3838.59	€15 000
Two	€116 791.59	€3503.75	€15 000
Three	€105 295.38		€15 000
Four			€15 000
Five			€15 000
Six			€15 000
Seven			€15 000
Eight			€15 000
Nine			€15 000
Ten			€15 000

Revision Exercise 5 (Extended Response Questions)

1. Assume that the APR charged by a bank is 5%, compounded annually.
   Copy and complete the following charts which compare the principal still owing after the repayments of
   (i) €6000 (ii) €12 000 per year on a principal loan of €100 000.
   Calculate the amount still owing after 10 years using each re-payment scheme.

Year	Principal	Interest	Payment
One	100 000	5000	6000
Two	99 000	4950	6000
Three	97 950		6000
Four			6000
Five			6000
Six			6000
Seven		4659.9	6000
Eight			6000
Nine			6000
Ten			6000

Year	Principal	Interest	Payment
One	100 000	5000	12 000
Two	93 000	4650	12 000
Three	85 650		12 000
Four			12 000
Five			12 000
Six			12 000
Seven			12 000
Eight		2150.3	12 000
Nine			12 000
Ten			12 000

2. You are 35 years-old today and you are planning for your retirement needs.
   You expect to retire at the age of 65 years and actuarial studies suggest that you will live to be a 100 year-old.
   You want to move to a country location when you retire.
   You estimate that it will cost you €300 000 to move (on your 65th birthday) and your living expenses will be €20 000 a year, starting at the end of the first year after retirement.
   Assume an average annual rate of 4% over the lifetime of the plan, including retirement.
   (i) How much will you need to have saved on your retirement to afford this plan?
   (ii) You have €40 000 in savings now.
       If you can invest this money (tax-free) at 5% per year, how much money do you need to save each year in order to afford your retirement plan?
   (iii) If you have no savings and could not start saving for another 5 years, how much would you then have to set aside each year to afford this plan assuming $i = 5\%$?

3. You want to take out a building society mortgage of €100 000 advertised at a rate of 9% p.a..
   However, you can only afford €800 per month repayments.
   (i) Write an equation for the repayments of a mortgage, explaining each term in the equation.
   (ii) Calculate the monthly interest rate equivalent to 9% p.a..
   (iii) Calculate the number of payments needed to clear the mortgage.
   (iv) How long would you need to clear this mortgage in full?

4. Richard and Natalie take out a loan of €150 000 over 30 years at 8.25% p.a. interest, compounding monthly. Their repayments are fixed at €1127 per month.
   (i) Using a spreadsheet similar to the one below, calculate the amount of the loan remaining after 5 years.

	A	B	C	D	E
1	Mortgage	Interest	Payment	Balance	
2	150000	994	1127	149867.2	
3	149867.2	993.32	1127	149733.5	
4	149733.5	992.43	1127	149599	
5	149599	991.54	1127	149463.5	
6	149463.5	990.64	1127	149327.1	
7					

(Note: By highlighting row 3 and by clicking and dragging the bottom right-hand cross, the balance on the account can be seen month-by-month.)
   (ii) After how many payments will this loan be cleared?
       Give your answer correct to the nearest month.
   After 5 years of repaying the loan, they make a lump-sum payment of €40 000.
   (iii) How long will it take to repay the loan after this payment?

5. A lottery game in the USA offers a first prize with an advertised jackpot of $21.5 million. This prize is to be given in 26 annual instalments each of $A, with the first instalment given immediately.

The value of the payment is guaranteed to increase by 4% each year.
  (i)   Write down, in terms of A, the amount of each of the first four payments.
  (ii) Hence write down a geometric series representing the jackpot of $21.5 million.
  (iii) Find, correct to the nearest dollar, the value of $A.
  (iv) Using your value for A and your answer to (i), complete a chart of the first four payments.

Payment number	1	2	3	4
Actual amount		$504 607		$545 783

  (v)   A cash-value option exists whereby the winner receives now the present value of each of the payments.
        The interest rate used for the cash option is 4.78%.
        Using the chart in (iv), complete the following table:

Payment number	1	2	3	4
Present value	$485 199		$478 002	

  (vi) Write down, in terms of n, an expression for the present value of the nth annual payment.
  (vii) Find the total sum of the present values, i.e., the prize money payable under the cash-value option.
  (viii) This jackpot was won recently and the winner received $7.9 million as the cash-value option after tax.
        Using your answer to (vii), find the percentage of tax charged on her winnings.
        (Adapted from SEC Leaving Certificate 2011.)

Length – Area – Volume

chapter

6

Key words

| polygon | area | perimeter | diagonal | trapezium | cyclic quadrilateral |
| arc | sector | radian | quadrilateral |

Section 6.1 Revision

In the following table, we revise key properties of 2-dimensional shapes already encountered in your study of mathematics.

Shape	Diagram	Properties
Square		› all sides have the same length › all angles are 90° › perimeter = $4x$ › area = x^2 › diagonal = $\sqrt{2}x$ › diagonals perpendicularly bisect each other
Rectangle		› opposite sides have the same length › all angles are 90° › perimeter = $2(x + y)$ › area = xy › diagonal = $\sqrt{x^2 + y^2}$ › diagonals have the same length › diagonals bisect each other
Parallelogram		› opposite sides have the same length › opposite angles are equal › perimeter = $2(x + y)$ › area = $yh = yx \sin \theta$ › diagonals bisect each other

| Triangle | 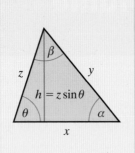 | > perimeter $= x + y + z$
 > area $= \frac{1}{2}x.h = \frac{1}{2}x.z.\sin\theta$
 > $\dfrac{y}{\sin\theta} = \dfrac{z}{\sin\alpha}$
 > types include isosceles, equilateral, scalene, right-angled
 > $\alpha + \beta + \theta = 180°$
 > special right-angled triangles with sides
     • $3, 4, 5$ ...... $(36.9°, 53.1°, 90°)$
     • $1, \sqrt{3}, 2,$ ...... $(30°, 60°, 90°)$
     • $1, 1, \sqrt{2}$ ...... $(45°, 45°, 90°)$ |

1. Trapezium

A **trapezium** is a quadrilateral which has one pair of parallel sides.

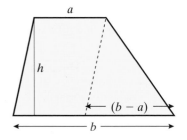

The area of a trapezium $= ah_{\text{parallelogram}} + \frac{1}{2}(b - a)\,h_{\text{triangle}}$

$$= ah + \tfrac{1}{2}bh - \tfrac{1}{2}ah$$

$$= \tfrac{1}{2}ah + \tfrac{1}{2}bh = \left(\frac{a+b}{2}\right)h$$

$$= \text{half the sum of the lengths of the parallel sides times the height.}$$

Example 1

If a parallelogram has a base of 10 cm, and a trapezium of the same area and height has a base of 14 cm, find x, the length of the other parallel side of the trapezium.

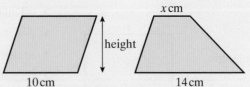

Area of parallelogram = Base × perpendicular height (h) = $10h$

Area of trapezium = $\frac{1}{2}(x + 14) \times$ perpendicular height (h) = $\frac{1}{2}(x + 14)h$

$\therefore\quad 10h = \frac{1}{2}(x + 14)h$

$\Rightarrow\quad 20 = x + 14$

$\Rightarrow\quad x = 6 \quad \Rightarrow\quad$ the other parallel side = 6 cm

POLYGONS

   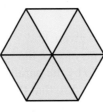 

| triangle | quadrilateral | pentagon | hexagon | heptagon |

2. Polygons

A **polygon** is a plane (2-dimensional) shape with straight edges.

Regular polygons are symmetrical, with a base triangle repeated in polygons with more than 4 sides. The interior angles of regular polygons are:

Triangle = 60°, Quadrilateral = 90°, Pentagon= 108°, Hexagon = 120°, Heptagon = 128.6°

Example 2

The area of the regular pentagon shown here is 600 cm². Calculate the length of one side, x, of the pentagon.

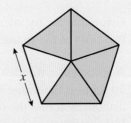

Since the total angle at the centre of the pentagon = 360°,

∴ each angle at the centre = $\dfrac{360°}{5}$ = 72°.

Each triangle is congruent and has equal base angles = $\dfrac{(180 - 72)°}{2}$ = 54°

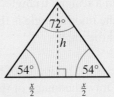

Each triangle has an area of $\left(\dfrac{600}{5}\right)$ cm² = 120 cm².

$\text{Tan } 54° = \dfrac{h}{\frac{x}{2}}$ ⇒ $h = \dfrac{x}{2}\tan 54°$

The area of the triangle $= \dfrac{1}{2} \times \text{base} \times h = \dfrac{1}{2} \times x \times h = 120 \text{ cm}^2$

$\qquad\qquad\qquad\qquad = \dfrac{1}{2} \times x \times \dfrac{x}{2}\tan 54° = 120 \text{ cm}^2$

⇒ $x^2 = \dfrac{480}{\tan 54°} = 348.74$ ⇒ $x = 18.675 = 18.7 \text{ cm}$

Exercise 6.1

1. A parallelogram is drawn inside a rectangle as shown.
   Using the measurements given, find
   (i) the fraction, in terms of a, of the rectangle's area that is taken up by the parallelogram
   (ii) the value of a required so that the area of the parallelogram $= \frac{4}{5}$ the area of the rectangle.

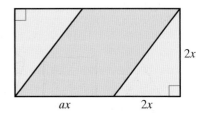

2. Calculate, in terms of x,
   (i) the area of the darker section of the rectangle
   (ii) the area of the lighter section of the rectangle
   (iii) the ratio of these areas.
   (Note; arrows indicate parallel lines.)

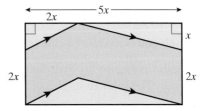

3. If the height of a triangle is 5 cm less than the length of its base, and if the area of the triangle is 52 cm², find the length of the base and also the height of the triangle.

4. Given that the hypotenuse of a right-angled triangle is 41 cm, and the sum of the other two sides of the triangle is 49 cm, find the lengths of these two sides.

5. A rectangular wooden frame is built to lay a concrete foundation for a patio.
   To support the frame while the concrete is being poured, steel cables are fixed diagonally across the rectangle and protrude out of the frame by 50 cm.
   If the perimeter of the frame is 14 m, and the length of the frame is one metre longer than its width, find the length of steel cable required.

6. In a scalene triangle, the smallest angle is two thirds the size of the middle angle, and the middle angle is three sevenths the size of the largest angle. Find the measure of all three angles.

7. E is the midpoint of [DC].
   Draw the image of the trapezium ABCD rotated by 180° about the point E.
   (i) What shape is made by the image and the original trapezium?
   (ii) What is the area of this composite shape?
   (iii) Explain how this proves the formula for the area of a trapezium.

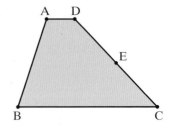

8. Three times the width of a certain rectangle exceeds twice its length by 3 cm, and four times its length is 12cm more than its perimeter.
   Find the dimensions of the rectangle.

9. Peter has three narrow rods of lengths p, q, and r, where $|p| > |q| > |r|$.
   He wants to make a trapezium shape with two right angles as shown. The dotted line completes the trapezium.
   Draw the three possible arrangements of rods.
   Given the inequality above, find which arrangement has the greatest area.
   (Note: if $a > b$, then $ac > bc$, given $c > 0$)

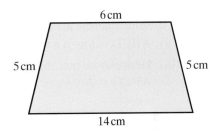

10. Using the measurements given, find the area of this trapezium.
    (Diagram not to scale.)

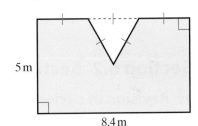

11. (i) The area of an equilateral triangle is $173\,\text{cm}^2$. Find the length of one side.

    (ii) The length of one side of an equilateral triangle is $10.75\,\text{cm}$.
    Find the perpendicular height of the triangle and hence find the area of the triangle.
    Verify your answer by using the triangle area formula $\frac{1}{2}ab \sin C$.

12. Find the area of this figure in square metres, correct to 3 decimal places.

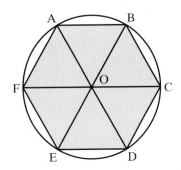

13. A regular hexagon is circumscribed by a circle of radius $5\,\text{cm}$. Find

    (i) the size of the angle EOD
    (ii) the size of the angle ODE
    (iii) the area of the hexagon ABCDEFA.

14. A composite design of regular polygons is shown.

    (i) Find the sizes of the angles α, β, θ
    (ii) If the square has a side of $4\,\text{cm}$, find the area of this composite shape correct to one place of decimals.

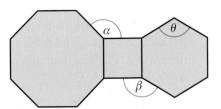

15. A drawing of the cross-section of a skip is shown. The skip company wants to draw a line along the side of the skip indicating half-full. By forming simultaneous equations using the dimensions given, find the

    (i) length of the line x and
    (ii) the height, y, of the line above the base.

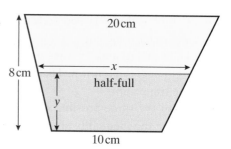

16.   (i) Show that the area of $\triangle ABD : \triangle CBD = |AD| : |DC|$.

    (ii) ABCD below is a trapezium. Prove that Area c = Area d.

    (iii) Hence show that the area of the trapezium
        ABCD = Area a + Area b + $2\sqrt{\text{Area } a.\text{Area } b}$.

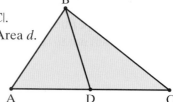

ICT: Using suitable computer software, similar trapeziums can be drawn with diagonals as shown.
This area formula can then be verified by using the software to calculate the separate areas.

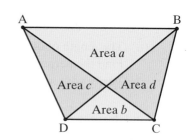

Section 6.2 Sectors of circles

1. Revision of circles and sectors of circles

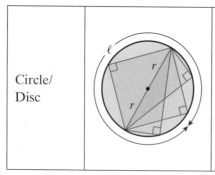

Circle/ Disc		• perimeter (circumference) = ℓ; since $\dfrac{\ell}{2r} = \pi$ $\Rightarrow \ell = 2\pi r$ • area = πr^2 • a cyclic quadrilateral is a quadrilateral inscribed in a circle • every triangle inscribed in a semicircle is a right-angled triangle • $360° = 2\pi$ **radians**

2. Arc of a circle

In the chapter on trigonometry, the length of an arc, the area of a sector, and radian measure were introduced. The length of an arc of a circle is found using the ratios

$$\frac{\ell}{2\pi r} = \frac{\theta(\text{degrees})}{360} = \frac{\theta(\text{radians})}{2\pi}$$

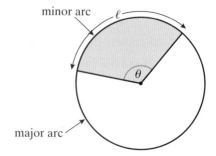

$$\therefore \text{ Length of arc } (l) = 2\pi r \frac{\theta(\text{degrees})}{360} = 2\pi r \frac{\theta(\text{radians})}{2\pi}$$
$$= r\theta \ (\theta \text{ in radians})$$

3. Area of a sector

Similarly, the area of a sector of a circle is found using the ratios

$$\frac{A}{\pi r^2} = \frac{\theta(\text{degrees})}{360} = \frac{\theta(\text{radians})}{2\pi}$$

$$\therefore \text{ Area of sector } (A) = \pi r^2 \frac{\theta(\text{degrees})}{360} = \pi r^2 \frac{\theta(\text{radians})}{2\pi} = \tfrac{1}{2}r^2\theta \ (\theta \text{ in radians})$$

Example 1

A flowerbed in the shape of a section of a sector of a circle is placed in the centre of a rectangular lawn, as shown in the diagram. Calculate

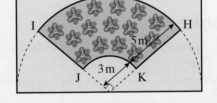

(i) the length of edging needed for the flowerbed
(ii) the area of grass in the garden.

Correct each answer to one place of decimals.

(i) length of large arc $\text{IH} = 2\pi r \dfrac{\theta(\text{degrees})}{360} = \left(\dfrac{90}{360}2\pi 8\right)\text{m} = 4\pi\,\text{m}$

length of small arc $\text{JK} = \left(\dfrac{90}{360}2\pi 3\right)\text{m}$

$= \dfrac{3\pi}{2}\,\text{m}$

Total perimeter =

$4\pi + \dfrac{3\pi}{2} + (2 \times 5) = \left(\dfrac{11\pi}{2} + 10\right)\text{m}$

$= 27.3\,\text{m}$

.... edging needed

(ii) The area of the sector (flowerbed portion) =
Area of large sector − Area of small sector

$= \left(\dfrac{90}{360}\right)\pi 8^2\,\text{m}^2 - \left(\dfrac{90}{360}\right)\pi 3^2\,\text{m}^2 = \left(\dfrac{90}{360}\right)55\pi\,\text{m}^2 = 43.197\,\text{m}^2$

Area of rectangle $= (8 \times 16)\,\text{m}^2 = 128\,\text{m}^2$

$\therefore$ The area of grass $= (128 - 43.197)\,\text{m}^2 = 84.8\,\text{m}^2$

Example 2

A minor arc CD of a circle, centre O and radius 20 cm, subtends an angle
x radians at O. The major arc CD of the circle subtends an angle $5x$ radians at O.
Find, in terms of π, the length of the minor arc.

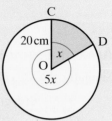

$$x + 5x = 2\pi$$

$$x = \frac{2\pi}{6} = \frac{\pi}{3}$$

The length of the minor arc $= r\theta = 20x = \dfrac{20\pi}{3}$ cm

(Note: This is an exact measurement. An approximate answer
is obtained when we substitute a value for π.)

ICT: Many of the questions below contain geometric shapes which are easily
displayed using computer software, e.g. Geogebra. Answers can therefore be
verified, and variations studied, as time allows.

Exercise 6.2

1. A drawing of a curved flower bed is shown.
   The scale in the drawing is 1 cm : 1 m.
   Calculate, correct to 1 place of decimals,

   (i) the perimeter of the bed
   (ii) the area of the bed.

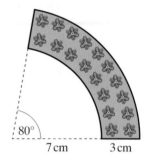

2. Find:
   (i) the total area, correct to the nearest cm^2
   (ii) the total perimeter enclosed by this composite figure,
   correct to the nearest cm.

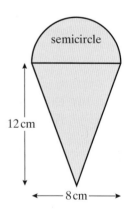

3. Write a formula for each of the following shaded areas.

(a)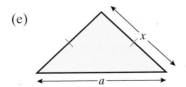

(b)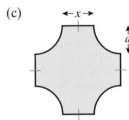

(c)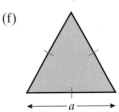

(d)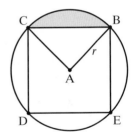

(e)

(f)

4. Write a formula for the radius of the sector of a circle in terms of the perimeter P of the sector and the angle θ radians subtended at the centre.

5. The points R and S lie on the circumference of a circle with centre O and radius 8.5 cm. The point T lies on the major arc RS.
Given that $|\angle RTS| = 0.4$ radians, calculate the length of the minor arc RS.

6. A square is inscribed inside a circle of radius r. Find
   (i) the area of the square BCDE
   (ii) the shaded area in terms of r.

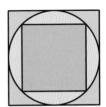

7. A farmer has 80 metres of fencing to make a circular chicken coop.
Find the radius and the area of the coop to a suitable degree of accuracy.
Explain why the radius cannot be measured with complete accuracy.

8. (i) A circle is shown with both an inscribed and a circumscribed square.

   Find the ratio of the area of the inner square to the area of the outer square.

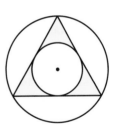

   (ii) An equilateral triangle is shown with both an inscribed and a circumscribed circle.

   Calculate the ratio of the area of the circumcircle to the area of the incircle.

9. A circle of circumference 12 cm is inscribed in a
    square which in turn is inscribed in an outer circle.
    This outer circle touches the parallel sides of a
    trapezium as shown.
    Find the area of the trapezium, giving your answer in the
    form $\dfrac{a\sqrt{b}}{\pi}$.

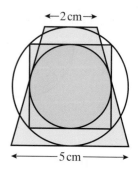

10. The shaded portion of the semicircle is to be cut
    from a large sheet of metal.

    (i)   Write down in radians the measure of the
          angle AOB.
    (ii) Find the **exact** length of the perimeter of
          the shaded portion.
    (iii) Find the area of the shaded portion and
    (iv) hence find the area of the non-shaded segment.

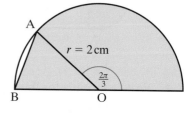

11. Derive a formula in terms of r and θ radians for the
    area of the minor segment under the chord BC.
    Hence, find the ratio of the area of the major
    segment to the area of the minor segment
    subtended by an angle of $\dfrac{\pi}{2}$ radians.

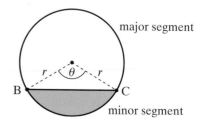

12. Five discs fit exactly into a rectangular frame of width 20 cm.
    Find the area of the remaining space in the frame.

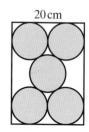

13. If the area of a sector of a circle is 48 cm², and its perimeter is 28 cm, find the length
    of the radius.

14. A farmer has a shed measuring 4 m by 5 m in the centre of a large field of grass.
    He ties a goat to one corner of this shed, and using a rope measuring 8 m, allows him
    to graze on the grass.
    (i)   Draw a diagram showing the grazing area.
    (ii) Indicate on the diagram the different sectors of circles represented by this area.
    (iii) Calculate this total grazing area correct to the nearest m².

Section 6.3 3-Dimensional objects

1. Prisms

A **prism** is a three-dimensional figure that
has the same cross-section all along its length.
Shown here is a prism with an equilateral triangular end.

The volume = $(A \times l)\,\text{m}^3$

The external surface area = $[2A + 3(l \times b)]\,\text{m}^2$

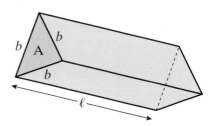

A rubbish skip is also a prism where the base is in the
shape of a trapezium.
Given that the width and perpendicular height of this
skip are both 1.8 m,

the volume $V = \text{Area}_{\text{trapezium}} \times 1.8\,\text{m}^3$

$$= \left(\frac{3.5 + 2.3}{2}\right) \times 1.8 \times 1.8\,\text{m}^3$$

$$= 9.369\,\text{m}^3 = 9.4\,\text{m}^3.$$

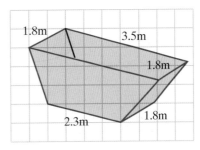

The surface area of a prism is best obtained by expanding the net of the prism.

The slant height is $\sqrt{0.6^2 + 1.8^2} = 1.9\,\text{m}$

The area of each end (E) = $(1.8 \times 1.9)\,\text{m}^2$

This skip has an external surface area of:

Area $= 2\left(\dfrac{3.5 + 2.3}{2}\right) \times 1.8 + 1.8 \times 2.3 + 2(1.8 \times 1.9)$

$= 21.42\,\text{m}^2$

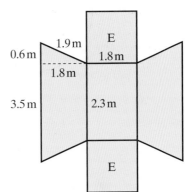

2. Revision of Cylinder, Cone and Sphere

Shape	Diagram	Properties
Cylinder		Volume = $\pi r^2 \times h$ Surface Area = $2 \times \pi r^2 + 2\pi r \times h$ Net of cylinder:

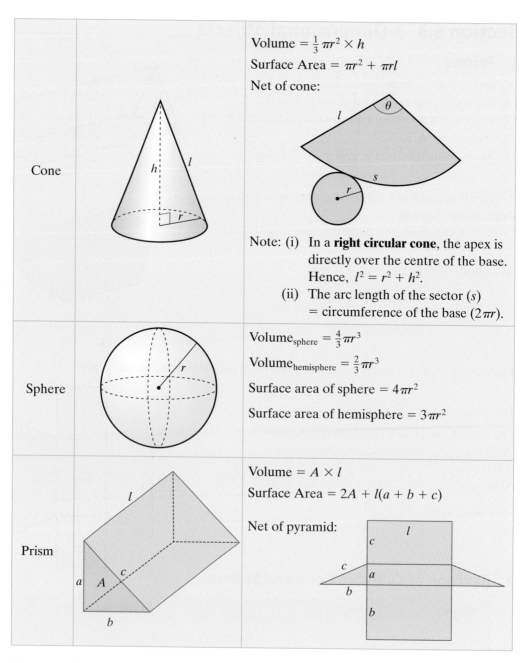

Cone		Volume $= \frac{1}{3}\pi r^2 \times h$ Surface Area $= \pi r^2 + \pi r l$ Net of cone: Note: (i) In a **right circular cone**, the apex is directly over the centre of the base. Hence, $l^2 = r^2 + h^2$. (ii) The arc length of the sector (s) = circumference of the base $(2\pi r)$.
Sphere		Volume$_{\text{sphere}} = \frac{4}{3}\pi r^3$ Volume$_{\text{hemisphere}} = \frac{2}{3}\pi r^3$ Surface area of sphere $= 4\pi r^2$ Surface area of hemisphere $= 3\pi r^2$
Prism		Volume $= A \times l$ Surface Area $= 2A + l(a + b + c)$ Net of pyramid:

Note: a prism can have many differently shaped (polygonal) bases.

Generally, the volume of a prism = (area of the base) × (length) l

3. Percentage Error / Tolerance / Degrees of accuracy

(i) Percentage error

During an experiment John *estimated* the volume of a liquid to be 100 ml.

He then measured it and found it to have a volume of 125 ml.

His percentage error is as shown.

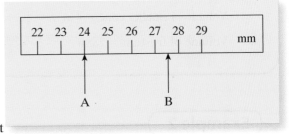

Estimated volume:	100 ml
True volume:	125 ml
Error:	25 ml
Relative error:	$\frac{25}{125} = \frac{1}{5} = 0.2$
Percentage error:	$\frac{25}{125} \times \frac{100}{1} = 20\%$

(ii) Tolerance

If a measurement is taken against a scale e.g. (i) a ruler measuring length in mm (ii) a balance measuring mass(weight) in g (iii) a clock measuring time in s. the accuracy of that measurement is limited by the size of the smallest unit on the scale.

The ***tolerance*** of that measurement is always $\pm\frac{1}{2}$ (the basic unit on the scale)

We say that the measurement is take ***to within*** ±0.5 of the basic unit.

If the measurement is the area or volume, each dimension will have a similar tolerance.

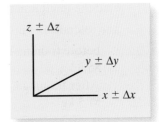

Reading A is 24 ± 0.5 mm

Reading B is 27.5 ± 0.5 mm

(iii) Degrees of accuracy

When a measurement is calculated to a given degree of accuracy e.g. correct to 1 place of decimals, an error on the measurement is created.

E.g. If a length is calculated as 10.3 cm, corrected to 1 place of decimals, this implies a minimum possible length of 10.25 cm and a maximum possible length of 10.34999....cm.

The actual length is within the range $10.25 \text{ cm} \le length < 10.34999...\text{cm}$

Example 1

Find the volume of the truncated cone shown (a frustum) correct to 1 place of decimals.

By drawing the cross-section through the centre of the truncated cone, we can see that by subtracting the smaller cone on the top from the larger cone, the remainder is the volume of the frustrum.

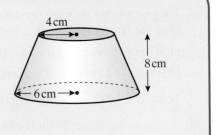

From similar triangles we have,

$$\frac{h-8}{4} = \frac{h}{6} \Rightarrow 6h - 48 = 4h$$

$$2h = 48$$

$$h = 24.$$

Volume of larger cone $= \frac{1}{3}\pi r^2 h = \frac{1}{3}\pi \times 6^2 \times 24 = 288\pi$

The height of the smaller cone $|PC| = h - 8 = 16\,\text{cm}$

$\therefore$ Volume of smaller cone $= \frac{1}{3}\pi r^2 h = \frac{1}{3}\pi \times 4^2 \times 16 = \frac{256}{3}\pi$

$\therefore$ Volume of frustum $= 288\pi - \frac{256}{3}\pi = \frac{608}{3}\pi = 636.7\,\text{cm}^3$

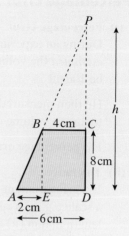

Example 2

Mat weighed 85 kg before training and 81 kg after. He took both measurements on a scales measuring in kg.

Find the minimum and maximum values for his weight loss.

The tolerance of his scales is $\pm\,0.5\,\text{kg}$

$\therefore$ before training his minimum weight was 84.5 kg and his maximum weight was 85.5 kg

After training his minimum weight was 80.5 kg and his maximum weight was 81.5 kg

$\therefore$ the maximum weight loss was $(85.5 - 80.5)\,\text{kg} = 5\,\text{kg}$

the minimum weight loss was $(84.5 - 81.5)\,\text{kg} = 3\,\text{kg}$

Note: the **tolerance interval** for his weight loss was $4 \pm 1\,\text{kg}$

Example 3

A company makes ball bearings (spheres) for a machine with a diameter of 12 mm. They claim that they are produced to an accuracy of $\pm 0.02\,\text{mm}$.

Find the largest and smallest ball bearing volumes produced.

Find the percentage error on   (i) the diameter   (ii) the volume.

Diameter $= 12\,\text{mm} \Rightarrow \text{Diameter}_{max} = 12.02\,\text{mm}, \text{Diameter}_{min} = 11.98\,\text{mm}$

Volume $= \frac{4}{3}\pi r^3 \Rightarrow$ Volume max $= \frac{4}{3}\pi(6.01)^3 = 909.310\,\text{mm}^3$

$\Rightarrow$ Volume min $= \frac{4}{3}\pi(5.99)^3 = 900.262\,\text{mm}^3$

Exercise 6.3

1. Examine each of the following shapes closely and

    (i) by drawing a suitable net of each, calculate the total area correct to one place of decimals

    (ii) find the volume of each shape correct to one place of decimals.

(a)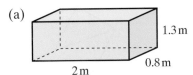
1.3 m
0.8 m
2 m

(b)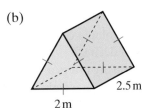
2.5 m
2 m

(c)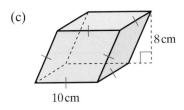
8 cm
10 cm

(d)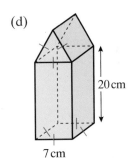
20 cm
7 cm

2. In a woodwork class, the students were asked to list in order from largest to smallest, the (i) volume (ii) **total** surface area of each of the following solid 3-dimensional objects, each answer given correct to the nearest whole number.
    Make two separate lists for (i) the areas (ii) the volumes, each arranged in descending order.

(a)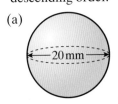
20 mm

(b)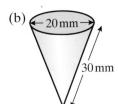
20 mm
30 mm

(c)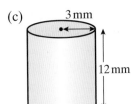
3 mm
12 mm

(d)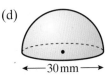
30 mm

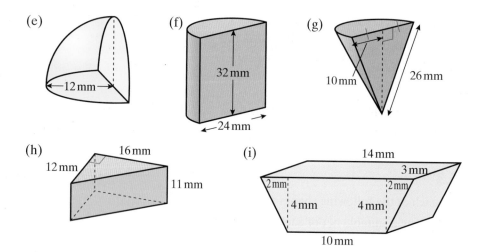

(e) ←12 mm→

(f) 32 mm   ←24 mm→

(g) 10 mm   26 mm

(h) 16 mm   12 mm   11 mm

(i) 14 mm   3 mm   2 mm   2 mm   4 mm   4 mm   10 mm

3. This model of a skip is used by a recycling company.

(i) Find the volume of the skip, correct to two places of decimals.

(ii) The company offers a 'volume pick-up' at €80 per m³ or a 'weight pick-up' at €30 per 100 kg, assuming a full skip weighs 1.3 tonnes. Which option represents the best "value for money" for the customer?

(iii) Write an equation for the volume of the skip in terms of a, h, w and θ.

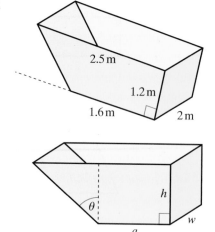

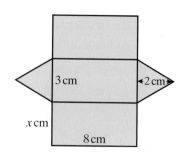

(iv) The recycling company wants to redesign the skip with a new angle $\theta = 45°$. If the width, height and overall volume must remain the same in order to fit on the truck, find, correct to one place of decimals, the new dimensions of the top and the bottom of the skip.

4. The net of a 3D figure is shown in the diagram. Both triangles are isosceles and congruent.

(i) Calculate the length of the side x cm.
(ii) Draw a sketch of the 3D figure and name it.
(iii) Calculate its volume.
(iv) Design a trapezoidal prism with the same volume.

3 cm   ←2 cm→ x cm   8 cm

5. **(i)** A student in a woodwork class is asked to fashion the largest sphere possible from the cube opposite. What volume of wood must be chipped away?

(ii) The student is then asked to calculate the volume of the smallest sphere that can enclose the cube fully.

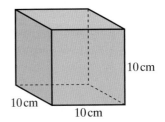

6. A water tank, in the shape of a cuboid(rectangular solid), is full of water. Water is drained from the tank at a rate of 8 litres per minute.
The dimensions of the tank are given to the nearest 10 cm.
The rate at which the water is drained from the tank is given to the nearest 0.5 litres per minute.
Calculate, correct to the nearest minute,

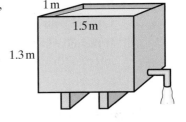

(i) the shortest time possible to drain the tank

(ii) the longest time possible to drain the tank.

7. The pyramid shown opposite has a rectangular base. The point X is directly above the midpoint of the base.

Draw two different possible nets of the pyramid and hence (using one of them) find the total external surface area of the pyramid.

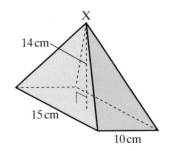

8. A steel support is to be made from a rectangular block of metal 4 cm thick, as shown.
If a quarter-circle is removed, calculate the total surface area and the total volume of the support.

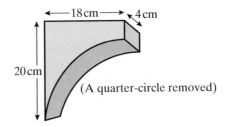

(A quarter-circle removed)

9. If x, y, and z represent lengths, and π and a are numbers with no dimensions, state whether each of the following formulae represents
    (i) a length   **(ii)** an area   **(iii)** a volume or **(iv)** a combination of these

(a) $\pi x^2 + \pi y^2 + \pi z^2$ **(b)** $ax + \pi y$ **(c)** axz **(d)** $a\pi y$

(e) $axy + \pi az$ **(f)** $ax + xy$ **(g)** $axyz$ **(h)** $x^2y + y^2z + z^2x$

10. If A represents area, V represents volume, and x, y, z are lengths, which of these formulae are consistent, and which are inconsistent, in terms of dimensions? Explain your answers.

   (i) $Ax = z^3$ (ii) $x = \dfrac{V}{Ay}$ (iii) $V = xy + z$ (iv) $A = x^2 + y^2 + z^2$

   (v) $V = A(x + y + z)$ (vi) $A = \dfrac{V}{x} + y$ (vii) $x = y + z$

11. A rectangular storage box measures 122 cm by 75 cm by 53 cm.
   (i) Find the percentage error made in rounding the volume of the box to $485\,000$ cm³. Correct your answer to 2 places of decimals.
   (ii) If the measurements were taken using a ruler scaled in cms, find the tolerance interval for the volume of the box.

12. A car travels at a constant speed of 56 km/h, correct to the nearest 1 km/h. It travels for 2.4 hours, correct to the nearest 0.1h. Calculate the minimum and maximum possible values for the distance travelled by the car.

13. The formula for the volume of a pyramid is
   $V = \frac{1}{3}$(base area) $\times$ perpendicular height.

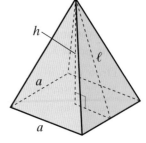

   (i) For the square-based pyramid opposite, find the volume in terms of a and h. Find the volume of a pyramid if the length of the base is 6 cm and the height is 7 cm.

   (ii) Another square-based pyramid has a base length of 5 cm and a volume of 100 cm³. Find its perpendicular height. Hence, and by drawing its net, find the total surface area.

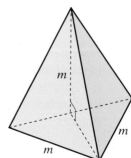

   (iii) The pyramid shown opposite has been cut from a square-based pyramid. Find its volume in terms of m. Describe this pyramid. Draw its net and find its total surface area in terms of m.

14. (i) A solid sphere just fits into a cubical box, as shown. If the edge of the box is 14 cm in length, and taking $\pi = \frac{22}{7}$, find

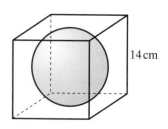

      (a) the volume of the box in cm³
      (b) the volume of the sphere in cm³
      (c) the percentage of space not occupied by the sphere.
      Give your answer correct to the nearest integer.

(ii) The same solid sphere fits exactly inside a cylinder.
Determine if the percentage of unoccupied space in the cylinder is greater or less than the space unoccupied in the cubical box.

15. Find, correct to 1 place of decimals, the volume of this rubber stopper.

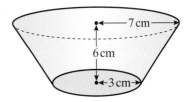

Section 6.4 Trapezoidal rule for calculating area

To calculate the areas of shapes with irregular boundaries, e.g. fields, lakes, etc., surveyors have usually divided the area into a series of parallel strips, each in the shape of a trapezium; a quadrilateral with two of the four sides parallel to each other.

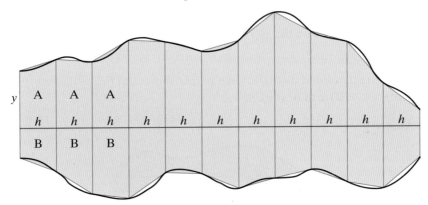

A straight line is drawn across the centre of the area, dividing it into a series of two different areas, A and B.

The area of each section, above and below the line, can be calculated separately using the formula for the area of a trapezium and then added together.

Along the line and at equal intervals of h, perpendicular lines are drawn up to the boundary. These ordinates (offsets) – y_1, y_2, y_3, etc – are the parallel sides of the trapezium.

Using the area formula for a trapezium, $\frac{a+b}{2} \times h$, we get

$A_1 = \frac{y_1 + y_2}{2} \times h$. Similarly, $A_2 = \frac{y_2 + y_3}{2} \times h$, and so on.

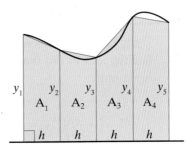

Therefore, the total area $A = A_1 + A_2 + A_3 + A_4$.

$$= \left(\frac{y_1 + y_2}{2} \times h\right) + \left(\frac{y_2 + y_3}{2} \times h\right) + \left(\frac{y_3 + y_4}{2} \times h\right) + \left(\frac{y_4 + y_5}{2} \times h\right)$$

$$= \frac{h}{2}(y_1 + y_2 + y_2 + y_3 + y_3 + y_4 + y_4 + y_5)$$

$$= \frac{h}{2}[y_1 + 2(y_2 + y_3 + y_4) + y_5]$$

In words, $\text{Area} \approx \dfrac{\text{interval width}}{2} [\text{first height} + \text{last height} + 2(\text{remaining heights})]$

When n strips are made, the Trapezoidal formula becomes

$$\text{Area} \approx \frac{h}{2}[y_1 + y_n + 2(y_2 + y_3 + y_4 + \ldots y_{n-1})]$$

Note 1: Because the top of each trapezium does not match the boundary at all points, the area obtained by this formula is only approximate.
Its accuracy depends on the gap width h; the smaller the gap width, the greater the accuracy.

Note 2: If offsets are measured from the same points above and below the line, then the area $(A + B)$ can be obtained using

$$\text{Area} \approx \frac{h}{2}[y_1 + y_7 + 2(y_2 + y_3 + y_4 + y_5 + y_6)]$$

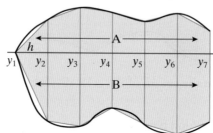

Example 1

Using the measurements provided, find the area of this shape given $h = 1$ unit.

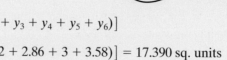

$y_1 = 0$, $y_2 = 3$, $y_3 = 3.62$, $y_4 = 2.86$,
$y_5 = 3$, $y_6 = 3.58$, $y_7 = 2.66$.

$$\text{Area} \approx \frac{h}{2}[y_1 + y_7 + 2(y_2 + y_3 + y_4 + y_5 + y_6)]$$

$$= \frac{1}{2}[0 + 2.66 + 2(3 + 3.62 + 2.86 + 3 + 3.58)] = 17.390 \text{ sq. units}$$

Example 2

The circle shown has equation $x^2 + y^2 = 25$.

(i) Find y in terms of x.

(ii) Hence complete this table.

x	0	1	2	3	4	5
y						

(iii) Use the table to estimate the area of the quarter-circle using intervals of $h = 1$ unit.

(iv) Complete the table below using intervals of $h = 0.5$ unit.

x	0	0.5	1	1.5	2	2.5	3	3.5	4	4.5	5
y											

(v) Compare both answers with the answer obtained from the area of a disc formula (correct to 3 places of decimals). What conclusion can be drawn?

(i) $x^2 + y^2 = 25 \Rightarrow y^2 = 25 - x^2$

$\qquad \Rightarrow y = \sqrt{25 - x^2}$

(ii)

x	0	1	2	3	4	5
y	5	$\sqrt{24}$	$\sqrt{21}$	4	3	0

(iii) $\therefore$ Area $\approx \frac{1}{2}\left[5 + 0 + 2(\sqrt{24} + \sqrt{21} + 4 + 3)\right] = 18.982$ sq. units

x	0	0.5	1	1.5	2	2.5	3	3.5	4	4.5	5
y	5	4.975	4.899	4.77	4.583	4.33	4	3.571	3	2.179	0

(iv) $\therefore$ Area $\approx \frac{0.5}{2}[5 + 0 + 2(4.975 + 4.899 + 4.77 + 4.584 + 4.33 + 4 + 3.571 + 3 + 2.179)] = 19.404$ sq. units

Area of $\frac{1}{4}$ disc $= \frac{1}{4}\pi r^2 = \frac{1}{4}\pi 5^2 = 19.635$ sq. units

(v) As h gets smaller, the answer approximates more closely to the disc formula answer. We also note that both the approximations are smaller than the true answer, as would be expected from the shape of the graph.

Note: If there are 5 strips, there are 6 ordinates.

If there are 10 strips, there are 11 ordinates.

If there are n strips, there are $n + 1$ ordinates.

Exercise 6.4

1. A farmer wants to find the area of one of his fields which is shaped as shown. He uses a map which has a scale of 1000 : 1. He divides the map of the field in two, using a horizontal line, and then draws perpendicular offsets at 10 mm intervals. By measuring the lengths of the offsets, use the trapezoidal rule to estimate the area of A + B.

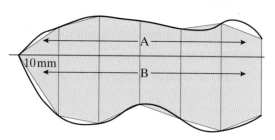

Give your answer in hectares, correct to 2 places of decimals.

(Note: One hectare = 10 000 m²)

2. If $h = 1$ cm and the lengths of the offsets are as shown, find the area of this map.

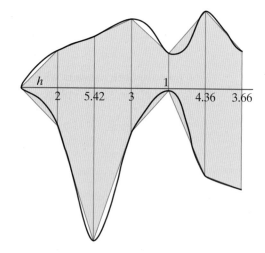

  (i) If the area of the map is 17.23 cm², find the percentage error in using the trapezoidal rule and $h = 1$ cm.

  (ii) By taking new measurements with $h = \frac{1}{2}$ cm, find a second estimate of the area.

3. Using the trapezoidal rule, and an interval value of (i) $h = 1$ cm and (ii) $h = 0.5$ cm, estimate the area under the curve
$y = 3x - (0.5)x^2$.

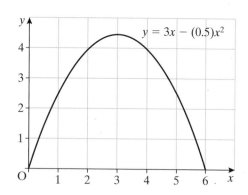

4. Copy these axes and use them to plot the function $y = \sqrt{x}$ for $0 \leqslant x \leqslant 2$.

Using four trapezoids, approximate the area under the curve for $0 \leqslant x \leqslant 2$.

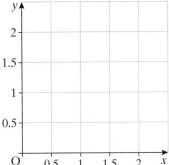

5.

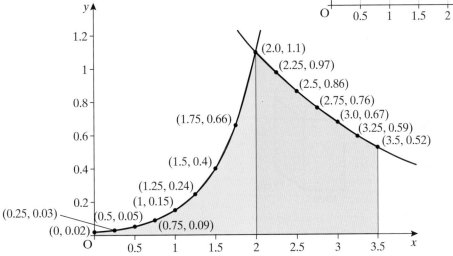

(i) Using an interval width of 0.25, find the ratio of the coloured areas under the curve.

(ii) Estimate, using trial and error, the maximum value of x so that both areas are equal.

6. An outline of the map of Ireland is given. If the scale used is $1\,\text{cm} = 20\,\text{km}$, use the trapezoidal rule to estimate the area of the island of Ireland.

Offsets are taken every 3 cm.

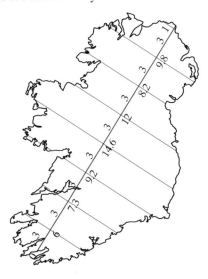

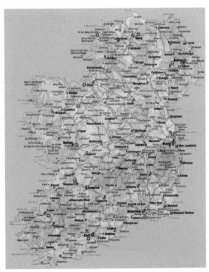

Revision Exercise 6 (Core)

1. The diagram shows a square, a diagonal and a line joining a vertex to the midpoint of a side.
What is the ratio of the area P to the area Q?

(ICT: Check your answer by drawing this figure with a computer graphics program, e.g. Geogebra)

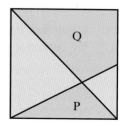

2. Find the total surface area and the volume of each of the following composite figures.
Correct your answers to the nearest whole number.

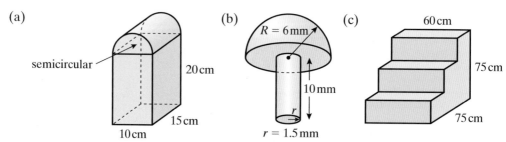

3. A circle of radius 5 cm has a centre O and a minor arc [CB] of length 6.4 cm, as indicated.

(i) Calculate, in radians, the size of the acute angle COB.

(ii) Calculate the area of the minor sector COB.

(iii) Calculate the ratio of
minor sector : major sector in the form $1 : p$, giving p correct to 3 significant figures.

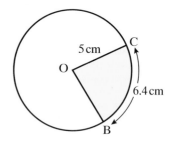

4. Determine the capacity of a swimming pool with the dimensions given.
If the water mains can supply water at a rate of 10 litre per minute, how long would it take to fill the pool?

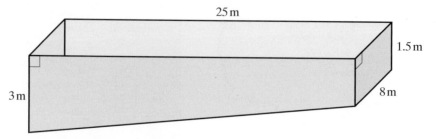

5. Find the value of x in each of the following circles.

(i)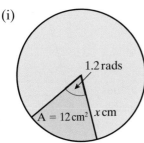

(ii)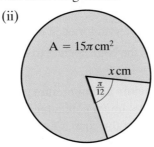

(iii)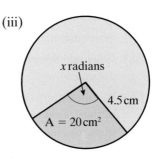

6. The net of a cone is shown in the diagram. Use this diagram to show that the curved surface area of a cone can be written as $A = \pi.r.\ell$, where r is the radius of the circular base and ℓ is the slant height of the cone. (Note: s is the length of the minor arc.)

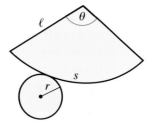

7. A card measuring 11.5 cm (using a ruler scaled in mm) is to posted in an envelope measuring 12 cm (using a ruler scaled in cm). Can you guarantee that the card will fit into the envelope? Explain your answer.

8. The dimensions of this box were measured using a cm ruler.

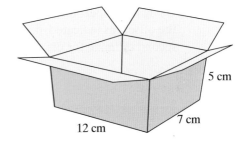

   (i) What was the tolerance of each measurement?

   (ii) Calculate the difference between the possible maximum and minimum volumes of the box. Give your answer correct to the nearest cm^3.

   (iii) The correct volume of the box is $450\,cm^3$.
   Find the percentage error in using the maximum volume of the box.
   Give your answer correct to 1 place of decimals.

9. Kris uses a protractor scaled in degrees to draw the given triangle as shown.

   Calculate the maximum and minimum possible values of the third angle.

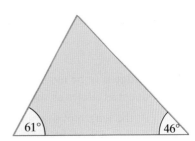

10. Using a millimetre scale Andre took the height and diameter measurements of a cone as shown.

    (i) Write down a tolerance interval for each measurement.

    (ii) Calculate the volume of the cone correct to 2 places of decimals.

    (iii) By calculating the maximum and minimum possible values of the volume find the maximum percentage error possible in measuring the volume of the cone. Give your answer correct to 2 places of decimals.

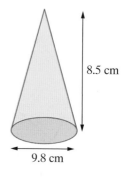

8.5 cm

9.8 cm

11. A crane using a cable with breaking load of 1500 kg, measured to two significant figures, is used to lift boxes to the top floor of a building.
Each box has a weight of 50 kg, measured to two significant figures.
What is the greatest number of boxes that can be lifted at same time to be sure that the cable does not break?

12. The graph of the function $y = (1 + 2x^2)^{0.3}$ is as shown.

    (i) By using the rectangle OPRQ and the triangle KPR, estimate the area under the graph for $0 < x < 5$.

    (ii) Using the trapezoidal rule, and the offsets as indicated, find a second estimate for the area.

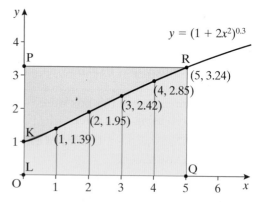

13. Find

    (i) the perimeter and

    (ii) the area of this composite figure, leaving your answers in surd form.

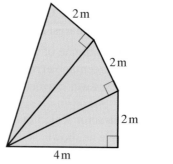

14. A badge is to be made from a series of connected circles as shown. Find

    (i) the length of the perimeter

    (ii) the area of the composite figure.

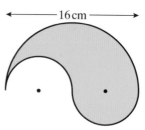

15. The cost of manufacturing a hemispherical glass dome is given by

Cost = €(5200 + 35*A*) where *A* is the surface area in square metres.

Find the cost of making a hemisphere of radius 10 m.

16. A spinning top is made from a cube, a cylinder
and a cone as shown in this diagram.
A cross-section drawing with dimensions is given.

Find the volume of the spinning top
correct to 1 place of decimals.

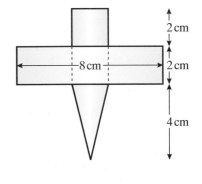

Revision Exercise 6 (Advanced)

1. The figure shows the minor sector BCE of a circle of
centre E and radius *r* cm. The perimeter of the sector
is 100 cm and the area of the sector is *A* cm².

   (i) Show that $A = (50r - r^2)\,\text{cm}^2$.
   (ii) Given that *r* can vary, find (by completing the square)
   the value of *r* for which *A* is a maximum and show
   that *A* is a maximum.
   (iii) Find the value of ∠CEB for this maximum area.

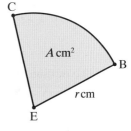

2.

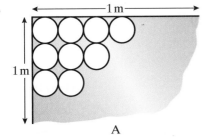

A

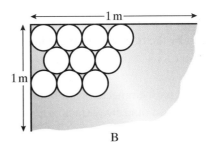

B

Circular holes, of radius 1 cm, are to be cut out of a sheet of metal. The sheet of metal
measures 1 m × 1 m. Two methods, A or B, could be used, as shown above.

   (i) Calculate the number of holes possible with each method.
   (ii) Calculate the percentage waste from each piece of metal.

3. In this diagram, the area of the shaded triangle
   PNQ is three times the area of the segment
   created by the chord [OQ].
   Find, in terms of r and θ,

   (i) the area of $\triangle$PQO

   (ii) the area of the segment formed by [OQ]

   (iii) the area of $\triangle$PQN.

   Hence show that $3\theta - 4\sin\theta = 0$.

   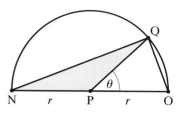

4. Find the total surface area and the volume of the metal in each of the following objects,
   correct to the nearest whole number.

   (a)   (b)   (c)

   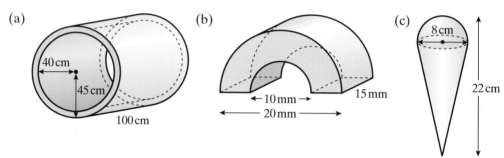

5. The outline of a design for a wind ornament is as
   shown. A circular wire holds a sector of a circle.

   If the angle of the minor sector is $\dfrac{2\pi}{3}$ radians,

   find the area   (i) of the minor sector

   (ii) of the minor segment.

   Show that if $\theta = 1.895$ radians, the area of the sector is
   bisected by the dotted horizontal line.

   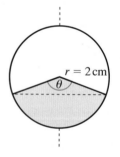

6. A straight path connects two points C and D on a
   curved section of railway track. The radius of the
   circular track is 44 m.

   (i) Show that the angle COD is 1.84 radians.

   (ii) Calculate the length of the railway track shown.

   (iii) Calculate the shortest distance from O to the path.

   (iv) Calculate the area bound by the path and the
   railway track.

   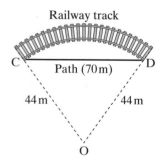

7. Show that the area of the minor segment is $\frac{1}{2}r^2(\theta - \sin\theta)$.

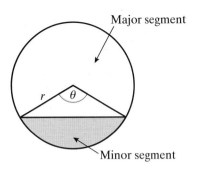

Major segment

Minor segment

(i) Given that the area of the major segment is 23.32 cm² when $\theta = 2$ radians, find r, correct to one place of decimals.

(ii) If this diagram represents the cross-section of a bowl containing water, find the surface area of the water. (Take $\theta = 2$ radians.)

8. The motion of a courier van is represented by a speed/time graph as shown.

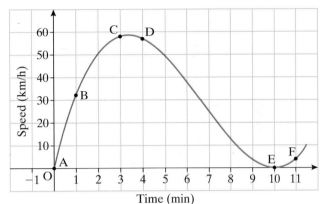

(i) Comment on the differences in the motion of the courier between points A to B, C to D and E to F.

(ii) What quantity is obtained when speed is multiplied by time?

(iii) Using the trapezoidal rule and readings from the graph, estimate the total distance travelled by the courier in 10 min.

9. A regular tetrahedron has four faces, each of which is an equilateral triangle.

One such tetrahedron is placed in a cylinder with one face flat against the bottom. If the length of one edge of the tetrahedron is $2a$, show that the volume of the smallest possible cylindrical container into which it will fit is $\dfrac{8\sqrt{6}}{9}\pi a^3$.

(Adapted from 2011 SEC sample paper.)

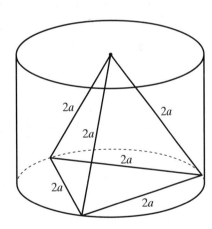

10. Find the area of the shaded trapezium. Note: the sides are not drawn to scale.

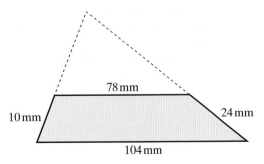

Revision Exercise 6 (Extended Response Questions)

1. A piece of wire of length 4 m is bent into the shape
   of a sector of a circle of radius r metres and angle θ radians.

   (i) State, in terms of θ and r,
   - (a) the length of the arc
   - (b) the area A of the sector.

   (ii) Hence, show that $A = 2r - r^2$.

   (iii) By completing the square, rewrite this equation in the form $A = q - (r - p)^2$.

   (iv) Draw a graph of A against r, $0 \leqslant r \leqslant 3$. Write down the maximum point on the
   graph and hence find the maximum value of r which will make the area
   a maximum.

   (v) Deduce the corresponding value of θ.

2. (i) Groups of students were asked to compare the areas
   of an equilateral triangle and a semicircle, where the
   base of the equilateral triangle had the same measurement
   as the diameter of the semicircle.
   Group one said that they had the same area.
   Group two said that the triangle was larger by 10.18%.
   Group three said that there was a 9.24% difference.
   Investigate the claims of each group.

   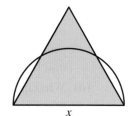

   (ii) The groups were then asked to calculate the size of
   the base angles of an isosceles triangle which
   had exactly the same area as the semicircle, and again
   where the base was the same size as the diameter of
   the semicircle.
   What size angle should they have come up with?

   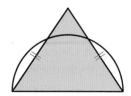

   (iii) If the equal areas are rotated about a line vertically through the apex of the
   triangle, a cone and a hemisphere are created. Investigate if the volumes are
   the same.

3. A diagram of the net of a drawer is given.
   When constructed, the drawer has the shape of an
   open-topped cuboid.

   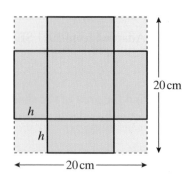

   (i) Find, in terms of h, an expression for
   the area of a square base.

   (ii) For what value of h would the drawer
   be an open-topped cube?

   (iii) Find an expression for the volume of
   the drawer in terms of h.
   Sketch a graph of the volume as a function
   of h from $h = 0$ cm to $h = 14$ cm.

   (iv) Use your graph to estimate the value of h
   that maximises the volume of the drawer.

(v) You need a drawer with a volume of 500 cm³.
Estimate from your graph the three different values of h that would create a volume of 500 cm³.

(vi) Explain why all values of h are not physically possible.

4. A programmer wants to make a program to estimate the area of a circle using the trapezoidal rule.
In his initial investigation he draws a semicircle of radius 10 cm. He then divides the diameter into 8 equal intervals.

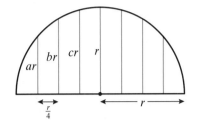

(i) Construct a semicircle of radius 10 cm and by measuring the length of each offset, estimate the area of the semicircle using the trapezoidal rule.

(ii) Find the percentage error in this method by comparing with the true area of $\frac{1}{2}\pi r^2$.

(iii) Using his construction, the programmer calculated the length of each offset in terms of r.
Using the diagram above, calculate the values for a, b, and c, correct to a reasonable degree of accuracy.

(iv) The programmer derived the approximate area as
$$\text{Area} = \frac{r^2}{4}(2a + 2b + 2c + 1).$$
Show clearly how this formula was derived.

(v) Using your calculated values for a, b and c in the programmer's equation, find a formula for the area of a semicircle of radius r cm.

(vi) Using this formula, estimate the areas of semicircles of radii 5 cm, 10 cm, and 15 cm.

(vii) Comment on the accuracy of the programmer's formula.

5. A large sheet of cardboard 22 cm × 31 cm is to be used to make a box.
The box is to have a volume of 500 cm³.
The shaded areas are flaps of width 1 cm.
The height of the box is h cm as shown in the diagram.

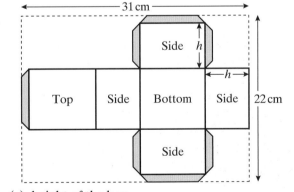

Write, in terms of h, the

(i) (a) length   (b) width   (c) height of the box.

(ii) Write an expression for the capacity of the box in terms of h.

(iii) Find the value of h for the box if it is to have a square base.

(iv) Show that this value of h gives the required capacity.

(v) Find, correct to 1 place of decimals, the other value of h that gives a capacity of $500\,\text{cm}^3$.

(vi) A graph of the capacity as a function of h is drawn. Indicate on this graph your answers to parts (iv) and (v).

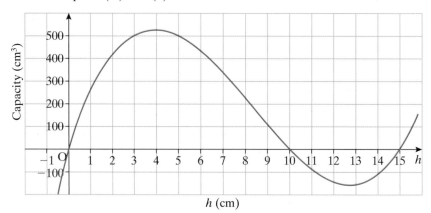

h (cm)

(vii) Is it possible to increase the capacity of the box by 10% using the same size piece of cardboard? Explain.

(Adapted from SEC, Project Maths sample paper, 2012)

Probability 2

Key words

tree diagram   probability distribution   expected value   random variable
fair game   binomial distribution   Bernoulli trials   multiplication rule
independent events   normal distribution   normal curve
Empirical rule   standard score   Probability simulations

In book 4, we dealt with permutations, combinations and the fundamentals of probability. In this chapter, we continue the study of probability and that will include more difficult concepts such as expected value and independent events as well as an introduction to the normal distribution.

Section 7.1 Tree diagrams

The possible outcomes of two or more events can be shown in a particular type of diagram called a **tree diagram**. Each branch represents a possible outcome of one event. The probability of each outcome is written on the branch.

Consider this problem:

A fair coin is tossed three times.
Determine the probability that exactly 2 heads are obtained.

Here is the sample space of possible outcomes:

HHH, HHT, HTH, HTT, THH, THT, TTH and TTT

Since 2 heads appear on 3 occasions,

$$P(2 \text{ heads}) = \frac{3}{8}$$

The same possibilities can be represented in a more structured way on a tree diagram.

The branches that contain 2 heads are highlighted.

Again $P(2 \text{ heads}) = \frac{1}{8} + \frac{1}{8} + \frac{1}{8} = \frac{3}{8}$

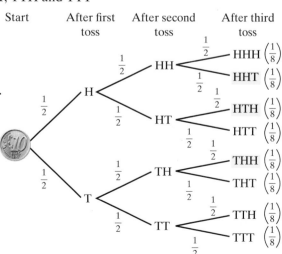

| Start | After first toss | After second toss | After third toss |

$$\text{H} \quad \frac{1}{2} \quad \text{HH} \quad \frac{1}{2} \quad \text{HHH} \left(\frac{1}{8}\right)$$
$$\frac{1}{2} \quad \text{HHT} \left(\frac{1}{8}\right)$$
$$\frac{1}{2} \quad \text{HT} \quad \frac{1}{2} \quad \text{HTH} \left(\frac{1}{8}\right)$$
$$\frac{1}{2} \quad \text{HTT} \left(\frac{1}{8}\right)$$
$$\frac{1}{2} \quad \text{TH} \quad \frac{1}{2} \quad \text{THH} \left(\frac{1}{8}\right)$$
$$\frac{1}{2} \quad \text{THT} \left(\frac{1}{8}\right)$$
$$\text{T} \quad \frac{1}{2} \quad \text{TT} \quad \frac{1}{2} \quad \text{TTH} \left(\frac{1}{8}\right)$$
$$\frac{1}{2} \quad \text{TTT} \left(\frac{1}{8}\right)$$

Example 1

Box A contains 3 red beads and 4 blue beads
Box B contains 2 red beads and 3 blue beads
One bead is taken at random from each box.
 (i) Draw a tree diagram to show all the outcomes.
 (ii) Work out the probability that they both will
   have the same colour.

A   B

 (i) The tree diagram below shows all the possible outcomes.
   Taking a red bead from box A and taking a red bead from box B are
   independent events.
   So P(red, red) = P(red) × P(red)
   $$\tfrac{3}{7} \times \tfrac{2}{5} = \tfrac{6}{35}$$

Box A	Box B	Outcome	Probability
	$\frac{2}{5}$ R	R R	$\frac{3}{7} \times \frac{2}{5} = \frac{6}{35}$
$\frac{3}{7}$ R	$\frac{3}{5}$ B	R B	$\frac{3}{7} \times \frac{3}{5} = \frac{9}{35}$
$\frac{4}{7}$ B	$\frac{2}{5}$ R	B R	$\frac{4}{7} \times \frac{2}{5} = \frac{8}{35}$
	$\frac{3}{5}$ B	B B	$\frac{4}{7} \times \frac{3}{5} = \frac{12}{35}$

 (ii) P(same colour) = P(both red or both blue)
     = P(R, R) + P(B, B)
     $= \tfrac{6}{35} + \tfrac{12}{35} = \tfrac{18}{35}$

OR implies addition

Note: Notice that the probabilities at the end of the branches sum to 1, i.e.,

$$\tfrac{6}{35} + \tfrac{9}{35} + \tfrac{8}{35} + \tfrac{12}{35} = \tfrac{35}{35} = 1$$

Tree diagrams for events without replacement

The tree diagram in the following example illustrates **events that are not independent**. The
outcome of the first event affects subsequent events.

Example 2

A box contains 12 beads. Five are yellow and the rest are green. A bead is removed
from the box and its colour is noted. It is not returned to the box. A second
selection is then made and the process is repeated, followed by a third selection.
 (i) Draw a tree diagram outlining this situation
 (ii) Find the probability of selecting exactly two green beads.

(i)   First selection   Second selection   Third selection

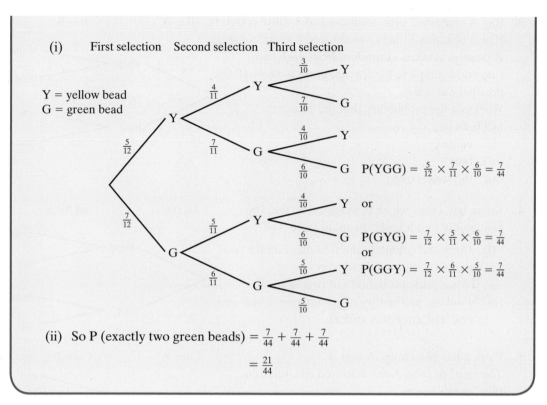

Y = yellow bead
G = green bead

$P(YGG) = \frac{5}{12} \times \frac{7}{11} \times \frac{6}{10} = \frac{7}{44}$

or

$P(GYG) = \frac{7}{12} \times \frac{5}{11} \times \frac{6}{10} = \frac{7}{44}$

or

$P(GGY) = \frac{7}{12} \times \frac{6}{11} \times \frac{5}{10} = \frac{7}{44}$

(ii) So P (exactly two green beads) $= \frac{7}{44} + \frac{7}{44} + \frac{7}{44}$

$= \frac{21}{44}$

Note: In the example above, the calculations of probabilities were confined to the relevant branches.

Exercise 7.1

1. (i) Draw a tree diagram for these two spinners.

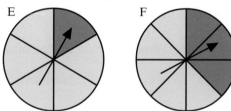

E   F

(ii) Find the probability that the two spinners show the same colour.

2. Paula has a die with 5 red faces and 1 green face.
    She rolls the dice twice.
    (i) Copy and complete the tree diagram.
    (ii) Find the probability that the die shows the same colour each time.
    (iii) Find the probability that the die shows green and red in that order.

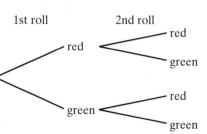

1st roll   2nd roll

red
  red
       green

green
  red
       green

3. Bag A contains 2 blue counters and 3 white counters.
   Bag B contains 3 blue counters and 4 white counters.
   A counter is taken at random from each bag.
   Copy and complete the tree diagram to show all the
   possible outcomes.
   Work out the probability that the counters
   will both be:
   (i)   white
   (ii) blue
   (iii) the same colour.

   Bag A

   Bag B

   $\frac{3}{5}$ — white $\frac{4}{7}$ — white
   — blue

   — blue — white
   — blue

4. Kevin has a coin which is weighted so that the
   probability that it lands 'head' is $\frac{3}{5}$ and 'tail' $\frac{2}{5}$.
   (i)   Copy and complete the tree diagram for two
         throws of the weighted coin.
   (ii) What is the probability of two heads?
   (iii) Find the probability of getting one 'head' and
         one 'tail' (in either order).

   1st throw   2nd throw
                      — head
   $\frac{3}{5}$ — head
                      — tail

                      — head
   — tail
                      — tail

5. Patrick has two cubes, A and B.
   The faces of cube A are coloured red, red, blue,
   blue, green, green.
   The faces of cube B are coloured red, blue, blue,
   blue, green, green.
   Patrick rolls the two cubes to see which colours
   come on top.
   (i)   Copy and complete the tree diagram,
         writing the probabilities on the branches.
   (ii) Find the probability that both cubes land
         with the same colour on top.
   (iii) Find the probability that one of the cubes lands blue and the other green.

   Cube A   Cube B
                      — red
   — red   — blue
                      — green

                      — red
   — blue   — blue
                      — green

                      — red
   — green   — blue
                      — green

6. Harry throws an ordinary die
   three times.
   (i)   Copy and complete this tree
         diagram.
   (ii) Find the probability that Harry
         gets two or more sixes in his
         three throws.

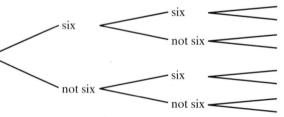

   1st throw   2nd throw   3rd throw
                      — six
   — six
                      — not six
                      — six
   — not six
                      — not six

7. A bag contains 2 black counters and 4 white counters.
   A counter is taken from the bag and not replaced.
   A second counter is then taken.
   Find the probability that the two counters are
   (i)   the same colour   (ii) different colours.

8. A bag contains 3 red cubes and 2 blue cubes.
   A cube is taken at random from the bag and not replaced.
   Then a second cube is taken at random.
   (i) Draw a tree diagram for this situation.
   (ii) Find the probability that both of the cubes taken out are the same colour.
   (iii) Find the probability that the two cubes are of different colours.

9. The probability that it will be raining tomorrow morning is $\frac{1}{3}$.
   If it is raining, the probability that Simon will be late for school is $\frac{1}{4}$.
   If it is not raining, the probability that he will be late is $\frac{1}{5}$.
   (i) Copy and complete this tree diagram.

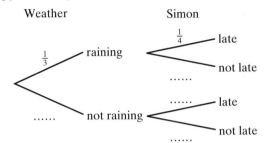

   (ii) Find the probability that Simon will be late for school tomorrow.

10. On his way to work, Nick goes through a set of traffic lights and then passes over a level crossing.
    Over a period of time, Nick has estimated the probability of stopping at each of these.
    The probability that he has to stop at the traffic lights is $\frac{2}{3}$.
    The probability that he has to stop at the level crossing is $\frac{1}{5}$.
    The probabilities are independent.
    (i) Construct a tree diagram to show this information.
    (ii) Calculate the probability that Nick will not have to stop at either the lights or the level crossing on his way to work.

11. Karen is looking at a job advert in the paper.
    On past experience, she estimates that she has a 70% chance of getting the job if she can get an interview.
    Karen thinks that she has a two in five chance of getting an interview.
    Draw a tree diagram to illustrate these events.
    Use the tree diagram to find each of these:
    (i) Given that she gets an interview, what then is the probability that she does not get the job?
    (ii) What is the probability that Karen does not get the job?

12. The probability that Aidan passes his driving test at the first attempt is $\frac{1}{3}$.
    If the test is failed, the probability that Aidan passes his driving test at the next attempt is $\frac{7}{12}$.
    Draw a tree diagram to illustrate the probabilities of these events.
    Hence calculate the probability that Aidan passes his driving test at his third attempt.

Section 7.2 Probability distributions – Expected value ——

Probability distributions

Consider the following experiments

  (i)   4 coins are tossed: x is the number of heads obtained
  (ii) Three dice are thrown: x is the number of sixes obtained
  (iii) A hand of 7 cards is dealt: x is the number of kings
  (iv) 100 people are selected: x is the number of people of weight $\geqslant 150\,\text{kg}$
  (v)   One person is selected at random: x cm is the height of that person
  (vi) One person is selected at random: x is the I.Q. of that person.

In each of the above experiments, x is called a **random variable** whose value depends, to some extent, on chance. In experiments (i) to (iv), x can take discrete values such as 0, 1, 2, 3... and for that reason x is said to be a **discrete random variable**. In experiments (v) and (vi), x can take any value within a certain range and is said to be a **continuous random variable**. In this section, we will consider only discrete random variables.

If a coin is tossed 3 times, the sample space of all possible outcomes is

$$TTT, \, TTH, \, THT, \, THH, \, HTT, \, HTH, \, HHT, \, HHH$$

If x is the number of heads obtained, a table of the results can be formulated as follows:

x	0	1	2	3
$P(x)$	$\frac{1}{8}$	$\frac{3}{8}$	$\frac{3}{8}$	$\frac{1}{8}$

This is called a **probability distribution**, where $P(x)$ is the probability that x occurs.

Probability distributions are particularly useful when dealing with expected values, as shown below.

Expected value

This circle is divided into 3 sectors.
When the spinner is spun, it will land on 4, 8 or 12.
If the spinner is spun twice and we get 4 and 12,
then the average of the two results is $\dfrac{4 + 12}{2} = 8$.

If the spinner is spun 100 times, is there a quick way of finding the 'average' of these spins?

Yes and it is found by multiplying each outcome (4, 8 or 12) by the probability of that outcome occurring and then adding the results.
This average is called the **expected value**.

This is set out in the table below:

Outcome (x)	Probability (P)	$x \times P$
12	$\frac{1}{2}$	6
8	$\frac{1}{4}$	2
4	$\frac{1}{4}$	1

When each outcome is multiplied by its corresponding probability, we get 6, 2 and 1.
The sum of these results is 9.
The number 9 is the **expected value**.

If the spinner above is spun a large number of times, the mean value of outcomes approaches the expected value, 9. Statisticians call this the *Law of large numbers*.

Notice that the expected value 9 is not one of the possible outcomes, i.e., 4, 8 and 12.

> In general, the expected value need not be one of the possible outcomes.

The expected value of the outcome of an experiment is denoted by E(X).

When all the outcomes are multiplied by their corresponding probabilities and the results added, the operation can be expressed in a concise way as follows

$$E(X) = \sum(x).P(x), \text{ where } \sum \text{ represents 'the sum of'.}$$

The expected value is widely used in the insurance industry and in the operation of casino games. If you would like to know whether or not a casino game is fair, you would need to know what the payout is and the probability of getting that payout. In simple terms, you need to know the expected value of the payouts.

You also have to take into account the money you pay to play the game.

Let us consider this fun-park spinning-wheel on the right.
It costs €8 to spin the wheel and you win the amount to which the arrow is pointing.

Is this a fair game?

First we calculate the expected value of the payout.

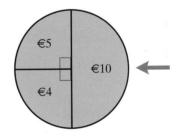

Payout (x)	Probability (P)	x × P
€10	$\frac{1}{2}$	€5
€5	$\frac{1}{4}$	€1.25
€4	$\frac{1}{4}$	€1

$$\sum x.P(x) = €5 + €1.25 + €1 = €7.25$$

The expected value of the payout is €7.25.
But it costs €8 to spin the wheel.
The final (net) position is €7.25 − €8.00 = −€0.75.
Thus if the wheel is spun a large number of times, you could expect to lose €0.75 on average on each spin.

When is a game fair?

To determine whether or not a game is **mathematically fair**, we need to take into account
  (i) the expected value of the payout
  (ii) the cost of playing the game.

Then (a) if the (expected value − cost) is zero, the game is fair
(b) if the (expected value − cost) is greater than zero, you will win in the long-run
(c) if the (expected value − cost) is less than zero, you will lose in the long-run.

A game is **equitable** or **fair** if the player's mathematical expectation is zero.

Example 1

This circle is divided into 6 equal sectors.

You pay €10 to spin the arrow and you win the amount in the sector where the arrow stops.

What is the expected amount you win or lose in this game?

We find the expected value of the payout by constructing the table below which shows the probability of each outcome.

Payout (x)	Probability (P)	Payout × Probability ($x \times P$)
€0	$\frac{2}{6}$	€0
€5	$\frac{1}{6}$	€$\frac{5}{6}$
€10	$\frac{2}{6}$	€$\frac{20}{6}$
€30	$\frac{1}{6}$	€5

Expected payout $= \sum x.P(x) = €0 + €\frac{5}{6} + €\frac{20}{6} + €5$

$$= €5 + €\frac{25}{6}$$

$$= €5 + €4\frac{1}{6} = €9\frac{1}{6} = €9.17$$

The expected payout is €9.17.

When you include the €10 you pay to play, the final (net) position is

$$€9.17 − €10 = −€0.83$$

So you can expect to lose €0.83 if you play this game.

Example 2

Luke rolls a pair of dice in a game of chance that costs €2 to play.

The table on the right gives the financial outcome for each event.
  (i) Calculate the financial expectation for this game.
 (ii) Is this game fair?
        Explain your answer.

Event	Financial outcome
Any double	Win €4
Total of 7	Win €3
Odd sum (except 7)	Money back (€2)
Even sum (except doubles)	Lose €3

There are 36 possible outcomes, as shown on the right.

(i) $P(\text{double}) = \dfrac{6}{36} = \dfrac{1}{6}$

$P(\text{total of 7}) = \dfrac{6}{36} = \dfrac{1}{6}$

$P(\text{odd sum – except 7}) = \dfrac{12}{36} = \dfrac{1}{3}$

$P(\text{even sum – except doubles}) = \dfrac{18-6}{36} = \dfrac{12}{36} = \dfrac{1}{3}$

6	7	8	9	10	11	12
5	6	7	8	9	10	11
4	5	6	7	8	9	10
3	4	5	6	7	8	9
2	3	4	5	6	7	8
1	2	3	4	5	6	7
	1	2	3	4	5	6

We now multiply each financial outcome by its probability.

$$\sum x.P(x) = €4 \times \tfrac{1}{6} + €3 \times \tfrac{1}{6} + €2 \times \tfrac{1}{3} - €3 \times \tfrac{1}{3}$$
$$= €\tfrac{4}{6} + €\tfrac{1}{2} + €\tfrac{2}{3} - €1$$
$$= €\tfrac{11}{6} - €1 = €1.83 - €1 = €0.83$$

We now deduct the cost to play the game which is €2.

$€0.83 - €2 = - €1.17$

The financial expectation is $-€1.17$ per game.

(ii) This game is not fair as you expect to lose €1.17 each time you play this game.

Exercise 7.2

1. Find the expected value when this spinner is spun.

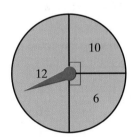

2. A card is selected at random from the cards shown and then replaced.
   The process is repeated several times.
   Find the expected value of the number selected.

   2   6   8

   12   9   2

3. When this spinner is spun, the amount in the sector in which the arrow stops is paid out.
   What is the expected value of the payout?

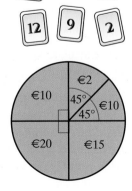

4. The probability of throwing each of the numbers 1 to 6 with a biased die are given below.

Outcome (x)	1	2	3	4	5	6
Probability (P)	0.1	0.05	0.25	0.15	0.25	0.2
$x \times P(x)$						

Find the expected value when this die is thrown.

5. The probability distribution of a set of numbers is shown in this table:
Find the expected value of x.

x	−2	−1	0	1	2
$P(x)$	0.3	0.1	0.15	0.4	0.05

6. The Garda chief of a city knows that the probabilities for 0, 1, 2, 3, 4 or 5 car thefts on any given day are, respectively, 0.21, 0.37, 0.25, 0.13, 0.03 and 0.01. How many car thefts can he expect per day?

7. List the eight different outcomes when three fair coins are tossed.
Now find the expected number of heads when the three coins are tossed.

8. In the given wheel, you win the amount in the sector in which the arrow stops.
It costs €10 to play the game.
How much would you expect to win or lose if you play this game?
Explain why the game is not fair.

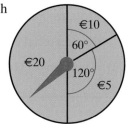

9. When a fair die is thrown, you win €10 when 1 or 2 shows and lose €5 when 3, 4, 5 or 6 shows.
Find the expected gain or loss when the die is thrown.
Is the game fair? Explain your answer.

10. Grandad bet €5 on each of these 5 horses in a horserace.

Horse	Probability of win	Payout from €5
Likely lad	0.32	€11
Just a Minute	0.07	€68
Everyone's a Critic	0.11	€42
Sauerkraut	0.01	€480
Solar Eclipse	0.05	€96

   (i) Calculate his financial expectation from this bet.
   (ii) On average, will Grandad make a gain or a loss?

11. For a particular age group, statistics show that the probability of dying is 1 in 1000 people and the probability of suffering some sort of disability is 3 in 1000 people. The *Hope Life Insurance Company* offers to pay out €50 000 if you die and €20 000 if you are disabled.
What profit is the insurance company making per customer, based on the expected value, if it charges a premium of €300 to its customers for the above policy?

12. The probability distribution of a random variable x is shown in this table:

x	1	2	3	4	5
$P(x)$	0.1	0.3	y	0.2	0.1

   (i) Find the value of y.
   (ii) Find the expected value of x.

13. In a casino, it costs €5 to throw a fair die.
    If you throw a 2 or a 6, you win €15.
    If you throw a 1, you win €1.
    For all other scores, you neither win nor lose.
    If you played this game 20 times, how much would you expect to win/lose?

14. The probability distribution of a random variable x is given below:

x	1	2	3	4	5
$P(x)$	0.1	p	0.3	q	0.2

   (i) Given $E(x) = 3$, write down two equations in p and q.
   (ii) Find the value of p and the value of q.

15. The table below gives details of claims made by households against the *Coverall Insurance Company* for a particular year.

	No. of households	No. of claims	Average cost per claim
Urban area	6250	480	€2840
Rural area	4600	210	€1705

   Use the table above to answer the following questions, giving your answer correct to two decimal places:
   (i) What is the probability that a rural household, selected at random, made a claim during the year?
   (ii) What is the expected value of the cost of a claim from a rural household?
   (iii) The urban households paid an average annual premium of €580. Calculate the average profit the insurance company made on each urban household premium.
   (iv) A rural household in County Galway has a probability of 0.05 of making a claim during the year. The average cost of such a claim is €1550. What premium should the insurance company charge this household to make a profit of €350 on the transaction?

16. A test consists of three sections:
    Section 1 has 20 multiple-choice questions in which students select 1 correct answer from 4 options (A, B, C, D).
    Section 2 has 10 true-or-false questions in which students choose either true or false.
    Section 3 has 10 multiple-choice questions in which students select 1 correct answer from 3 options (A, B, C).

    If every question in the test is randomly answered, what is the expected number of correct answers?

17. On one table in a casino there is a deck of normal playing cards.
    On another table there are two fair dice.
    It costs €10 to play at each table.
    At the card table, you select one card from the deck.
    You win €30 if you draw a heart but win €2 if you draw any other suit.
    At the other table, you throw the two dice and add the numbers showing.
    If you get a total of 10, 11 or 12 you win €50.
    For any other total you win €2.
    Which game should you play to get the better expected return?
    What is the difference between the two expected returns?

Section 7.3 Bernoulli trials – Binomial distribution

The Swiss mathematician James Bernoulli(1654–1705) studied the probabilities occurring when several trials of the one experiment were carried out.

The characteristics of a Bernoulli trial are:

1. Each trial can have only two outcomes often referred to as **success** and **failure**.
2. The trials are independent (the outcome of one has no influence over the outcome of another trial)
3. The probability of *success* / *failure* remains constant from trial to trial.
4. There is a fixed number of trials.

The probability of a success is generally called p.

The probability of a failure is q, where $p + q = 1$.

The three main applications of his study are as follows:

1. To find the probability of a first success after n trials

> ### Example 1
>
> Find the probability of getting a six on the fourth throw of an unbiased die.
>
> The probability of getting a six on a single throw, $P(6) = \frac{1}{6} = p$
>
> The probability of not getting a six on a single throw, $P(1, 2, 3, 4, 5) = \frac{5}{6} = q$
>
> To get a six (success) on the fourth throw assumes no six (failure) on the first three throws.
>
> $\therefore$ P(success on the fourth throw) $= q \times q \times q \times p = \frac{5}{6} \times \frac{5}{6} \times \frac{5}{6} \times \frac{1}{6} = \frac{5^3}{6^4} = \frac{125}{1296}$

2. To find the probability of k successes in n trials

A coin is biased in such a way that the probability of a head is always $\frac{2}{5}$.

Consider tossing the coin four times. We would like to know the probability of getting three heads.

This could happen in the four different ways {H, H, H, T} or {H, H, T, H} or {H, T, H, H} or {T, H, H, H}.

$$P(\text{H, H, H, T}) = \tfrac{2}{5} \times \tfrac{2}{5} \times \tfrac{2}{5} \times \tfrac{3}{5} = \left(\tfrac{2}{5}\right)^3 \times \tfrac{3}{5}$$

$$P(\text{H, H, T, H}) = \tfrac{2}{5} \times \tfrac{2}{5} \times \tfrac{3}{5} \times \tfrac{2}{5} = \left(\tfrac{2}{5}\right)^3 \times \tfrac{3}{5}$$

$$P(\text{H, T, H, H}) = \tfrac{2}{5} \times \tfrac{3}{5} \times \tfrac{2}{5} \times \tfrac{2}{5} = \left(\tfrac{2}{5}\right)^3 \times \tfrac{3}{5}$$

$$P(\text{T, H, H, H}) = \tfrac{3}{5} \times \tfrac{2}{5} \times \tfrac{2}{5} \times \tfrac{2}{5} = \left(\tfrac{2}{5}\right)^3 \times \tfrac{3}{5}$$

The total probability for 3 heads and 1 tail $= 4 \times \left(\tfrac{2}{5}\right)^3 \times \tfrac{3}{5} = \tfrac{96}{625}$

In book 4 we stated that $\binom{n}{r}$ represents the number of ways of choosing r objects from n different objects.

So the number of ways of selecting 3 heads from 4 (tosses of the) coins is $\binom{4}{3}$

Thus the probability of 3 heads and 1 tail $= \binom{4}{3}\left(\tfrac{2}{5}\right)^3 \times \tfrac{3}{5}$

The example above is a special type of probability model called the **binomial distribution**.

In general, the probability of r successes in n trials is given by the general term of the binomial expansion of $(p + q)^n$, where p is the probability of success and q is the probability of failure.

$$P(r \text{ successes}) = \binom{n}{r}(p)^r(q)^{n-r}$$

Consider the event of obtaining a 6 from a single throw of an unbiased die.

$$P(\text{success}) = \tfrac{1}{6} \quad \text{and} \quad P(\text{failure}) = \tfrac{5}{6}$$

If there are 4 such trials, then the probability of 0, 1, 2, 3, 4 successes from 4 attempts is given by the terms of the expansion of $\left(\tfrac{1}{6} + \tfrac{5}{6}\right)^4$

$$P(\text{no six}) = \binom{4}{0}\left(\tfrac{1}{6}\right)^0\left(\tfrac{5}{6}\right)^4$$

$$P(\text{one six}) = \binom{4}{1}\left(\tfrac{1}{6}\right)^1\left(\tfrac{5}{6}\right)^3$$

$$P(\text{two sixes}) = \binom{4}{2}\left(\tfrac{1}{6}\right)^2\left(\tfrac{5}{6}\right)^2$$

$$P(\text{three sixes}) = \binom{4}{3}\left(\tfrac{1}{6}\right)^3\left(\tfrac{5}{6}\right)^1$$

$$P(\text{four sixes}) = \binom{4}{4}\left(\tfrac{1}{6}\right)^4\left(\tfrac{5}{6}\right)^0$$

Example 2

An unbiased die is thrown 5 times. Find the probability of obtaining

    (i)   1 six   (ii)   3 sixes   (iii)   at least 1 six.

Let $p = P(\text{success, i.e. getting a six})$ and $q = P(\text{failure})$.

$$\Rightarrow p = \tfrac{1}{6} \quad \text{and} \quad q = \tfrac{5}{6} \quad \text{and} \quad n = 5$$

(i) To find $P(1 \text{ six})$, we substitute 1 for r and 4 for $(n - r)$ in the formula $\binom{n}{r} p^r q^{n-r}$.

$$\Rightarrow \quad P(1 \text{ six}) = \binom{5}{1} p^1 q^4 = \binom{5}{1} \left(\frac{1}{6}\right) \left(\frac{5}{6}\right)^4$$

$$= 5 \cdot \frac{1}{6} \cdot \frac{5^4}{6^4} = \frac{5^5}{6^5} = \frac{3125}{7776}$$

(ii) $P(3 \text{ sixes}) = \binom{5}{3} \left(\frac{1}{6}\right)^3 \left(\frac{5}{6}\right)^2$

$$= 10 \cdot \frac{1}{6^3} \cdot \frac{25}{36} = \frac{250}{7776} = \frac{125}{3888}$$

(iii) $P(\text{at least 1 six}) = 1 - P(\text{no six})$

$$P(\text{no six}) = \binom{5}{0} \left(\frac{1}{6}\right)^0 \left(\frac{5}{6}\right)^5 = \left(\frac{5}{6}\right)^5$$

$$\Rightarrow \quad P(\text{at least 1 six}) = 1 - \left(\frac{5}{6}\right)^5 = \frac{4651}{7776}$$

Example 3

Given that 10% of apples are bad, find the probability that in a box containing 6 apples, there is
  (i) no bad apple
 (ii) just one bad apple
(iii) at least one bad apple.

$$P(\text{bad apple}) = \frac{1}{10} \quad \Rightarrow \quad P(\text{good apple}) = \frac{9}{10}$$

$$\Rightarrow \quad p = \frac{1}{10} \quad \text{and} \quad q = \frac{9}{10} \quad \text{and} \quad n = 6$$

(i) $P(\text{no bad apple})$ is the term where the power of p is zero.

$$= \binom{6}{0} \left(\frac{1}{10}\right)^0 \left(\frac{9}{10}\right)^6 = \left(\frac{9}{10}\right)^6 = \frac{9^6}{10^6}$$

(ii) $P(1 \text{ bad apple}) = \binom{6}{1} \left(\frac{1}{10}\right)^1 \left(\frac{9}{10}\right)^5$ .... the power of $p = 1$

$$= 6 \cdot \frac{1}{10} \cdot \left(\frac{9}{10}\right)^5 = \frac{6.9^5}{10^6}$$

(iii) $P(\text{at least 1 bad apple}) = 1 - P(\text{no bad apple})$

$$= 1 - \frac{9^6}{10^6}$$ .... from (i) above

3. To find the probability of kth success on the nth Bernoulli trial

In example 2 on the previous page, we worked out the probability of getting 3 sixes when a dice is thrown 5 times. If the same dice is thrown continuously until a six appears for the fourth time, how do we find the probability that the 4th six appears on the tenth throw?

For a 4th six to appear on the 10th throw,
  (i) we need to get 3 sixes on the first nine throws, and then
 (ii) get a six on the 10th throw.

Three sixes on the first nine throws is given by

$$\binom{9}{3} p^3 q^{9-3} \quad \text{i.e.} \quad \binom{9}{3}\left(\frac{1}{6}\right)^3 \left(\frac{5}{6}\right)^6$$

$$84 \times \frac{5^6}{6^9} = 0.13$$

$P(\text{six on the 10th throw}) = \frac{1}{6}$

Thus $P(\text{4th six on the 10th throw}) = 0.13 \times \frac{1}{6} = 0.0217.$

Example 4

A card is drawn at random from a normal deck of playing cards and then replaced. The process is repeated until the third diamond appears. Find the probability that this happens when the tenth card is drawn.

$P(\text{drawing a diamond}) = \frac{1}{4}$

The probability of drawing the third diamond on the 10th draw is

$$P(\text{drawing 2 diamonds in the first nine draws}) \times$$
$$P(\text{drawing a diamond on the 10th draw})$$

$P(\text{2 diamonds on 1st nine draws}) = \binom{9}{2}\left(\frac{1}{4}\right)^2\left(\frac{3}{4}\right)^7$

$$= 0.3$$

$P(\text{diamond on 10th draw}) \qquad = \frac{1}{4} = 0.25$

Thus $P(\text{third diamond on the 10th draw}) = 0.3 \times 0.25$
$$= 0.075$$

Exercise 7.3

1. A fair die is thrown repeatedly. Find the probability of getting the first 6 on the fourth throw.

2. Two dice are rolled and their numbers added. Find the probability of getting the first 7 on the third roll.

3. The probability that a horse will win any race is $\frac{2}{5}$. What is the probability that he will win his first race on his fifth attempt.

4. On average 10% of bolts produced by a machine are defective. Find the probability that the first defective bolt occurs on the sixth investigation correct to 3 places of decimals.

5. A card is drawn at random from a normal deck of playing cards. Find the probability that:
   (i) the first picture card occurs on the third attempt
   (ii) the first diamond occurs on the fourth attempt
   (iii) the first red card occurs on the second attempt.

6. A fair coin is tossed 8 times.
   We require the probability of getting 3 heads on these 8 tosses.
   (i) Explain why the binomial distribution is a suitable method of solving this problem.
   (ii) If p = probability of getting a head
           q = probability of not getting a head
     and n = number of trials,
     write down the values of p, q and n.

7. A coin is tossed 5 times. What is the probability of getting
   (i) exactly 1 head   (ii) exactly 3 heads?

8. Find the probability that, in five throws of a fair dice, a 3 will occur
   (i) on no occasion   (ii) once only   (iii) twice.

9. The probability that a marksman hits the target is $\frac{1}{3}$.
   What is the probability that, in 7 attempts, he hits the target three times?

10. Assuming that a couple are equally likely to produce a boy or a girl, find the probability that in a family of 5 children there are 3 boys and 2 girls.

11. Jean either walks to school or goes by bus. The probability that she walks to school on a summer morning is 0.7. For a school week of five days during the summer, find the probability that
    (i) she walks to school only once
    (ii) she walks to school exactly three times.

12. The probability that a person votes for Party X is $\frac{3}{5}$.
    Find the probability that, in a randomly selected sample of 8 voters, there are exactly 3 who vote for Party X.

13. The probability that a first-year university student will complete four years of study is $\frac{1}{3}$. What is the probability that, of four first-year students, at least three will complete four years of study?

14. If 20% of the bolts produced by a machine are defective, determine the probability that, out of 4 bolts selected at random,
    (i) 2 bolts are defective
    (ii) not more than 2 bolts are defective.

15. The probability that any child in a certain class travels to school by bus is $\frac{2}{5}$. If four children from the class are selected at random, what is the probability that
    (i) none of them travels to school by bus
    (ii) three of them travel to school by bus
    (iii) at least one of them travels to school by bus?

16. A certain golfer estimates that the probability that he will sink any one putt is $\frac{7}{10}$. Find the probability that
    (i) he will sink two putts in three attempts
    (ii) he will miss three putts in four attempts.

17. The probability that horse A will win any given race is $\frac{2}{5}$.
    What is the probability that in five races
    (i) A will win exactly 3 races
    (ii) A will win the first, third and fifth races and lose the others?

18. Out of 2000 families with 4 children each, how many would you expect to have
    (i) 2 boys   (ii) no girls   (iii) at least one boy?

19. In a multiple-choice test, each question has three alternative answers with only one answer correct.
    Part A of the test consists of four of these questions.
    (i) Explain why the binomial distribution is appropriate in this situation.
    (ii) If Ray guesses each answer, calculate the probability that he gets all answers correct.
    (iii) Calculate the probability that he gets the first answer correct.
         Hence calculate the probability that he gets exactly one answer correct.

20. A fair coin is tossed repeatedly until the third head appears.
    Explain how you would use the binomial distribution to work out the probability of this happening.

21. A fair dice is thrown repeatedly.
    (i) Find the probability of getting two fives in the first ten throws.
    (ii) Hence find the probability of getting the third five on the eleventh throw.

22. A card is drawn at random from a normal deck of playing cards and then replaced.
    (i) What is the probability that the card drawn is a picture card?
    (ii) A card is drawn repeatedly and then replaced until the third picture card is drawn.
         Find the probability that the third picture card is drawn on the thirteenth attempt.

23. When a spinner is spun, the probability that it lands on red is 0.3. The spinner is spun until four reds are got.
    Find the probability that the fourth red is got on the tenth spin.

24. A bag contains counters of which 40% are red and the rest yellow. A counter is taken from the bag, its colour is noted and then replaced. This is performed eight times.
    (i) Find the probability that exactly three counters will be red.
    (ii) If the process is repeated until a fourth red counter is drawn, find the probability that this happens on the ninth draw.

25. In a multiple-choice test, there are ten questions and for each question there is a choice of four answers, only one of which is correct. If a student guesses at each of the answers, find the probability that he gets

   (i) none correct   (ii) 7 correct.

Now find the probability that he gets his third correct answer on the tenth question.

Section 7.4 How to show events are independent ───

In book 4, it was stated that two events are **independent** when the outcome of one event does not affect the outcome of the other event.

We also used conditional probability to get a multiplication rule for independent events as follows:

$P(A|B) = \frac{P(A \cap B)}{P(B)}$ ... (conditional probability)

$\therefore$ $P(A \cap B) = P(A|B) \times P(B)$ ... (general multiplication rule)

In the case of independent events A and B, where the occurrence of one event has no effect on the other we conclude that;

$P(A|B) = P(A)$

$\therefore$ $P(A \cap B) = P(A) \times P(B)$

> ***Multiplication rule for*** $P(A \cap B) = P(A).P(B)$
> ***independent events:*** $P(A \text{ and } B) = P(A).P(B)$

In this section, we will use the multiplication rule to determine whether or not two events are independent. The following examples will illustrate the procedure.

Example 1

In a group of 60 students, 20 study History, 24 study French, 8 study both History and French and 24 study neither.

Illustrate this information on a Venn diagram.

Now investigate if the events 'a student studies History' and 'a student studies French' are independent.

$P(\text{History}) = \frac{20}{60} = \frac{1}{3}$

$P(\text{French}) = \frac{24}{60} = \frac{2}{5}$

$P(\text{History and French}) = \frac{8}{60} = \frac{2}{15}$

Now $P(\text{History}) \times P(\text{French}) = \frac{1}{3} \times \frac{2}{5} = \frac{2}{15}$

Thus $P(\text{History and French}) = P(\text{History}) \times P(\text{French}) = \frac{2}{15}$

The two events are independent.

Example 2

Two events A and B are such that $P(A) = 0.5$, $P(B) = 0.4$ and $P(A|B) = 0.3$.
(i) Find $P(A \cap B)$.
(ii) Investigate whether or not the events A and B are independent.

(i) Using the conditional probability rule, we have:

$$P(A|B) = \frac{P(A \cap B)}{P(B)}$$

$$\therefore \quad 0.3 = \frac{P(A \cap B)}{0.4}$$

$$\therefore \quad P(A \cap B) = (0.3)(0.4) = 0.12$$

$$\therefore \quad P(A \cap B) = 0.12$$

(ii) $P(A \cap B) = 0.12 \qquad P(A) = 0.5 \qquad P(B) = 0.4$

$\qquad P(A) \times P(B) = 0.5 \times 0.4 = 0.2$

Since $P(A \cap B) = 0.12 \Rightarrow P(A \cap B) \neq P(A) \times P(B)$

Thus the events A and B are not independent.

Example 3

Two ordinary fair dice, one red and one blue, are to be rolled once.
(i) Find the probability of the following events:

Event A: the number showing on the red dice will be a 5 or a 6.
Event B: the total of the numbers showing on the two dice will be 7.
Event C: the total of the numbers showing on the two dice will be 8.

(ii) Show that events A and B are independent.
(iii) Investigate if events A and C are independent.

(i) The events A, B and C are shown on the right.

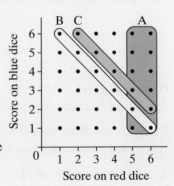

$\#A = 12 \quad \therefore \quad P(A) = \frac{12}{36} = \frac{1}{3}$

$\#B = 6 \quad \therefore \quad P(B) = \frac{6}{36} = \frac{1}{6}$

$\#C = 5 \quad \therefore \quad P(C) = \frac{5}{36}$

(ii) There are two ways to score 7 with the red dice showing 5 or 6.

These are $(5, 2)$ and $(6, 1)$

So $\#(A \cap B) = 2 \Rightarrow P(A \cap B) = \frac{2}{36} = \frac{1}{18}$

Now $P(A) \times P(B) = \frac{1}{3} \times \frac{1}{6} = \frac{1}{18}$

Since $P(A \cap B) = P(A) \times P(B) = \frac{1}{18}$, events A and B are independent.

(iii) From the diagram #(A ∩ C) = 2.

These are (5, 3) and (6, 2).

Thus #(A ∩ C) = 2 ⇒ $P(A \cap C) = \frac{2}{36} = \frac{1}{18}$

Now $P(A) \times P(C) = \frac{1}{3} \times \frac{5}{36} = \frac{5}{108}$

Since $\frac{5}{108} \neq \frac{1}{18}$, then $P(A \cap C) \neq P(A) \times P(C)$.

Thus events A and C are not independent.

Remember: **1.** If two events are **independent**,

$P(A \ and \ B) = P(A \cap B) = P(A).P(B)$ ... $(P(A|B) = P(A))$.

2. If two events are **mutually exclusive**,

$P(A \ or \ B) = P(A \cup B) = P(A) + P(B)$ ... $(P(A \cap B) = 0)$.

Exercise 7.4

1. The given Venn diagram shows the number of elements in the different regions.

   Find   (i) $P(A)$ (ii) $P(B)$ (iii) $P(A \cap B)$.

   Hence show that A and B are independent events.

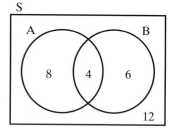

2. From the given Venn diagram, write down
   (i) $P(A)$ (ii) $P(B)$.

   Now show that A and B are independent.

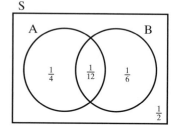

3. Given that $P(A) = 0.8$, $P(B) = 0.6$ and $P(A \cap B) = 0.48$.
   Are A and B independent events? Explain your answer.

4. Events A and B are such that $P(A) = 0.4$ and $P(B) = 0.25$.
   If A and B are independent events, find $P(A \cap B)$.

5. A and B are two independent events.
   If $P(A) = 0.4$ and $P(A \cup B) = 0.7$, use the formula
   $P(A \cup B) = P(A) + P(B) - P(A \cap B)$ to find $P(B)$.

6. The events A and B are such that

   $P(A) = 0.45$, $P(B) = 0.35$ and $P(A \cup B) = 0.7$.

   (i)   Find the value of $P(A \cap B)$.
   (ii) Explain why the events A and B are not independent.
   (iii) Find the value of $P(A|B)$.

   Remember:

   $P(A|B) = \dfrac{P(A \cap B)}{P(B)}$.

7. Given that $P(A) = 0.8$, $P(B) = 0.7$ and $P(A|B) = 0.8$.
   (i) Find $P(A \cap B)$
   (ii) Show that A and B are independent.

8. The events A and B are such that $P(A) = \frac{2}{5}$, $P(B) = \frac{1}{6}$ and $P(A \cup B) = \frac{13}{30}$.
   (i) Find $P(A \cap B)$.
   (ii) Explain why A and B are not independent.

9. Given that events C and D are independent and that $P(C|D) = \frac{2}{3}$ and $P(C \cap D) = \frac{1}{3}$, find
   (i) $P(C)$ (ii) $P(D)$.

10. Given $P(B) = 0.7$, $P(C) = 0.6$ and $P(C|B) = 0.7$, find $P(B \cap C)$.
    Now investigate if B and C are independent.

11. A and B are two independent events such that
    $$P(A) = 0.2 \text{ and } P(B) = 0.15$$
    Evaluate the following probabilities:
    (i) $P(A \cap B)$ (ii) $P(A|B)$ (iii) $P(A \cup B)$

12. Two events A and B are such that
    $$P(A) = 0.2, P(A \cap B) = 0.15 \text{ and } P(A' \cap B) = 0.6.$$
    (i) Copy and complete the given Venn diagram.
    (ii) Find the probability that neither A nor B happens.
    (iii) Find the conditional probability, $P(A|B)$.
    (iv) State whether A and B are independent and justify your answer.

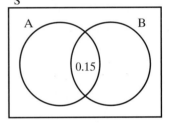

13. Two events A and B are such that $P(A) = \frac{8}{15}$, $P(B) = \frac{1}{3}$, $P(A|B) = \frac{1}{5}$.
    Calculate the probability that
    (i) both events occur
    (ii) only one of the two events occurs
    (iii) neither event occurs.

14. (i) Given that two events, A and B, are such that $P(A \text{ and } B) = P(A) \times P(B)$, state what you can say about the events A and B.
       If event A is 'obtaining a 6 on a single throw of a dice', suggest a possible description for event B.
    (ii) Given that two events, C and D, are such that $P(C \text{ or } D) = P(C) + P(D)$, state what you can say about the events C and D.
        Write down the value of $P(C \text{ and } D)$.

15. Two events, A and B, are such that $P(A|B) = 0.4$, $P(B|A) = 0.25$ and $P(A \cap B) = 0.12$.
    (i) Calculate the value of $P(A)$ and $P(B)$.
    (ii) Give a reason why A and B are not independent.
    (iii) Find $P(A \cap B')$

16. Two events, E and F, are such that $P(E) = \frac{2}{5}$, $P(F) = \frac{1}{6}$ and $P(E \cup F) = \frac{13}{30}$.
    Show that E and F are neither mutually exclusive nor independent.

Section 7.5 Probability involving permutations and combinations

Many of the more difficult problems in probability involve the use of permutations or combinations to identify the number of possible outcomes or the number of favourable outcomes. While many problems can be solved in more than one way, the following worked examples will illustrate how combinations, in particular, can be used to solve certain types of problem.

Remember $\binom{n}{r}$ = the number of ways of selecting r objects from n.

e.g. the number of ways of selecting 3 students from 6 is $\binom{6}{3} = 20$

Example 1

In Class 6A, two boys and four girls study music.
In Class 6B, four boys and six girls study music.
Two pupils are chosen at random from each of the two classes to perform at a concert.
  (i)   In how many ways can the 4 pupils be selected?
 (ii)   Calculate the probability that the four chosen consist of 2 boys from 6A and 2 girls from 6B.
(iii)   Calculate the probability that the four pupils are of the same gender.

For convenience, we will set out the information in the form of a table.

6A	2 Boys	4 Girls
6B	4 Boys	6 Girls

  (i)   The number of ways 2 pupils can be selected from 6A and 2 pupils from 6B is,
$$\binom{6}{2} \times \binom{10}{2} = 675 \text{ ways.}$$

 (ii)   Two boys from 6A and two girls from 6B can be chosen in
$$\binom{2}{2} \times \binom{6}{2} = 1 \times 15 = 15 \text{ ways}$$
$$P(2 \text{ boys from 6A and 2 girls from 6B}) = \frac{15}{675} = \frac{1}{45}$$

(iii)   If the four pupils are of the same gender, they will consist of
        (a) 2 girls from 6A and 2 girls from 6B
     or (b) 2 boys from 6A and 2 boys from 6B.

$$P(a) = \frac{\binom{4}{2} \times \binom{6}{2}}{675} = \frac{6 \times 15}{675} = \frac{90}{675}$$

$$P(b) = \frac{\binom{2}{2} \times \binom{4}{2}}{675} = \frac{1 \times 6}{675} = \frac{6}{675}$$

$$\therefore \quad P(a \text{ or } b) = P(a) + P(b) = \frac{90}{675} + \frac{6}{675} = \frac{96}{675} = \frac{32}{225}$$

Example 2

Three cards are drawn at random, and without replacement, from a pack of 52 playing cards. Find the probability that

(i) the three cards drawn are the Jack of spades, the Queen of clubs and the King of clubs

(ii) the three cards are aces

(iii) two cards are red and the third one is a club

(iv) the three cards are of the same colour.

(i) Three cards can be selected from 52 cards in $\binom{52}{3}$ ways.

$$\binom{52}{3} = \frac{52 \times 51 \times 50}{3 \times 2 \times 1} = 22100$$

The three cards mentioned can be selected in $\binom{3}{3}$ i.e. 1 way

$\therefore \quad P(\text{J..Q..K}) = \frac{1}{22100}$

(ii) Three aces can be selected from four aces in $\binom{4}{3}$ ways

$\therefore \quad P(\text{3 aces}) = \frac{\binom{4}{3}}{\binom{52}{3}} = \frac{4}{22100} = \frac{1}{5525}$

(iii) Two red cards and one club can be selected in

$$\binom{26}{2} \times \binom{13}{1} = \frac{26 \times 25}{2 \times 1} \times 13 = 4225 \text{ ways}$$

$\therefore \quad P(\text{2 red and 1 club}) = \frac{4225}{22100} = \frac{169}{884} = \frac{13}{68}$

(iv) $P(\text{3 cards of the same colour}) = P(\text{3 black or 3 red})$

$$= P(\text{3 black}) + P(\text{3 red})$$

$$= \frac{\binom{26}{3}}{\binom{52}{3}} + \frac{\binom{26}{3}}{\binom{52}{3}} = \frac{5200}{22100} = \frac{4}{17}$$

Events occurring at least once

Many questions in probability contain phrases such as "at least once", "at least one red disc", etc. Take, for example, the probability of getting at least one 4 when a pair of dice are thrown.

First get the probability that no 4 is thrown.

$P(\text{no 4}) = P(\text{no 4 on 1st throw}) \times P(\text{no 4 on 2nd throw}) = \frac{5}{6} \times \frac{5}{6} = \frac{25}{36}$

$P(\text{at least one 4}) = 1 - P(\text{no 4}) = 1 - \frac{25}{36} = \frac{11}{36}$

Similarly, if a coin is tossed four times, the probability of getting at least two heads is

$$P(\text{at least 2 heads}) = 1 - P(\text{no head}) - P(\text{1 head})$$

In general, if E is any event, then

$$P(E \text{ occurring}) = 1 - P(E \text{ not occurring})$$

Exercise 7.5

1. A hand of four cards is dealt at random from a normal pack of 52 cards.
    Find the probability that the hand contains
    (i) exactly two queens   (ii) four spades
    (iii) four red cards   (iv) four cards of the same suit.

2. A team of four people is chosen at random from six men and five women.
    In how many ways can the team be chosen?
    Now find the probability that the team will consist of
    (i) 2 men and 2 women   (ii) 1 man and 3 women   (iii) all women.

3. There are sixteen discs in a board-game: five blue, three green, six red and two yellow.
    Four discs are chosen at random.
    What is the probability that
    (i) the four discs are blue
    (ii) the four discs are the same colour
    (iii) all four discs are different in colour
    (iv) two of the discs are blue and two are not blue?

4. Nine discs were each given a natural number from two to ten inclusive, each number
    different from the others. All nine were placed in a box.
    (i) A disc was picked at random and replaced. A second disc was then picked.
        Find the probability that both discs showed prime numbers.
    (ii) Three discs were picked at random. What is the probability that three odd-
        numbered discs or three even-numbered discs were picked?

5. Nine cards are numbered from 1 to 9, with each number different from the others.
    Three cards are drawn at random from the nine cards.
    (i) Find the probability that the card numbered 8 is not drawn.
    (ii) Find the probability that all three cards drawn have odd numbers.

6. In a class of 24 students, there are 14 boys and 10 girls.
    In a particular week three students celebrate their birthdays.
    What is the probability that these three students
    (i) are three boys or three girls
    (ii) have their birthdays falling on different days of the week?

7. In an examination a candidate is required to select any seven questions from ten.
   (i) In how many ways can this be done?
   (ii) How many of the selections contain the first and second questions?
   Now calculate the probability that the candidate selects
   (iii) both the first and second questions
   (iv) at least one of the first two questions.

8. A class of 16 pupils consists of 10 girls, 3 of whom are left-handed, and 6 boys, only one of whom is left-handed. Two pupils are to be chosen at random from the class to act as prefects. Calculate the probability that the chosen pupils will consist of
   (i) one girl and one boy
   (ii) one girl who is left-handed and one boy who is left-handed
   (iii) two left-handed pupils
   (iv) at least one pupil who is left-handed.

9. Three dice, each numbered 1 to 6 are rolled. One dice is fair and the others are biased so that, for each of them, a six is twice as likely as any other score.
   Find the probability of rolling exactly two sixes.

10. A box contains letters used in a word-game. At a certain stage in the game, the 8 letters in the box are A, A, C, E, L, P, P, P. One player draws, at random, 3 letters in succession without replacing them. Calculate the probability that
    (i) the letters P, E, A are drawn in that order
    (ii) the letters P, E, A are drawn in any order
    (iii) the 3 letters drawn do not include E or P
    (iv) the 3 letters drawn are either all consonants or all vowels.

Section 7.6 Probability simulations

The word **simulate** means to imitate or model. The use of simulation is becoming an increasingly-powerful tool in the modern world of business. In the past, when an engineer was designing a new car or aeroplane, he would build a physical model first and test its performance in wind tunnels. Now, initial tests are done on computers through the use of simulation programmes.

A **probability simulation** is the use of some method to model or represent a real experiment or situation.

Simulations can involve

> dice, spinners, discs and counters
> calculators and computers to generate random numbers
> random number tables

You may also use experiments in simulation.

Example 1

With every breakfast cereal pack there is a free coloured toy. There are 6 different colours of toys.

How many packs of breakfast cereal do you need to buy to collect the 6 different-coloured toys?

A simulation can give you some indication of how many packets you need to buy.

(i) Match each colour to a number on a dice.

(ii) Roll the dice until each colour has appeared once.

2, 2, 6, 4, 2, 2, 5, 1, 4, 5, 4, 3

All six numbers have occurred in the first 12 rolls.
Based on this simulation, you would need to buy 12 packets.

(iii) Repeat the simulation.

3, 1, 3, 1, 4, 6, 6, 5, 3, 5, 6, 3, 5, 2

This time you would need to buy 14 packets.

(iv) Repeat this as many times as you like.

The more times you repeat the experiment, the more confidence you have in the results.

Think!
Can you propose an alternative way to find how many packets you need to buy?
Perhaps your method might include the following:

> generate a random number table
> use a spreadsheet
> use a spinner
> get your friends to buy some boxes to see how many you need to buy to get a full set.

The **advantages** of simulation are:
> It is quick and inexpensive
> When using a spreadsheet, you can get several hundred pieces of data
> You can adjust the probability to cater for events that are not equally likely.

Example 2

In families that have 5 children, we wish to investigate the probability that boys outnumber girls.

Devise a simulation of this situation and use it to determine whether the probability is more than, less than, or equal to $\frac{1}{2}$.

Assume that each child has an equal chance of being a boy or a girl.
Suppose you choose to toss 5 coins at a time to simulate the genders of the 5 children in the family, where head stands for boy and tail stands for girl.
In 4 tosses we get the following results:

TTTTT	5 girls	Girls outnumber boys
THHHH	1 girl, 4 boys	Boys outnumber girls
THTHH	2 girls, 3 boys	Boys outnumber girls
HHTTT	3 girls, 2 boys	Girls outnumber boys

After 100 tosses, we get the following results:

Outcome	Frequency
Boys outnumbering	53
Girls outnumbering	47

It appears that the outcomes are fairly even and that the probability that boys outnumber girls is about $\frac{1}{2}$.

Using a spreadsheet, this experiment was simulated and the result is shown in the table below:

Outcome	Frequency
Boys outnumbering	48
Girls outnumbering	52

This outcome shows a similar result.

This example could also be modelled by
 (i)   Rolling a dice with $1 - 3$ indicates boy and $4 - 6$ indicates girl
 (ii) Random numbers using a calculator or a table of random numbers:

       $0 - 4$ indicates boy and $5 - 9$ indicates girl

 (iii) selecting from a deck of playing cards:

       red indicates girl and black indicates boy

Example 3

Four people are selected at random from a large crowd.
What is the probability that two or more of them have birthdays in the same month?
  (i) Devise a simulation that could determine the probability of this happening.
  (ii) Run the simulation 100 times and approximate the probability.

  (i) Possible simulations:
> Write down the 12 months of the year on separate cards and draw them out of a box.
> Remove all the kings from a deck of cards, then select a card from the remaining 48:
  Ace = January, 2 = February, ... etc.
> Use a calculator or spreadsheet to generate random numbers from 1 to 12.
> Toss a dice and coin together (there are 12 possible outcomes).
  H1 = January, H2 = February, ... etc.

  (ii) **Simulation result**   **Shared birthday**

6	8	1	2	No
1	8	1	11	Yes
5	11	6	10	No
8	8	10	12	Yes
10	8	2	4	No
5	6	12	10	No

> The above 6 results were found using the random number function on a calculator.
> When this experiment was conducted 100 times, the following results were recorded.

Shared birthday	Frequency
Yes	45
No	55

From these results, we can conclude that the probability of two, three or more people, from a random group of four sharing the same birthday, is about 45%.

Note: This answer seems surprisingly high but the true (calculated) probability is 42.7%.

Exercise 7.6

1. One of twenty different vouchers are given away in packets of crisps.
   You need a full set of vouchers to get a model car.
   Carry out a simulation to estimate the number of packets of crisps you would need to buy to get a car.

2. A menu has three options – meat, fish and vegetarian.
   $\frac{2}{8}$ of diners choose fish; $\frac{1}{8}$ choose vegetarian; $\frac{5}{8}$ choose meat.
   Explain how you would simulate the choices of the next ten customers.

3. Carry out a simulated experiment to determine the probability, correct to two decimal places, that in a family with four children
   (i) the girls outnumber the boys
   (ii) all the children are girls.

4. At a road junction, it is known that 80% of cars turn left and 20% of cars turn right.
   Suggest how you might allocate numbers to simulate the probability of cars turning right or left when approaching this junction.

5. The *Ringdogs* have a 0.7 chance of winning their home games and a 0.4 chance of winning their away games.
   (i) If they play 12 home games and 13 away games, how many games should they win?
   (ii) Make a simulation of this situation and find out how many of the 25 games they should win.
        Does your result agree with part (i)?

6. Every packet of *Chocopops* breakfast cereal contains a superhero figure for children to collect. David wants to collect the entire set of eight different superhero figures.
   Devise a simulation to determine the approximate number of packets of *Chocopops* he will need to purchase to collect the full set.

7. What is the probability of rolling at least one 6 in four rolls of a fair dice?
   Give your answer correct to 2 decimal places.
   Simulate an experiment over a number of trials to determine an approximate probability of rolling a 6.
   Compare your result to the answer already found.

8. What is the likely size of a family that contains one child of each gender?
   Explain how you could simulate this experiment.

Revision Exercise 7 (Core)

1. In a random experiment $P(A) = 0.5$, $P(B) = 0.4$ and $P(A \cup B) = 0.7$ Find:

   (i) $P(A \cap B)$
   (ii) $P(A|B)$
   (iii) $(B|A)$

2. Which of these events can be illustrated by this tree diagram?

    (i) tossing a coin three times

    (ii) selecting two counters from a bag of red, blue and yellow counters.

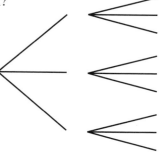

3. A golfer estimates that the probability she will sink a 1-metre putt is 0.7. Find the probability that she will sink three 1-metre putts in four attempts.

4. Five children are selected at random from a class containing 10 boys and 20 girls.
    (i) In how many ways can this be done?
    (ii) How many of the selections have 2 boys and 3 girls?
    (iii) What is the probability that exactly two boys are selected?

5. A local football team wins 80% of its home matches. Find the probability that (i) the first win occurs in the 4th match.
                (ii) the first loss occurs in the 4th match.

6. 20% of the items produced by a machine are defective. Four items are chosen items are defective. Four items are chosen at random for inspection.
    (i) Find the probability that none of the chosen items is defective.
    (ii) Find the probability that the first defective item is found on the 4th inspection.

7. The school team has two tennis matches to play.

The probability that they win the first match is $\frac{2}{5}$.

If they win the first match, the probability that they win the second is $\frac{3}{4}$.

If they lose the first match, the probability that they win the second is $\frac{1}{3}$.

Copy this tree diagram. Fill it in.

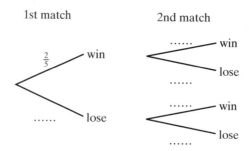

Find the probability that the team:
(i) loses both matches   (ii) wins only one match.

8. From the given Venn diagram, write down

   (i) $P(E)$

   (ii) $P(F)$

   (iii) $P(E \cup F)$

   Now show that E and F are independent.

   Find also $P(E|F)$.

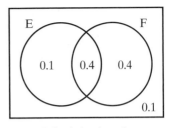

9. At a bazaar held to raise money for a charity, it costs €1 to try one's luck in drawing an ace from an ordinary deck of 52 playing cards.

   What is the expected profit per customer if the prize is €10 if, and only if, the person draws an ace?

10. Jack takes a card at random from this pack.

   He keeps the card and then takes a second card at random.

   What is the probability that the second number he takes is higher than the first?

Revision Exercise 7 (Advanced)

1. A tennis player A has a probability of $\frac{2}{3}$ of winning a set against a player B. The match is won by the player who first wins two sets.

   Find the probability that A wins the match.

2. The probability that my football club has all their first-team players fit is 70%. When they do have a fully-fit team, they win 90% of their home games. When their first team is not fully-fit, they win 40% of their home games.

   Calculate the probability that they win their next home game.

3. Two events E and F are independent.

   If $P(E) = \frac{1}{5}$ and $P(F) = \frac{1}{7}$, find

   (i) $P(E \cap F)$ (ii) $P(E \cup F)$.

4. In a class of 56 students, each studies at least one of the subjects Biology, Chemistry, Physics. The Venn diagram shows the numbers of students studying the various combinations of subjects.

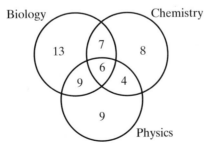

   (i) A student is picked at random from the whole class.

      Find the probability that the student does not study Biology.

   (ii) A student is picked at random from those who study at least two of the subjects.

      Find the probability that the student does not study Biology.

(iii) Two students are picked at random from the whole class.
Find the probability that they both study Physics.

(iv) Two students are picked at random from those who study Chemistry.
Find the probability that exactly one of them studies Biology.

5. (i) Events C and D are shown in the Venn-diagram over.
Show that C and D are independent events.

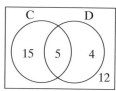

(ii) Events X and Y are such that $P(X) = \frac{2}{3}$, $P(X|Y) = \frac{2}{3}$ and $P(Y) = \frac{1}{4}$.
Find (a) $P(X \cap Y)$ (b) $P(Y|X)$.

6. Two athletes, A and B, are attempting to qualify for an international competition in both the 5000 m and 10 000 m races.
The probabilities of each qualifying are shown in the following table:

Athlete	5000 m	10 000 m
A	$\frac{3}{5}$	$\frac{1}{4}$
B	$\frac{2}{3}$	$\frac{2}{5}$

Assuming that the probabilities are independent, calculate the probability that
(i) athlete A will qualify for both races
(ii) exactly one of the athletes qualifies for the 5000 m race
(iii) both athletes qualify for the 10 000 m race.

7. (i) Amy throws a biased dice three times.
For each throw, the probability of Amy not scoring a 6 is $\frac{2}{3}$.
Using a tree diagram, or otherwise, find the probability that she gets at least one 6 in the three throws.

(ii) For events A and B, it is known that $P(A) = \frac{2}{3}$, $P(A \cup B) = \frac{3}{4}$ and $P(A \cap B) = \frac{5}{12}$.
Find $P(B)$.

8. The given diagram shows a roulette wheel in a casino.
It costs €25 to spin the spinner once and you win the money in the sector in which it stops.
How much do you expect to win or lose if you play this game?
Explain why the game is not fair.

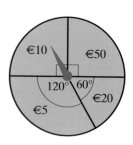

9. A fair die is rolled several times. Calculate the probability that
(i) two sixes occur on the first six rolls
(ii) the second six occurs on the seventh roll.

10. Events E and F are such that $P(E) = \frac{2}{3}$, $P(E|F) = \frac{2}{3}$ and $P(F) = \frac{1}{4}$.

Find   (i) $P(E \cap F)$ (ii) $P(F|E)$

Investigate if E and F are independent events.

Explain your answer.

Revision Exercise 7 (Extended Response Questions)

1. A marble falls down from A and must follow one of the paths indicated on the diagram. All paths from A to the bottom row are equally likely to be followed.

    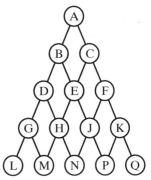

    (i) One of the paths from A to H is A-B-D-H.
    List the other two possible paths from A to H.
    (ii) Find the probability that the marble passes through H or J.
    (iii) Find the probability that the marble lands at N.
    (iv) Two marbles fall from A, one after the other, without affecting each other.
    Find the probability that they both land at P.

2. A soccer player knows that he has a 70% success rate when taking penalties.
    He takes ten penalty shots against the same goalkeeper.
    Calculate, correct to three decimal places, the probability that
    (i) he scores his first goal on his third attempt
    (ii) he scores exactly three goals in five attempts
    (iii) he scores his third goal on his seventh attempt.

3. (a) A and B are two events such that $P(A) = \frac{13}{25}$, $P(B) = \frac{9}{25}$ and $P(A|B) = \frac{5}{9}$.
    Determine each of these probabilities:
    (i) $P(A \text{ and } B)$ (ii) $P(B|A)$ (iii) $P(A \cup B)$.
    (b) A dice is biased in such a way that the probability of rolling a six is p.
    The other five numbers are all equally likely. This biased dice and a fair dice are rolled simultaneously. Show that the probability of rolling a total of 7 is independent of p.

4. In a class of 28 students there are 15 girls. Of the students in the class, 6 girls and 8 boys play basketball.
    (i) Represent this information in the chart below.

	Girl	Boy	Total
Basketball			
Does not play basketball			
Total			

A student is chosen at random from the class.

If G represents the event of choosing a girl and B represents the event of choosing a student who plays basketball, find:

(ii) $P(G)$ (iv) $P(B')$ (vi) $P(B|G)$ (viii) $P(B \cap G)$

(iii) $P(B)$ (v) $P(G|B)$ (vii) $P(B|G')$

5. A bag contains 4 red counters and 6 green counters.
    Four counters are drawn at random from the bag.
    Calculate the probability that
    (i)   all counters drawn are green
    (ii) at least one counter of each colour is drawn
    (iii) at least two green counters are drawn
    (iv) at least two green counters are drawn, given that at least one of each colour is drawn.
          State, giving a reason, whether or not the events "at least two green counters are drawn" and "at least one counter of each colour is drawn" are independent.

6. Consumer research on the reception of broadband was based on feedback from 150 households in a given area. The results of the survey was summarised as follows:

	Good reception (G)	Poor reception (G')
Provider A(P)	48	16
Provider B(P')	24	62

If one of the households is chosen at random, calculate the following probabilities:

(i) $P(G|P)$, the probability that the household is getting a good reception from Provider A.
(ii) $P(G \cap P)$, the probability that the household is getting a good reception and is using Provider A.
(iii) $P(G \cup P)$, the probability that the household is using Provider A or is getting a good reception or both.
(iv) Are the events G and P independent? Explain.
(v)   Are the events G and P mutually exclusive? Explain.

7. (a) The random variable X has the following probability distribution.

x	1	2	3	4	5
$P(x)$	0.1	a	b	0.2	0.1

(i) Write down the value of $a + b$.
(ii) Given that E(x), the expected value of x, is 2.9, find the value of a and the value of b.

(b) There are 16 girls and 8 boys in a class. Half of these 24 students study French. The probability that a randomly-selected girl studies French is 1.5 times the probability that a randomly-selected boy studies French.
How many of the boys in the class study French?

8. In a game, Ann uses a dice and Jane uses two equilateral
   triangle spinners, adding the scores together.
   Ann rolls the dice and Jane spins the spinners.
   After each turn they compare the scores.
   (i)   If the winner gets 1 point, who do you think is the
         more likely to reach 20 points first?
   (ii) To test if your judgement is correct, now construct a
         probability distribution for each event and, by finding
         the expected values, state which of the two has the better chance of reaching
         20 points first.

9. Five unbiased coins are tossed.
   (i)   Find the probability of getting three heads and two tails.
   (ii) The five coins are tossed eight times. Find the probability of getting three heads
         and two tails exactly four times.
         Give your answer correct to three decimal places.

10. A bag contains the following cardboard shapes:
    10 red squares, 15 green squares, 8 red triangles and 12 green triangles.
    One of the shapes is drawn at random from the bag.
    E is the event that a square is drawn.
    F is the event that a green shape is drawn.
    (i)   Find $P(E \cap F)$.
    (ii)   Find $P(E \cup F)$.
    (iii) State whether E and F are independent events, giving a reason for your answer.
    (iv)   State whether E and F are mutually exclusive events, giving a reason for your answer.

Functions and Graphs

Key words

function   domain   mapping diagram   codomain   range   domain intervals
inverse functions   composite functions   injective, surjective and bijective
functions   limit   continuous functions   asymptote   exponential function
logarithmic function   related graphs

Section 8.1 Introduction to functions

In our study of maths so far, we have dealt with points such as (2, 4) and (−3, 2) and learned how to plot these points on the coordinated plane.

Points such as (2, 4) and (−3, 2) are examples of **ordered pairs**.
An ordered pair, denoted by (x, y), is a pair of elements x and y in which x is considered to be the first element and y is the second element.

A set of ordered pairs such as $A = \{(1, 2), (2, 4), (3, 6), (4, 8)\}$ is called a **relation**.
Every relation determines two sets.
The set of all the first elements of the ordered pairs is called the **domain**.
The set of all the second elements of the ordered pairs is called the **range**.

Some relations may be defined by a **rule** relating elements in the domain to their corresponding elements in the range.

In order to define the relation fully, we need to specify both the rule and the domain.

For example, $\{(x, y)|y = 2x + 1, x \in \{1, 2, 3, 4\}\}$ is the relation

$\{(1, 3), (2, 5), (3, 7), (4, 9)\}$.

The domain is the set $\{1, 2, 3, 4\}$ and the range is the set $\{3, 5, 7, 9\}$.

The relation above may be represented
by a **mapping diagram**, as shown.

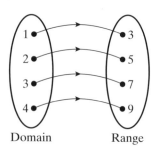

Domain   Range

Functions

Functions are special relations with individual properties.
They are often referred to as "number machines", with inputs and outputs.

When is a relation a function?
A **function** is a relation for which **each x-value** in an input set, there is a **unique y-value** of an output set.

When a function is represented by a mapping diagram, each element of the domain maps onto **one and only one** element of the range.

Consider these two mapping diagrams:

(i) 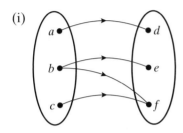   (ii)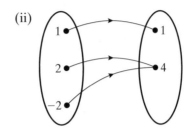

Diagram (i)   is not a function since the element *b* is paired with 2 different elements in the range.

Diagram (ii)   is a function since each element in the domain is mapped onto **one and only one** element in the range.

> *Remember*
>
> 1. In the mapping of a function, only one arrow comes from each element of the domain.
> 2. Each element of the domain is operated on by the function.

Notation – domain – range

Consider this rule for a function: "Square the input and add six."
If we input *x*, the output will be $x^2 + 6$.

The rule for this function may be written in any of the three ways shown on the right.

> (i) $f(x) = x^2 + 6$
> (ii) $f: x \rightarrow x^2 + 6$
> (iii) $y = x^2 + 6$

When dealing with the domain and range of a function, it is important to know what the basic number systems are. These are given below:

$N = \{1, 2, 3, ...\}$, the set of **natural** numbers,

$Z = \{...-3, -2, -1, 0, 1, 2, 3, ...\}$, the set of **integers**,

$Q = \{$fractions, $\frac{a}{b}, a, b \in Z, b \neq 0\}$, the set of **rational** numbers,

$R \backslash Q = $ the set of **irrational** numbers, e.g. $\pi, \sqrt{2}, e$, etc.

When all these numbers are combined, we get the set of **real numbers, R**.
R⁺ is the set of **positive** real numbers.

Consider the function $f: N \to N : x \to x^2$.
This means that the set of input numbers comes from N, the set of natural numbers.
The output numbers also come from the set N.
The set of possible output numbers is called the **codomain**.
However, the outputs generated by the function $f: N \to N : x \to x^2$ are the square numbers 1, 4, 9, 16, ...
The set of **actual outcomes** of a function is called the **range**.
The range is always a subset of the codomain.
However, in some functions, the range and codomain may be the same set.

The function $f: N \to N : x \to x^2$ is shown on the right.

Domain = N
Codomain = N
Range = {1, 4, 9, 16, ...}

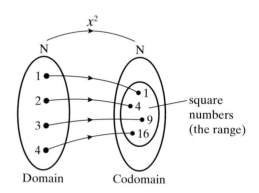

Now consider the function $f: R \to R : x \to x^2 + 2$.
The domain of f is the set of real numbers R.
The codomain is also R.

Domain intervals: When we have an input, a function gives certainty about the output. To create functions from certain relations, it is necessary to restrict the domain and create **intervals** in which the relation is a function.

1. When dealing with the log function $f: R^+ \to R : x \to \ln x$, the domain must be restricted to values of $x > 0$, that is, $x \in R^+$.
   We cannot get the log of a negative number.

2. For the function $f(x) = \sqrt{4 - x^2}$, the domain must exclude the values $x < -2$ or $x > 2$ as these values for x result in the square root of a negative number which is not a real number.
   Thus, the domain is $-2 \leq x \leq 2$.

The main features of a function are highlighted below:

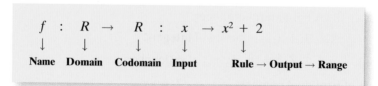

Vertical line test for a function

A very useful way to identify whether or not a relation is a function is to draw a graph of the relation and apply the **vertical line test**.

If a vertical line can be drawn anywhere on the graph, and it intersects the graph **more than once,** then the relation is **not** a function.

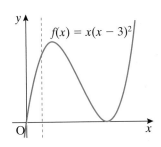

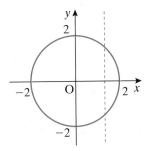

$f(x) = x(x - 3)^2$ is a function.

$x^2 + y^2 = 4$ is not a function.

Example 1

$f(x) = 4x + 3$ and $g(x) = 3x^2$ are two functions.

Find   (i) $f(3)$ (ii) $g(-1)$ (iii) $f(2k)$ (iv) $g(k - 3)$.

(i) $\quad f(x) = 4x + 3$
$\Rightarrow f(3) = 4(3) + 3$
$\qquad\quad = 15$

(ii) $\qquad g(x) = 3x^2$
$\Rightarrow g(-1) = 3(-1)^2$
$\qquad\qquad = 3$

(iii) $\quad f(x) = 4x + 3$
$\quad f(2k) = 4(2k) + 3$
$\qquad\quad = 8k + 3$

(iv) $\qquad g(x) = 3x^2$
$g(k - 3) = 3(k - 3)^2$
$\qquad\quad = 3(k^2 - 6k + 9)$
$\qquad\quad = 3k^2 - 18k + 27$

Example 2

Determine which of the following are the graphs of functions:

(i)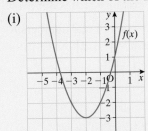

(ii)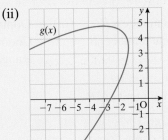

(iii)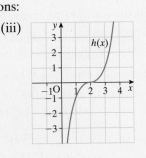

(i)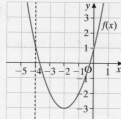

(ii)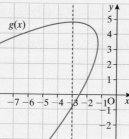

(iii)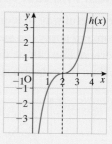

(i) $f(x)$ is a function as any vertical line intersects the graph once only.

(ii) $g(x)$ is not a function. It fails the vertical line test and there are some values of x that would not produce real values of y.

(iii) $h(x)$ is a function as any vertical line intersects the graph once only.

When describing intervals, the parentheses shown on the right are generally used.

1. $\{x \in R \mid a \leqslant x \leqslant b\} = [a, b]$
2. $\{x \in R \mid a < x < b\} = (a, b)$
3. $\{x \in R \mid a \leqslant x < b\} = [a, b)$
4. $\{x \in R \mid a < x \leqslant b\} = (a, b]$

Example 3

Examine each of the given functions and their graphs. State the domain, codomain and range of each.

(i) $f: R \to R: x \to x^2 - 2x + 8$ (ii) $g: (0, 2] \to R: x \to \dfrac{1}{x}$ (iii) $h: R \to [-1, 1]: x \to \cos x$

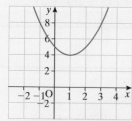

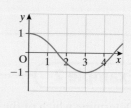

(i) f: Domain = set of real numbers R
    Codomain = set of real numbers R
    Range = $[4, \infty)$

(iii) h: Domain = set of real numbers R
    Codomain = $[-1, 1]$
    Range = $[-1, 1]$

(ii) g: Domain = $\{x \in R \mid 0 < x \leqslant 2\}$
    Codomain = set of real numbers R

    $g(x) = \dfrac{1}{x} \Rightarrow$ at $x = 2$, $g(2) = \dfrac{1}{2}$

    Range = $[\frac{1}{2}, \infty)$

Example 4

Write down the domain, codomain and range of the following functions:

(i) $f: R^+ \to R$, where $f(x) = x^2 - 4$ (ii) $g: R \to R: f(x) = 3x + 2$

(i) The domain of f is R^+, the set of positive real numbers.
The codomain of f is R.
$f(x) = x^2 - 4 \Rightarrow$ the lowest value of $f(x)$ is -4 since x^2 is always positive.
The range of f is $[-4, \infty)$.

(ii) The domain of g is R.
The codomain of g is R.
The range of g is R.

> R^+ is the set of positive real numbers.
> It does not include zero.

Note: The graph of $y = x^2 + 2$ is drawn in the domain $[-2, 1]$.

The range is $[2,6]$.

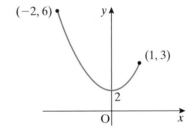

Exercise 8.1

1. Say why the following set of couples is not a function:

$\{(2, 5), (3, 6), (5, 8), (2, 10)\}$.

2. Investigate if each of these sets of couples represents a function.
   If it is not a function, state the reason why.

   (i) $\{(0, 0), (1, 1), (2, 4), (3, 9), (4, 16)\}$
   (ii) $\{(-2, 1), (-1, 3), (-2, 5), (1, 6), (2, 9)\}$
   (iii) $\{(-3, 4), (0, 11), (2, 9), (4, 11)\}$

3. State whether each of the following mapping diagrams represents a function.
   Give a reason for your answer in each case.

(i)

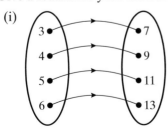

(ii)

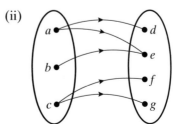

(iii) 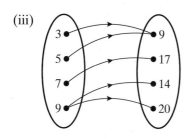   (iv)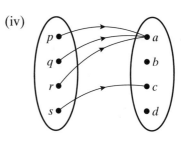

4. A set of couples is defined by the rule $y = 2x - 4$.
   If $x \in \{-1, 0, 1, 2, 3\}$, list all the couples.
   Write down the range generated.

5. If $f(x) = 3x - 2$, find
   (i) $f(2)$ (ii) $f(-3)$ (iii) $f(k)$ (iv) $f(2k - 1)$.

6. Given that $g(x) = (x - 2)^2$, find
   (i) $g(4)$ (ii) $g(-4)$ (iii) $g(8)$ (iv) $g(a)$.

7. The function f is defined by $f : R \rightarrow R : x \rightarrow 3x - 4$.
   For what value of k is $f(k) + f(2k) = 0$?

8. $f : x \rightarrow 4x$ and $g : x \rightarrow x + 1$ define two functions.
   If $g(3) + k[f(3)] = 8$, find the value of k.

9. $f(x) = 2x^2 - 1$ and $g(x) = x + 2$ define two functions.
   Solve these equations:
   (i) $f(x) = 3$ (ii) $g(x) = f(3)$ (iii) $f(x) = g(x)$

10. A function $f(x)$ is defined by $f(x) = 1 + \dfrac{2}{x}$.
    (i) Evaluate $f(-4)$ and $f\left(\frac{1}{5}\right)$.
    (ii) Find the value of x for which $f(x) = 2$.
    (iii) Find the value of k if $kf(2) = f\left(\frac{1}{2}\right)$.

11. $g(x) = 1 - 4x$ defines a function.
    (i) Find $g(k + 1)$.
    (ii) Solve the equation $g(k + 1) = g(-3)$.

12. If $g(x) = 3x - 2$, solve these equations:
    (i) $g(-x) = 6$ (ii) $g(2x) = 4$ (iii) $\dfrac{1}{g(x)} = 6$

13. Solve each of the following equations:
    (i) $f(x) = x^2 - 2x$, given $f(x) = 3$
    (ii) $g(x) = x^2 - x - 6$, given $g(x) = 0$
    (iii) $h(x) = x + \dfrac{1}{x}$, given $h(x) = 2$.

14. Use the vertical line test to determine if each of the following is the graph of a function where $x \in R$.

(i)

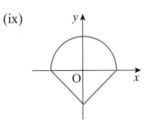

(ii)

(iii)

(iv)

(v)

(vi)

(vii)

(viii)

$y = x^3$

(ix)

15. The graphs and the ranges of six relations are given below.
Connect each graph to its correct range.

Ⓐ $(4, 5)$

Ⓑ $(0, 1)$

Ⓒ $(1, 4)$

Ⓓ

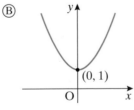

Ⓔ $(2, 2)$, $(-1, -1)$, $(0, -2)$

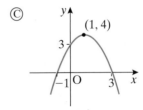

Ⓕ

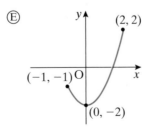

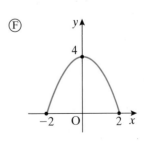

① Range $= (-\infty, 4]$ ② Range $= [-2, 2]$ ③ Range $= (-\infty, 2]$

④ Range $= [0, 4]$ ⑤ Range $= (-\infty, 5]$ ⑥ Range $= [1, \infty)$

16. State the domain and range for the relations represented by each of the following graphs:

(i)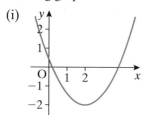

(ii)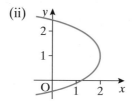

(iii)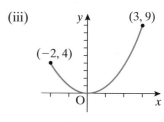

(iv)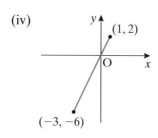

(v)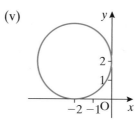

(vi)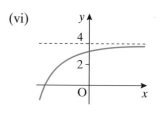

17. Which of the graphs shown in Question 16 above represent functions?

18. The equation of the quadratic curve shown is of the form $f(x) = kx(x - 6)$.

What is the value of k?

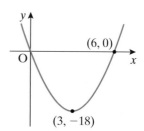

19. $f: x \to x^2 + px + q$ defines a function.

Given that $f(3) = 4$ and $f(-1) = 4$, find the values of p and q.

Using these values for p and q, solve the equation $x^2 + px + q = 0$.

20. The function $f(x) = x^2 + bx + c$ is graphed on the right.

(i) Use the graph to find two equations in b and c.

(ii) Solve the equations to find the value of b and the value of c.

(iii) Using these values for b and c, solve the equation $x^2 + bx + c = 0$ to find the coordinates of the point D.

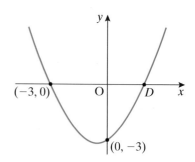

Section 8.2 Composition of functions

The diagram below shows a function f illustrated by the mapping diagram from A to B, and the function g illustrated by the mapping diagram from B to C.

The red arrows represent the couples of a new function combining f and g.

It is called the **composite function** g after f.
It is written as $g \circ f$, or simply **gf**.

$g \circ f$ is read 'g after f'.

The couples $g \circ f$ from the diagram are
{(1, 11), (3, 15), (5,19)}.

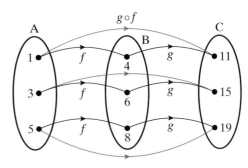

We will now consider two functions, $f(x) = 2x + 5$ and $g(x) = x - 3$, to find the rule for the composite function $gf(x)$.

These functions are illustrated on the right.
In f, the output is $(2x + 5)$ when the input is x.

We will now use $(2x + 5)$ as the input for the function g.

Since $g(x) = x - 3$, then $gf(x) = g(2x + 5)$
$$= (2x + 5) - 3 \quad \text{... replacing } x \text{ with } (2x + 5)$$
$$gf(x) = 2x + 2$$

We will now consider what happens when the order of the functions is changed.

$fg(x) = f(x - 3)$
$$= 2(x - 3) + 5 \quad \text{... replacing } x \text{ with } (x - 3)$$
$$fg(x) = 2x - 1$$

Since $2x + 2 \neq 2x - 1$, this shows that $gf(x) \neq fg(x)$.

> In general, if f and g are two functions,
> $$\text{then } fg(x) \neq gf(x)$$
> i.e. the composition of functions (generally) is **not commutative**

Example 1

Given that $f(x) = x + 3$ and $g(x) = x^2 - 1$, find
(i) $fg(2)$ (ii) $gf(-1)$ (iii) $fg(x)$ (iv) $gf(x)$.
Find also the value of x for which $fg(x) = gf(x)$.

(i) $fg(2) = f(3) = 6 \quad \text{... } g(2) = 2^2 - 1 = 3$
(ii) $gf(-1) = g(2) = 3$
(iii) $fg(x) = f(x^2 - 1) = (x^2 - 1) + 3 = x^2 + 2$
(iv) $gf(x) = g(x + 3) = (x + 3)^2 - 1 = x^2 + 6x + 9 - 1$
$$= x^2 + 6x + 8$$

$$fg(x) = gf(x) \Rightarrow x^2 + 2 = x^2 + 6x + 8$$
$$0 = 6x + 6$$
$$\text{i.e.} \quad 6x + 6 = 0$$
$$6x = -6 \Rightarrow x = -1$$

Note: $f \circ f(x)$ is written as $f^2(x)$.

Example 2

Given $f(x) = 2x + 1$, $g(x) = \dfrac{1}{x}$ and $h(x) = x^2 - 4$, find

(i) $gf(x)$ (ii) $f^2(x)$ (iii) $gh(x)$ (iv) $h^2(x)$

(v) $hfg(x)$ (vi) the values of x for which $gh(x) = \dfrac{1}{12}$.

(i) $gf(x) = g(2x + 1)$

$\qquad = \dfrac{1}{2x + 1}$

(ii) $f^2(x) = f(2x + 1)$ $\ldots f^2 = f \circ f$
$\qquad = 2(2x + 1) + 1$
$\qquad = 4x + 3$

(iii) $gh(x) = g(x^2 - 4)$

$\qquad = \dfrac{1}{x^2 - 4}$

(iv) $h^2(x) = h(x^2 - 4)$
$\qquad = (x^2 - 4)^2 - 4$
$\qquad = x^4 - 8x^2 + 12$

(v) $hfg(x) = hf\left(\dfrac{1}{x}\right)$

$\qquad = h\left(2\left(\dfrac{1}{x}\right) + 1\right) = h\left(\dfrac{2 + x}{x}\right)$

$\qquad = \left(\dfrac{2 + x}{x}\right)^2 - 4$

$\qquad = \dfrac{4 + 4x + x^2 - 4x^2}{x^2}$

$\qquad = \dfrac{4}{x^2} + \dfrac{4}{x} - 3$

(vi) $gh(x) = \dfrac{1}{x^2 - 4}$

$\qquad \dfrac{1}{12} = \dfrac{1}{x^2 - 4}$

$\qquad x^2 - 4 = 12$

$\qquad x^2 = 16$

$\qquad x = \pm 4$

Exercise 8.2

1. If $f(x) = x^2 + 1$ and $g(x) = 2x - 1$, find the value of each of the following:

(i) $f(3)$ (ii) $gf(3)$ (iii) $g(3)$ (iv) $fg(3)$

(v) $f^2(3)$ (vi) $g^2(3)$ (vii) $gf(-4)$ (viii) $fg\left(\dfrac{1}{2}\right)$

2. $f: x \to 2x + 1$ and $g: x \to 4x - 3$ are two functions.

Find (i) $f(3)$ (ii) $gf(3)$ (iii) $fg(-2)$ (iv) $gf(x)$.

For what value of x is $fg(x) = 19$?

3. The functions f and g are defined as follows:

$$f: x \rightarrow 2x - 1 \quad \text{and} \quad g: x \rightarrow x^2 + 2.$$

Find (i) $fg(-2)$ (ii) $gf\left(\frac{1}{2}\right)$ (iii) $fg(x)$ (iv) $gf(x)$.

For what values of x is $gf(x) = fg(x)$?

4. If $f(x) = 2^{x-1}$ and $g(x) = 3 + 4x$, find (i) $fg(x)$ (ii) $gf(x)$.

5. If $f(x) = 3x^2$ and $g(x) = 2x + 1$, find $fg(x)$.
Hence, solve the equation $fg(a) = g(1)$.

6. Two functions f and g are defined by $f(x) = 2x + 3$ and $g(x) = 2x - 3$.
(i) Find expressions for $fg(x)$ and $gf(x)$.
(ii) Determine the least possible value of the product $fg(x) \times gf(x)$.

7. If $f(x) = 2x + 1$ and $g(x) = 3x + c$,
(i) find c if $gf(x) = fg(x)$ for all values of x.
(ii) Find m if $f^2(m) = m$.

8. $f(x) = s + tx$, $g(x) = x^2 - 4$ and $h(x) = 3x + 1$ define three functions.
If $hgf(x) = 4(3x^2 + 3x - 2)$, find the values of s and t for $s, t \in N$.

9. Functions f and g are defined by $f(x) = \cos x$ and $g(x) = x + \frac{\pi}{6}$.
Find the value of $fg\left(\frac{\pi}{6}\right)$.

10. Functions f, g and h are defined as follows:

$$f(x) = x^2 - x + 10, \quad g(x) = 5 - x \quad \text{and} \quad h(x) = \log_2 x.$$

(i) Find expressions for $hf(x)$ and $hg(x)$.
(ii) Hence, solve $hf(x) - hg(x) = 3$.

11. If $f(x) = 2x + 3$, find (i) $f^2(x)$ (ii) $f^3(x)$ (iii) $f^4(x)$.
Hence, find an expression for $f^n(x)$ in terms of n.

12. Functions f and g are defined by $f(x) = x^2 + 1$ and $g(x) = 1 - 2x$.
Show that $gf(x) \neq fg(x)$.
What property of operations does your result suggest?

13. Let f and g be functions defined by

$$f(x) = \frac{1}{2}\left(\frac{1}{x} + 1\right), x \neq 0 \quad \text{and} \quad g(x) = \frac{1}{2x - 1}, x \neq \frac{1}{2}.$$

Investigate if $fg(x) = gf(x)$.

14. $p(x) = (3x - 4)^3$ defines a function.
If $f(x) = 3x$, $g(x) = x - 4$ and $h(x) = x^3$, show that $hgf(x) = p(x)$.

15. Use what you have discovered in Question 14 to perform each of these operations:
    (i) If $h(x) = (3x - 1)^2$, find two functions f and g such that $fg(x) = h(x)$.
    (ii) If $h(x) = \dfrac{1}{5x + 3}$, find two functions f and g such that $gf(x) = h(x)$.
    (iii) If $h(x) = \sin^2(3x)$, find three functions f, g and k such that $fgk(x) = h(x)$.
    (iv) If $b(x) = \cos(\sqrt{2x})$, find three functions f, g and h such that $hgf(x) = b(x)$.

16. If $f(x) = 2^{x-1}$ and $g(x) = 3 + 4x$, find an expression for $fg(x)$.
    Hence, solve the equation $fg(x) = 64$.

17. A stone is dropped into the centre C of a pool.
    A crest is formed and moves a distance of 5m
    in 4 seconds.
    Write an equation for the radius (r) as a function
    of time (t).
    Write an equation for the area of the circle formed as
    (i) a function of r
    (ii) a function of t by using composition of functions.

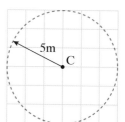

18. A salesman in a company gets 4% commission on sales of amounts over €4000.
    If €x is the average sales per week, explain the functions
    (i) $f(x) = €0.04x$
    (ii) $g(x) = €(x - 4000)$

    Which of the functions $fg(x)$ or $gf(x)$ represents the average weekly commission?
    Use the appropriate composite function to calculate the commission on sales valued
    at €8000.

Section 8.3 Types of functions

In Section 8.1 of this chapter, a function was described as a relation where there is
a **unique** output value for each input value.
In this section, we will discuss types of functions such as injective, surjective and
bijective functions.

1. Injective functions

A function f, from A to B, is said to be **injective** or
one-to-one if every output in B has a unique input in A.

In a mapping diagram, no two inputs in A will have the
same output in B; hence, the phrase 'one-to-one'.

Note: It is not necessary that every element in the
codomain has a corresponding element in
the domain.
In the diagram on the right, 8 has no corresponding
input; however, the mapping diagram still represents
an injective function.

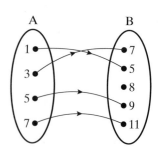

Examples

1 $f: R \to R: y = x + 5$.

This function generates the couples such as $(0, 5)$, $(1, 6)$, $(-2, 3)$, $(-7, -2)$, ...

Each element in the domain has a unique corresponding element in the codomain.

Hence, f is an injective function.

2 The function $f(x) = x^2$ is **not** a one-to-one function as, for example, $f(-3) = 9$ and $f(3) = 9$; hence, 9 does not have a unique input.

Horizontal line test for injective functions

The diagram on the right shows the graph of $y = x^3$.

If $y = x^3$ is an injective function, then any line drawn parallel to the x-axis will intersect the curve **at most once**.

The diagram shows that $y = x^3$ is an injective function.

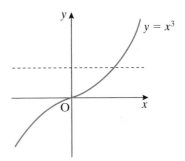

2. Surjective (many-to-one) functions

A function f is **surjective** if **every** element of the codomain is the image of **at least one** element of the domain.

A surjective function may also be described as a mapping of A **onto** B.

No element of the codomain is left unused.
Hence, the range and the codomain are equal.

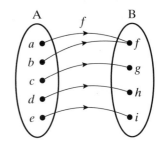

> For any function f, if the range and the codomain are equal, then the function is surjective.

Horizontal line test for surjective functions

Consider the function $f: R \to R$.
If f is surjective, then every horizontal line drawn must intersect the graph **at least once**.
The function $y = x^3$, where $x \in R$, is surjective as every horizontal line intersects the graph at least once.

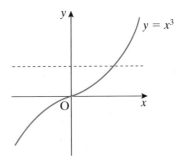

3. Bijective functions

A function *f* is **bijective** if for every element *y* in B, there is exactly one element *x* in A such that $f(x) = y$.

Therefore, a bijective function is both injective and surjective.

From the diagram, it can be seen that there is an exact one-to-one match between the elements in A and B. This function is bijective.

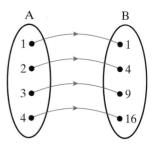

Example 1

State whether the following maps A → B are
   (i) functions   (ii) injective   (iii) surjective   (iv) bijective.
Give reasons for your answers.

(a) 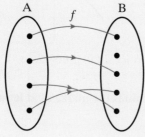   (b)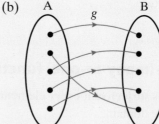

(c)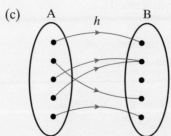

(a) *f* is a function; only one arrow from each element in A.
    f is injective; each element in A maps to only one element in B.
    f is not surjective; an element in B is not in the range of *f*.
    f is not bijective as it is not both injective and surjective.

(b) *g* is a function; only one arrow from each element in A.
    g is injective; each element in A maps to only one element in B.
    g is surjective; each element in B is the image of some element in A.
    g is therefore bijective.

(c) *h* is a function; only one arrow from each element in A.
    h is not injective; more than one element in A maps to the same element in B.
    h is not surjective; all the elements in B are not included in the mapping.
    h is not bijective.

___

Example 2

The graph of the function

$$f: R \rightarrow R : x \rightarrow x^2 - 2 \text{ is shown.}$$

(i) What is the range of f?
(ii) Explain why f is not injective.
(iii) Explain why f is not surjective.
(iv) Suggest a domain for f to make the
function injective.
(v) Suggest a codomain for f to make the function surjective.

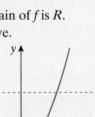

$f(x) = x^2 - 2$

(-2, 2)   (2, 2)

(i) The lowest y-value of the graphed function is $y = -2$.
∴ The range of f is $y \geqslant -2$ or $[-2, \infty)$.
(ii) f is not injective as any horizontal line in the given range will intersect the
curve at more than one point.
[OR: -2 is mapped onto 2, and also 2 is mapped onto 2.
Hence, there is not a unique output for each input.]
(iii) f is not surjective as the range of f is $y \geqslant -2$ and the codomain of f is R.
Since the codomain and range are not equal, f is not surjective.
(iv) If the domain is restricted to $x \geqslant 0$, we get the
graph shown on the right.
Since a horizontal line will intersect this graph
at one point only, this function is injective.
(v) If the codomain of f is restricted to $y \geqslant -2$,
then the codomain and range are the same.
Hence, the function would be surjective.

___

Exercise 8.3

1. State whether the following maps are
   (i) functions   (ii) injective   (iii) surjective.

   Give a reason for your answer in each case.

   (a) 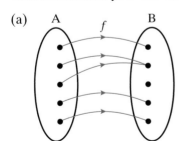   (b)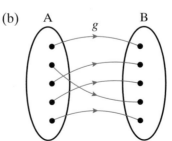

   Explain why the function g is bijective.

2. The function h from set A to set B is shown.

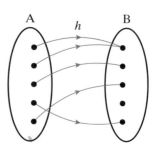

   (i) Is h a function? Explain.

   (ii) Is h injective? Explain.

   (iii) Is h surjective? Explain.

   (iv) Explain why h is not bijective.

3. Of the three mapping diagrams shown below, one is injective, one is surjective and one is bijective.

Connect each mapping to one of these descriptions.

(a) 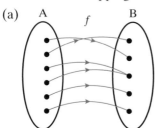   (b) 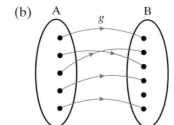   (c)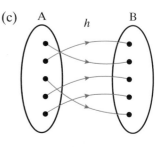

4. Does the given mapping diagram represent

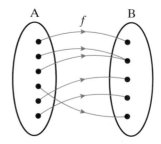

   (i) a function

   (ii) an injective function

   (iii) a surjective function ?

Explain why f is not bijective.

5. State whether each of the following relations is

   (i) a function   (ii) an injective function.

(a) $\{(2, 3), (3, 4), (5, 4), (4, 6)\}$ (b) $\{(1, 2), (2, 3), (3, 4), (4, 6)\}$

(c) $\{(1, 2), (3, 2), (4, 2), (9, 4), (9, 3)\}$ (d) $\{(1, 1), (2, 3), (3, 2), (4, 4), (5, 1)\}$

(e) $\{(0, -1), (-1, 2), (-2, 0), (-3, 1)\}$ (f) $\{(5, 5), (4, 3), (3, 1), (2, -1), (1, 2), (0, 3)\}$

6. The graph of the function $f(x) = 2x + 1$ is shown.

Explain why f is both injective and surjective.

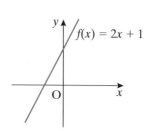

7. Use the horizontal line test to determine whether the given graph represents

   (i) an injective function

   (ii) a surjective function.

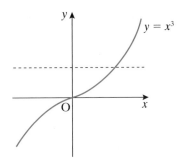

8. The graph of a function $f: R \to R$ is shown on the right.

   (i) What is the range of the graphed function?

   (ii) What is the codomain of f?

   (iii) By comparing the codomain and range, explain why f is not surjective.

   (iv) Suggest a restriction on the codomain to make f a surjective function.

   (v) Use the horizontal line test to show that f is not injective.

   (vi) Suggest a restriction on the domain to make f an injective function.

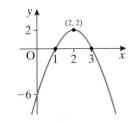

9. The graph of a quadratic function $g(x): R \to R$ is shown.

   (i) Is $g(x)$ an injective function? Explain.

   (ii) Is $g(x)$ a surjective function in the range $y \leqslant 2$? Explain.

   (iii) Suggest a restriction on the domain to make $g(x)$ an injective function.

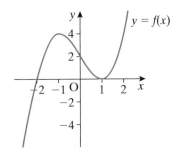

10. Use the horizontal line test to investigate if the given function $y = f(x)$ is

   (i) injective   (ii) surjective.

   Is the function bijective? Explain.

11. Explain why the graph on the right does not represent a function.

Suggest a restriction on the range to make the graph represent a function.

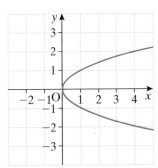

12. Let $f: N \to N : x \to 2x$ define a function.

(i) What is the domain of f?
(ii) What is the codomain of f?
(iii) What is the range of f?
(iv) Using the codomain and range, explain why f is not a surjective function.
(v) Is f a one-to-one function?
(vi) Suggest a restriction on the codomain to make f a surjective function.

13. The given graph represents the function $f(x) = \sin \frac{x}{2}$.

(i) Does the graph represent an injective function? Explain.
(ii) Does the graph represent a surjective function in the given range? Explain.
(iii) Suggest a restricted domain so that the function is injective.

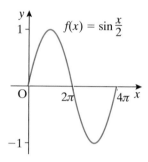

14. This is the graph of $f: R \to R^+ : f(x) = |x|$.

(i) Is f surjective? Explain.
(ii) Is f injective? Explain.
(iii) Suggest a restricted domain and range to make f bijective.

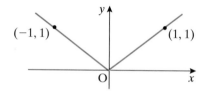

15. The given diagram shows the graph of the function $y = e^x$.

(i) Write down the range of the function.
(ii) Is the function injective? Explain.
(iii) Is the function surjective in the range $y > 0$?
(iv) Explain why the function is bijective for $x \in R$ and $y > 0$.

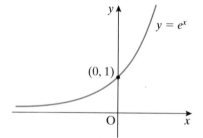

Section 8.4 Inverse functions

In previous sections, we have seen that a function generates a set of y-values, called the range, from a set of x-values, called the domain.

In this section, we will deal with the reverse of this procedure by finding the elements of the domain when given the elements of the range.

In the given mapping diagram, the couples of f are:

$$f = (1, 4), (3, 7), (5, 10), (7, 13)$$

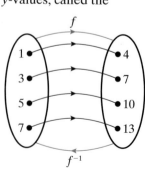

If we reverse these couples, we get a new function called f^{-1}.

f^{-1} is said to be the **inverse function** of f.

From the mapping diagram, $f^{-1} = (4, 1), (7, 3), (10, 5), (13, 7)$.

For every couple (a, b) that f creates, f^{-1} will create the couple (b, a).

Thus, f and f^{-1} create points that are reflections of one another in the line $y = x$.

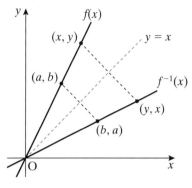

Note: As can be seen from the diagram, a function f has an inverse if and only if it is bijective, i.e. the function must be *one to one* and *onto*.

Take the function $f(x) = x^2$.

$(2, 4)$ and $(-2, 4)$ are couples of f.

So the couples $(4, 2)$ and $(4, -2)$ are couples of f^{-1}.

This shows that f^{-1} is not a function as the input 4 does not have a **unique** output.

Since $f(x) = x^2$ is not bijective, it does not have an inverse.

How to find the inverse of a function

$$\text{Let} \quad f(x) = 3x - 2$$
$$\Rightarrow \quad y = 3x - 2$$
$$3x = y + 2$$
$$x = \frac{y + 2}{3} \quad \text{... express } x \text{ in terms of } y$$
$$\therefore \quad f^{-1}(x) = \frac{x + 2}{3} \quad \text{... replace } y \text{ with } x$$
$$f^{-1}(x) = \frac{x + 2}{3} \text{ is the inverse function of } f(x).$$

We can verify that the inverse function is correct by showing that $f(3) = 7$ and $f^{-1}(7) = 3$.

Example 1

(i) If $f(x) = 5x - 3$, find $f^{-1}(x)$.

(ii) Hence, show that $f^{-1}f(x) = x$.

(i) Let $y = 5x - 3$

$5x = y + 3$

$x = \dfrac{y + 3}{5}$

$\therefore f^{-1}(x) = \dfrac{x + 3}{5}$

(ii) $f^{-1}f(x) = f^{-1}(5x - 3)$

$= 5\left(\dfrac{x + 3}{5}\right) - 3$

$= x + 3 - 3$

$= x$

In Example 1 above, it was shown that $f^{-1}f(x) = x$.

It can also be shown that $ff^{-1}(x) = x$.

For any two functions
f and f^{-1}, then
(i) $ff^{-1}(x) = x$.
(ii) $f^{-1}f(x) = x$.

Example 2

The diagram on the right shows the reflection of the curve $f(x) = x^3 + 1$ in the line $y = x$.
Find the equation of $f^{-1}(x)$.

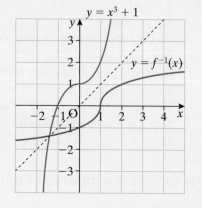

Let
$$y = x^3 + 1$$
$$x^3 = y - 1 \quad \text{... get } x \text{ in terms of } y$$
$$x = \sqrt[3]{y - 1}$$
$$\therefore \ f^{-1}(x) = \sqrt[3]{x - 1} \quad \text{... change } y \text{ to } x$$

Restricted domain

Consider the two graphs shown below:

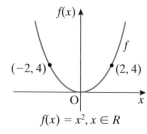

$f(x) = x^2, x \in R$

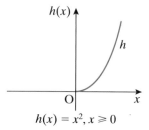

$h(x) = x^2, x \geqslant 0$

$f(x) = x^2, x \in R$ is a function but it is not injective (therefore not bijective) as a horizontal line will intersect the graph more than once. Since it is not bijective, it has no inverse.
$h(x) = x^2, x \geqslant 0$ is a function in the restricted domain $x \geqslant 0$.
$h(x)$ is a bijective function and hence has an inverse.
The inverse function $h^{-1}(x)$ is $y = \sqrt{x}$, for $x \geqslant 0$.
If f and f^{-1} are inverse functions, the domain of f is the range of f^{-1}.

Example 3

The relation $f(x) = x^2 - 4x - 4$ is a function with domain $x > 2$.
Find $f^{-1}(x)$ and write down its range.

Let
$$y = x^2 - 4x - 4$$
$$y = x^2 - 4x + \left(\tfrac{4}{2}\right)^2 - \left(\tfrac{4}{2}\right)^2 - 4 \quad \text{... completing the square}$$
$$= x^2 - 4x + 4 - 4 - 4$$
$$y = (x - 2)^2 - 8$$
$$(x - 2)^2 = y + 8$$
$$x - 2 = \sqrt{y + 8}$$
$$x = 2 + \sqrt{y + 8} \quad \text{... finding } x \text{ in terms of } y$$
$$\therefore \ f^{-1}(x) = 2 + \sqrt{x + 8} \quad \text{... replace } y \text{ with } x$$

We take the positive value for $\sqrt{y + 8}$ as $x > 2$.

The range of $f^{-1}(x)$ is $y > 2$ ... the same as the domain of f

Exercise 8.4

Find the inverse of each of the functions in numbers (1–9).

1. $f(x) = x - 4, x \in R$
2. $f(x) = 2x - 3, x \in R$
3. $f(x) = 5x + 3, x \in R$

4. $f(x) = 3x, x \in R$
5. $f(x) = \dfrac{2x}{5}, x \in R$
6. $f(x) = \dfrac{4x - 3}{2}, x \in R$

7. $f(x) = \dfrac{x - 6}{x}, x \in R, x \neq 0$

8. $f(x) = \dfrac{3x}{x - 1}, x \in R, x \neq 1$

9. $f(x) = \dfrac{10 - 2x}{3}, x \in R$

10. Given $f(x) = 4x + 5, x \in R$, find $f^{-1}(x)$.
    Hence, show that $ff^{-1}(x) = x$.
    Now investigate if $f^{-1}f(x) = ff^{-1}(x)$.

11. If $f(x) = \dfrac{x}{3} - 2$, find $f^{-1}(x)$ and hence show that $ff^{-1}(x) = x$.

12. Copy each of the following graphs and on the same set of axes, draw the inverse of each of the corresponding functions:

(i)
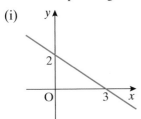

(ii)
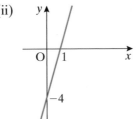

(iii)
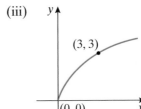

(iv)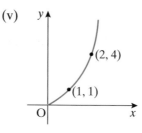

(v)

(vi)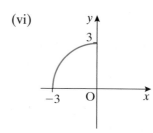

(vii)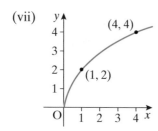

(viii)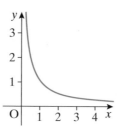

(ix)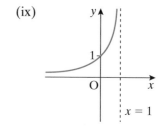

13. The given diagram shows two lines l and m.

   (i) Find the equations of l and m.

   (ii) Verify that the equation of l is the inverse of the equation of m.

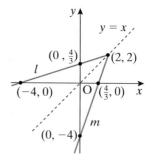

14. $g(x) = \dfrac{1}{x-2}, x \in R, x \neq 2$ is the inverse of the function $f(x) = \dfrac{1+kx}{x}, x \in R, x \neq 0$.

   Find the value of k, where $k \in N$.

15. $f(x) = 2x - 3$ and $g(x) = x - 4$ define two functions.

   (i) Find $gf(x)$ and $[gf(x)]^{-1}$.

   (ii) Investigate if $[gf(x)]^{-1} = f^{-1}g^{-1}(x)$.

16. Given $f(x) = \dfrac{x+3}{2}, x \in [0, 5]$, find $f^{-1}(x)$.

   By drawing the graphs of $f(x)$ and $f^{-1}(x)$ in the given domain, show that the domain of f is the range of $f^{-1}(x)$.

   Write down the domain and range of $f^{-1}(x)$.

17. Find the inverse function of each of the following by completing the square:

   (i) $f(x) = x^2 + 4x - 6, x \geqslant -2$
   (ii) $f(x) = x^2 - 2x - 5, x \geqslant 1$
   (iii) $f(x) = x^2 - 8x - 3, x \geqslant 4$
   (iv) $f(x) = x^2 + 8x + 20, x \geqslant -4$

18. Given $f(x) = \dfrac{3 - x}{2}$, $-1 \leqslant x \leqslant 4$.

Sketch the graph of the given function and on the same set of axes, sketch the graph of the inverse function.
State the domain and range of the inverse function.

19. Let $f: A \to R$, $f(x) = \sqrt{3 - x}$.
If A is the set of all real values of x for which $f(x)$ is defined, find A.

20. Let $g: [b, 2] \to R$ where $g(x) = 1 - x^2$.
If b is the smallest real value such that g has an inverse function, find b and $g^{-1}(x)$.

Section 8.5 Sketching the graphs of functions

In our study of algebra so far, we will have learned how to construct a table of ordered pairs, then plot these points and draw the graph of the function.

In this section, we will show how to draw a rough sketch of a graph by concentrating on the shape of the graph, as well as the main features of the graph.

The important features of any graph include

> the general shape of the graph, e.g. the graph of a quadratic function
> the point(s) where the graph crosses the x-axis and the y-axis
> the turning points of a quadratic and cubic graph.

1. Linear functions

The graph of a line such as $y = 2x - 4$ can be drawn by finding the points where the line intersects the x-axis and y-axis.
When $x = 0$, $y = 2(0) - 4$, i.e. $y = -4$.
When $y = 0$, $2x - 4 = 0$, i.e. $x = 2$.
∴ $(0, -4)$ and $(2, 0)$ are points on the line.

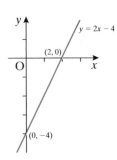

2. Quadratic functions

The general form of a **quadratic function** is $f(x) = ax^2 + bx + c$, where a, b and c are constants and $a \neq 0$.

When $a > 0$, the graph of $f(x)$ looks like this:

The lowest point of the curve is called the **minimum point**.

When $a < 0$, the graph of $f(x)$ looks like this:

The highest point of the curve is called the **maximum point**.

To draw a rough sketch of a quadratic function, we require
- (i) the points where the graph intersects the x-axis and y-axis
- (ii) the turning point of the curve.

The turning point can be found by either of these methods:
- (i) expressing the function in **completed square** form, or
- (ii) using calculus. (chapter 4)

Here is an example of how to express a quadratic function in 'completed square' form.

$$x^2 - 8x + 9$$
$$= x^2 - 8x + 16 - 16 + 9 \quad \text{... add and subtract (half the coefficient of } x)^2$$
$$= (x - 4)^2 - 7$$

The turning point is $(4, -7)$.
The axis of symmetry is $x = 4$.

> For the function
> $$y = k(x - p)^2 + q,$$
> ➤ the turning point is (p, q)
> ➤ the minimum value is q.

Example 1

By finding the points where the curve crosses the x-axis and y-axis and the turning point by completing the square, sketch the graph of $f(x) = -x^2 + 4x + 5$.

$$-x^2 + 4x + 5$$
$$= -[x^2 - 4x - 5]$$
$$= -[x^2 - 4x + 4 - 4 - 5] \quad \text{... add and subtract (half the coefficient of } x)^2$$
$$= -[(x - 2)^2 - 9]$$
$$= -(x - 2)^2 + 9$$

∴ The turning point is $(2, 9)$.

To find where the curve intersects the x-axis, we solve the equation
$$-x^2 + 4x + 5 = 0$$
$$\Rightarrow \quad x^2 - 4x - 5 = 0 \Rightarrow (x + 1)(x - 5) = 0 \Rightarrow x = -1 \text{ or } x = 5$$

The curve intersects the x-axis at $x = -1$ and at $x = 5$.

To find where the curve intersects the y-axis, let $x = 0$.

$$y = -x^2 + 4x + 5$$
$$x = 0 \Rightarrow y = 0 + 0 + 5, \text{ i.e. } 5$$

The curve intersects the y-axis at $(0, 5)$.

A sketch of the curve is shown.

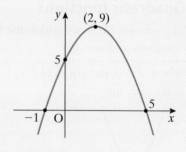

Note: In the example above if $f(x) = -x^2 + 4x + 5$ then $f'(x) = -2x + 4$
∴ turning point occurs at $f'(x) = 0 = -2x + 4$
∴ $x = 2$ and $f(2) = -2^2 + 4(2) + 5 = 9$ ∴ $(2, 9)$ is the turning point.

3. Cubic functions

A cubic function generally takes the form

$$f(x) = ax^3 + bx^2 + cx + d, \text{ where } a, b, c \text{ and } d \in R.$$

The graph of a cubic function $f(x) = ax^3 + bx^2 + cx + d$, generally consists of a smooth curve with two turning points as follows:

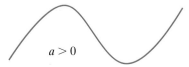 **OR**

When $a > 0$, the graph begins by rising from left to right.

When $a < 0$, the graph begins by falling from left to right.

We can sketch a graph of a cubic function by finding the points where the curve intersects the axes. The accuracy of the sketch can be improved by locating the local maximum and minimum turning points if required.

Example 2

Sketch the graph of $y = x(x + 1)(x - 2)$.

$$y = x(x + 1)(x - 2)$$
$$\Rightarrow \quad y = x^3 - x^2 - 2x$$

... The shape of the graph will look like this as the coefficient of x^3 is positive.

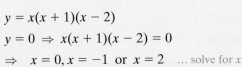

$$y = x(x + 1)(x - 2)$$
$$y = 0 \Rightarrow x(x + 1)(x - 2) = 0$$
$$\Rightarrow \quad x = 0, x = -1 \text{ or } x = 2 \quad \text{... solve for } x$$

∴ The curve crosses the x-axis at

$$x = 0, x = -1, x = 2.$$

We let $x = 0$ to find where the curve intersects the y-axis.

$$x = 0 \Rightarrow y = 0$$

∴ The curve crosses the y-axis at $(0, 0)$.

A sketch of the curve is shown on the right.

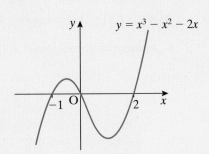

Example 3

Sketch the graph of $f(x) = -x^3 - 2x^2 + 5x + 6$.

We first factorise $f(x)$ to find the points where the curve intersects the x-axis.

$$f(x) = -x^3 - 2x^2 + 5x + 6$$
$$f(1) = -1 - 2 + 5 + 6 \neq 0$$
$$f(-1) = 1 - 2 - 5 + 6 = 0$$
$$\therefore \ (x + 1) \text{ is a factor of } f(x)$$

A sketch of the curve is shown below:

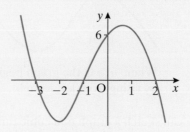

By division, $y = (x + 1)(-x^2 - x + 6)$
$$y = -(x + 1)(x^2 + x - 6)$$
$$y = -(x + 1)(x + 3)(x - 2)$$

$y = 0 \Rightarrow x = -1, -3$ or 2
$x = 0 \Rightarrow y = 6$

$\therefore$ The curve intersects the y-axis at $(0, 6)$.

The curve has this shape as the coefficient of x^3 is negative.

Example 4

For the function $f: R \to R, f(x) = -\dfrac{x^3}{3} + 4x - 1$:

  (i) Find the stationary points and determine their nature.
  (ii) Sketch the graph.

(i) $f(x)$ has stationary points where $f'(x) = 0$:

$$f(x) = -\frac{x^3}{3} + 4x - 1 \Rightarrow f'(x) = -x^2 + 4 = 0 \ \ \therefore \ x = \pm 2.$$

$$f''(x) = -2x \ \Rightarrow f''(2) = -2(2) = -4 \quad \text{(negative)}$$
$$\Rightarrow \text{a maximum turning point at } x = +2$$

Also $f''(-2) = -2(-2) = +4 \quad \text{(positive)}$
$$\Rightarrow \text{a minimum turning point at } x = -2$$

At $x = 2, f(2) = -\dfrac{(2)^3}{3} + 4(2) - 1 = \dfrac{13}{3} = 4\dfrac{1}{3}$

At $x = -2, f(-2) = -\dfrac{(-2)^3}{3} + 4(-2) - 1 = \dfrac{17}{3} = -6\dfrac{1}{3}$

$\Rightarrow$ a maximum turning point at $\left(2, \dfrac{13}{3}\right)$, a minimum turning point at $\left(-2, -\dfrac{19}{3}\right)$

(ii) Since $f(x) = -\dfrac{x^3}{3}$ ....the curve has the general shape:

At $x = 0, f(0) = -1$ $\therefore$ $(0, -1)$ is a point on the curve.

Also at $f''(x) = 0$ the curve has a point of inflection.

$\therefore$ $-2x = 0 \Rightarrow x = 0$

The point $(0, -1)$ is the point of inflection.

Note: the table function on your calculator can give some extra points if a more accurate sketch is required.

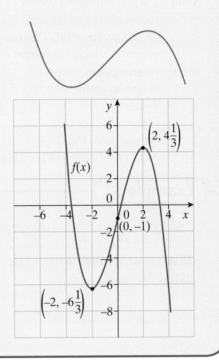

4. Finding equations for given cubic graphs

The graph of a function is shown on the right.

It intersects the x-axis at $x = -2, 0$ and 2.

This function will contain $x(x + 2)(x - 2)$ as part of the expression.

Notice that the graph also contains the point $(1, 1)$.

To accommodate this condition, the equation of the function will take the form $y = kx(x + 2)(x - 2)$, where k is a number to be found.

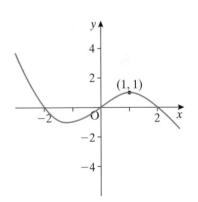

We use the fact that $(1, 1)$ is on the graph to find the value of k.

$(1, 1) \in$ of the graph: $\qquad y = kx(x + 2)(x - 2)$
$\Rightarrow \quad 1 = k(1)(3)(-1)$
$\Rightarrow \quad -3k = 1 \Rightarrow k = -\dfrac{1}{3}$

$\therefore$ The equation of the function is $y = -\dfrac{1}{3}x(x + 2)(x - 2)$

i.e. $y = -\dfrac{x}{3}(x + 2)(x - 2)$

or $y = -\dfrac{1}{3}x^3 + \dfrac{4}{3}x$

Note: If a graph touches (but does not cross) the x-axis at a point, a double root occurs at this point. This point can either be a local maximum or minimum turning point.
As in the graph over $f(x) = (x - 4)^2$
$\Rightarrow$ roots at, $0 = (x - 4)(x - 4)$
$\Rightarrow$ a double root at $x = 4$.
We also note that $f'(x) = 2x - 8$
$\Rightarrow f'(x) = 0$ at $x = 4$ i.e. a turning point at $x = 4$.

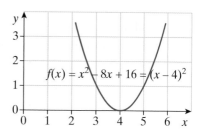

$f(x) = x^2 + 8x + 16 = (x - 4)^2$

Example 5

Find the equation of the given graphed function and prove (using calculus) that the function has stationary points at $(2, 0)$ and $(0, 2)$.

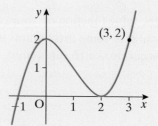

$(3, 2)$

The graph intersects the x-axis at $x = -1$ and it touches the x-axis at $x = 2$.

The equation has the form $y = k(x + 1)(x - 2)^2$

Put $(3, 2)$ into the equation: $2 = k(4)(1)^2$

$\qquad\qquad\qquad 2 = 4k$

$\qquad\qquad\qquad k = \dfrac{1}{2}$

The equation of the function is $y = \dfrac{1}{2}(x + 1)(x - 2)^2$

$y = \dfrac{1}{2}(x + 1)(x - 2)^2 = \dfrac{x^3}{2} - \dfrac{3x^2}{2} + 2$

$\dfrac{dy}{dx} = \dfrac{3x^2}{2} - 3x = x\left(\dfrac{3x}{2} - 3\right)$

$\Rightarrow \dfrac{dy}{dx} = 0 = x\left(\dfrac{3x}{2} - 3\right) \Rightarrow x = 0, 2$

at $x = 0$, $y = \dfrac{1}{2}(1)(2)^2 = 2$

at $x = 2$, $y = \dfrac{1}{2}(2 + 1)(2 - 2)^2 = 0$

$\therefore$ stationary points occur at $(0, 2)$ and $(2, 0)$

Note: Stationary points are explained in detail in Chapter 4.

Exercise 8.5

1. Construct a table of ordered pairs similar to that shown on the right.

   Hence, draw a graph of the function $f(x) = 2x^2 + 3x - 4$ in the domain $-3 \leqslant x \leqslant 2$.

x	$2x^2 + 3x - 4$	y
-3	$18 - 9 - 4$	5
-2		
2		

2. Find the coordinates of the points where these functions intersect the x-axis and y-axis.
   Hence draw a rough sketch of the graph of each function.
   (No need to identify the turning point in each graph.)
      (i) $f(x) = x^2 - 4x$ (ii) $f(x) = x^2 - 2x - 8$ (iii) $f(x) = -x^2 + 2x + 3$

3. Express each of the following in completed square form:
      (i) $x^2 - 4x + 2$ (ii) $x^2 - 12x + 36$ (iii) $-x^2 + 8x - 12$

4. Express $y = x^2 + 4x - 12$ in its completed square form.
   Now draw a sketch of the curve $y = x^2 + 4x - 12$, clearly showing where it intersects
   the x-axis and y-axis and its turning point.

5. Find the points where the graph of $y = x^2 + 4x - 5$ intersects the x-axis and y-axis.
   Express $y = x^2 + 4x - 5$ in the form $(x + a)^2 + b$ and hence write down the
   coordinates of the turning point.
   Draw a rough sketch of the graph of $y = x^2 + 4x - 5$.

6. Express $x^2 + 3x - 10$ in the completed square form.
   Hence, write down the coordinates of the turning point of the curve.
   Draw a sketch of the curve $y = x^2 + 3x - 10$, indicating clearly where the curve
   intersects the x-axis and y-axis.

7. A quadratic rule for a particular parabola is of the form $y = ax^2 + c$.
   The parabola passes through the points with coordinates $(-1, 4)$ and $(0, 8)$.
   Find the value of a and of c.

8. Determine the equation of each of the following parabolas:

(i) 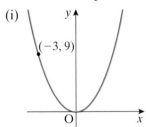   (ii) 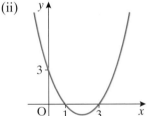   (iii)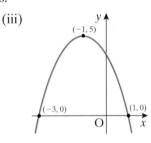

9. Which of the graphs shown below could represent the graph of
   the equation $y = (x - 4)^2 - 3$?

Ⓐ 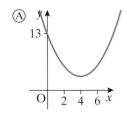   Ⓑ 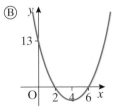   Ⓒ 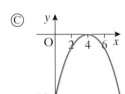   Ⓓ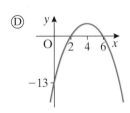

10. Which of the graphs in Question 9 could represent $y = 3 - (x - 4)^2$?

11. A parabola has a turning point at $(-1, 3)$ and cuts the y-axis at $(0, 4)$.
Find the equation of this parabola.

12. Find where each of these cubic functions
   (i) intersects or touches the x-axis   (ii) intersects the y-axis.
   (a) $y = (x + 1)(x + 2)(x - 3)$ (b) $y = x(x - 6)(x + 3)$
   (c) $y = (x - 1)(x + 2)^2$ (d) $y = x(x^2 - 9)$

13. Draw a sketch of the graph of each of these functions.
   Label your sketch graph showing the points of intersection with the axes.
   (There is no need to determine the coordinates of the turning points.)
   (i) $y = x(x - 1)(x - 3)$ (ii) $y = (x - 2)(x + 3)(2x - 1)$
   (iii) $y = -(x - 1)(x + 2)(x - 4)$ (iv) $y = x^3 - 9x$

14. Here are the graphs of three cubic functions, $f(x) = \dots\dots$

Ⓐ 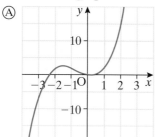   Ⓑ 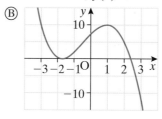   Ⓒ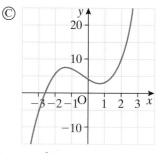

   (i) Which graph represents a function in which the coefficient of x^3 is negative?
   (ii) Which graph has only one real root for the equation $f(x) = 0$?
   (iii) In which graph is $f(x)$ positive and decreasing for $1 < x < 2.4$?
   (iv) Which graph is negative and decreasing for $x > 2.4$?

15. Associate each sketch-graph below with one of the given equations:

$y = x^3 - x^2$ $y = 1 - x^2$ $y = x - x^2$ $y = -\frac{3}{4}x + 3$ $y = x^2 + 3x$ $y = 9x - x^3$

Ⓐ 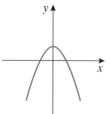   Ⓑ 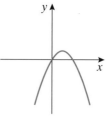   Ⓒ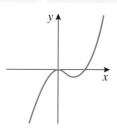

Ⓓ 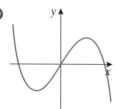   Ⓔ 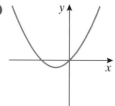   Ⓕ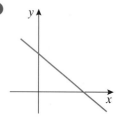

16. Here is the graph of the function
$$f(x) = x^3 - 3x^2 - 9x.$$

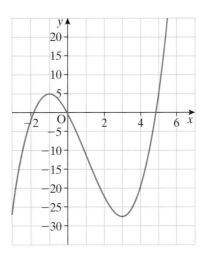

Use your graph to estimate
  (i) $f(3)$
  (ii) the maximum turning point
  (iii) the roots of the equation $x^3 - 3x^2 - 9x = -20$
  (iv) the range of values of x for which $f(x)$ is decreasing.
  (v) Explain why the equation $f(x) = 10$ has only one root.
  (vi) Explain why the equation $f(x) = -10$ has three roots.
  (vii) If $f(x) = k$ has three real roots, estimate the range of values for k.

17. Draw sketches of the graphs of $y = x(x - 2)(x + 4)$ and $y = x - 3$ and state the number of points of intersection.

18. Work out the equation of the cubic function graphed on the right.

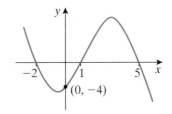

19. A farmer has 60m of fencing with which to construct three sides of a rectangular yard connected to an existing fence.
  (i) If the width of the yard is xm, and the area inside the yard is Am², write down the rule connecting A and x.
  (ii) Sketch the graph of A against x.
  (iii) Use the graph to estimate the maximum area that can be formed for the yard.

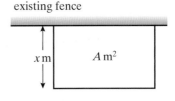

20. The graph of a cubic function is shown.
  (i) Use the information given to find the equation for this function.
  (ii) Explain why the function is not injective.
  (iii) Is the function surjective in the range $0 \leqslant y \leqslant 2$?
  (iv) Explain why the function is not bijective.
  (v) Use calculus to show that stationary points occur at $(2, 0)$ and $(0, -2)$.

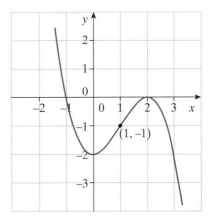

21. Sketch the graphs of each of the following by finding:
    (i) stationary points   (ii) axes intercepts.
    (a) $y = 3x^3 - x^2$ (b) $y = x^3 + 6x^2 + 9x + 4$

22. Show that the function, $y = x^3 - 6x^2$ has stationary points at $(0, 0)$ and $(4, -32)$. Determine the nature of the stationary points and draw a sketch of the function indicating the x-axis intercepts and point of inflection.

23.   (i) A stationary point of a curve is one in which the slope of the tangent to the curve is zero. Name 3 types of stationary points
    (ii) Find the range of values of x for which, $y = 4x^3 - 3x^4$, is an
       (a) increasing   (b) decreasing function.
    (iii) Find the stationary points and the x-axis intercept of the function, $y = 4x^3 - 3x^4$ and hence draw a sketch of the function.

24. Given that $f(x) = x^2 - 6x + 18, x \geqslant 0$ is the equation of a curve C.
    (i) Express $f(x)$ in the form $(x - a)^2 + b$, where a and b are constants.

The curve C with equation $y = f(x), x \geqslant 0$, meets the y-axis at P and has a minimum point at Q.
    (ii) Sketch the graph of C, showing the coordinates of P and Q.

The line $y = 41$ meets C at the point R.
    (iii) Find the x-coordinate of R, giving your answer in the form $p + q\sqrt{2}$, where p and q are integers.

Section 8.6 Exponential and logarithmic functions ———

Any function of the form $f(x) = a^x$, where the base a is a positive real number other than 1, is called an **exponential function** (or index function). $y = 2^x$ and $y = 10^x$ are examples of exponential functions.

The function $f(x) = e^x$ is a special exponential function where e is the real number 2.718, correct to three decimal places.

The graph of an exponential function has a very recognizable shape. Two types of graphs will be examined.

1. Graphs of $y = a^x, a > 1$

Example 1

Plot the graph of $y = 2^x$ for $-3 \leqslant x \leqslant 3$.

The table of values is set out below:

x	-3	-2	-1	0	1	2	3
$y = 2^x$	0.125	0.25	0.5	1	2	4	8

The graph is shown on the right.

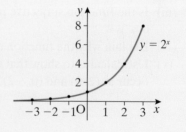

The graph above shows that as x decreases in value, the curve approaches the x-axis but never touches it. The x-axis is said to be an **asymptote** to the curve.

The graph intersects the y-axis at $(0, 1)$.

The range of the function is R^+, i.e. the range is $y > 0$.

All graphs of the form $y = a^x$ intersect the y-axis at $(0, 1)$.

Graphs of $y = 2^x$, $y = 3^x$ and $y = 4^x$ are drawn on the same diagram, as shown.

The larger the value of x, the steeper the rise in the curve.

Each curve crosses the y-axis at $(0, 1)$.

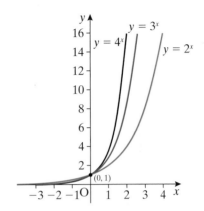

2. Graphs of $y = a^x$, $0 < a < 1$

Example 2

Plot the graph of $y = \left(\frac{1}{2}\right)^x$ in the domain $-3 \leqslant x \leqslant 3$.

Here is the table of values:

x	-3	-2	-1	0	1	2	3
$y = \left(\frac{1}{2}\right)^x = 2^{-x}$	8	4	2	1	0.5	0.25	0.125

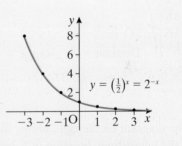

In the graph shown on the previous page, the y-values decrease as the x-values increase.
The graph contains the point $(0, 1)$.
The range of the function is R^+.
The graph of $y = 2^{-x}$ is a reflection in the y-axis of the graph of $y = 2^{+x}$.

Graphs of Exponential Functions

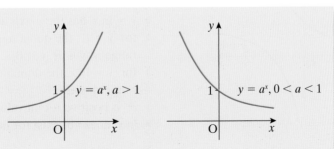

263

On the right is the graph of $y = 3.2^x$.
It is similar to the graph of $y = 2^x$, but each y-value
is multiplied by 3.
Notice that this graph intersects the y-axis at $(0, 3)$.

In general, the graph of $y = k.2^x$ intersects the
y-axis at $(0, k)$.

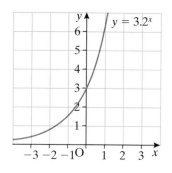

Graphing logarithmic functions

A table of values for $y = \log_{10} x$ is given below.
The values are given to 1 decimal place.

x	0.1	1	2	3	4	5
$y = \log_{10} x$	-1	0	0.3	0.5	0.6	0.7

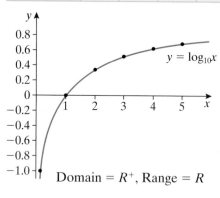

Domain $= R^+$, Range $= R$

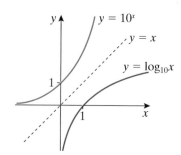

The graph of $y = \log_{10} x$ is the
reflection in the line $y = x$ of the
graph of $y = 10^x$.

The diagram on the right above illustrates that the inverse of the exponential function $y = e^x$
is the **logarithmic function** $y = \log_e x$.

$\log_e x$ is generally written as $\ln x$.

The function $y = e^x$ has the inverse function $y = \ln x$.

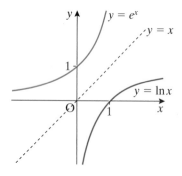

> the graphs are reflections of each other in
>   the line $y = x$
> $y = e^x$ has the x-axis as an asymptote
> $y = \ln x$ has the y-axis as an asymptote
> for $y = e^x$, the domain is $x \in \mathbb{R}$ and the
>   range is $y \in \mathbb{R}, y > 0$
> for $y = \ln x$, the domain is $x \in \mathbb{R}, x > 0$ and the
>   range is $y \in \mathbb{R}$
> e^x is positive for all values of x
> $\ln x$ does not exist for negative values of x.

Note: The inverse of the function $f(x) = e^x$ may also be found algebraically as follows:

$$y = e^x$$
$$\Rightarrow \quad x = \log_e y \qquad \text{... using the definition of a log.}$$
$$x = \ln y \qquad \text{... } \log_e = \ln$$
$$\therefore \quad y = f^{-1}(x) = \ln x \qquad \text{... changing } y \text{ to } x \text{ and } x \text{ to } y$$
$$\qquad \text{where } y = f^{-1}(x) \text{ the inverse function}$$

$$\therefore \quad \text{if } y = f(x) = e^x \text{ then } f^{-1}(x) = \ln x$$

If $y = f(x) = e^x$
then $f^{-1}(x) = \ln x$

Example 3

The graph of the function $f(x) = a \cdot b^x$ is shown.
Find the values of a and b.

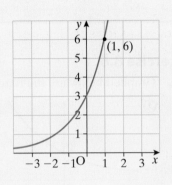

$f(x) = a \cdot b^x$
$f(0) = 3 \Rightarrow a \cdot b^0 = 3$
$\qquad \Rightarrow a = 3 \quad \text{... } b^0 = 1$
$(1, 6) \in f(x)$
$\Rightarrow 6 = 3 \cdot b^1 \qquad \text{... } y = 6, x = 1, a = 3$
$\Rightarrow 3b = 6 \Rightarrow b = 2$
$\therefore \quad a = 3 \text{ and } b = 2$

Example 4

The size of the human population, N, can be modelled using the equation
$N = N_0 e^{rt}$ where N_0 is the population in 2006, t is the time in years since 2006,
and r is the annual rate of increase in the population.

(i) In 2006, the population of a certain country was approximately 61 million,
with an annual rate of increase of 1.6%. Assuming this growth remains
constant, what would be the population in 2020? (i.e. after 14 years.)

(ii) In 2006, the population of another country was approximately 5.1 million,
with an annual rate of increase of 0.43%.
Assuming this growth rate remains constant, how long would it take for this
country's population to double in size?

(i) $N = N_0 e^{rt}$
$N = 61\,000\,000\, e^{0.016(14)} \quad \text{... express 1.6\% as a decimal (i.e. 0.016)}$
$N = 61\,000\,000\, e^{0.224}$
$N = 61\,000\,000\, (1.25107)$
$N = 76{,}315{,}270$
$\therefore \quad$ the population in 2020 will be 76.3 million

(ii) $N = N_0 e^{rt}$

$10.2 = 5.1 e^{0.0043t}$　　... $r = 0.43\% = \dfrac{0.43}{100} = 0.0043$　$[N = 2N_0]$

$e^{0.0043t} = \dfrac{10.2}{5.1} = 2$

$\Rightarrow 0.0043t = \log_e 2 = \ln 2$　　... using the definition of a log.

$\therefore\ t = \dfrac{\ln 2}{0.0043} = 161.197 = 161.2$ years.

It will take 161.2 years for the population to double in size.

Exercise 8.6

1. Graphed below are the functions $f(x) = a^x, a > 1$ and $f(x) = a^x, 0 < a < 1$.

   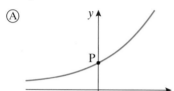   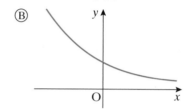

   (i)   Associate each graph with its function.
   (ii) Write down the coordinates of the point P.
   (iii) Write down the equation of the asymptote to each graph.

2. Copy and complete the table below.

x	-2	-1	0	1	2
2^x	$\frac{1}{4}$				
4.2^x	1				

   Use the table to draw a sketch of the function $f(x) = 4.2^x$ in the domain $-2 \leqslant x \leqslant 2$.
   Use your graph to find an estimate for $f(0.5)$.

3. Three graphs Ⓐ, Ⓑ and Ⓒ are sketched on the right.

   Associate each graph with one of the functions given below:

   $f(x) = 2^x$　　　$f(x) = 3^x$　　　$f(x) = 3.3^x$

   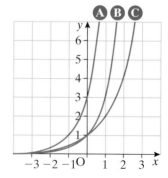

4. The given curve represents either
   (a) $f(x) = k \cdot 2^x$ or (b) $f(x) = k \cdot 3^x$

   (i) Find the value of k.
   (ii) Write down the function that the
        curve represents.

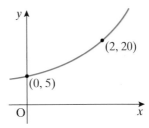
(2, 20)
(0, 5)

5. The curve $y = a(2^x)$ passes through the point $(1, 3)$.
   Find the value of a.

6. Copy and complete the table below and hence draw the graph of
   the function $f(x) = 3^{-x}$ in the domain $-2 \leqslant x \leqslant 3$.

x	-2	-1	0	1	2	3
$f(x) = 3^{-x}$						

   Use your graph to estimate
   (i) $f(-1.5)$ (ii) the value of x when $f(x) = 4$.

7. Draw a sketch of the function $f(x) = 3 \cdot 2^x + 2$ in the domain $-2 \leqslant x \leqslant 3$.
   Write down the range of the function.

8. The graph of the function $y = ae^x + b$ is shown.
   Find the values of a and b in terms of e.

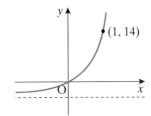
(1, 14)

9. Two variables x and y satisfy the equation $y = 3 \times 4^x$.
   (i) Find the value of a if $(a, 6)$ lies on the graph with equation $y = 3 \times 4^x$.
   (ii) If $\left(-\frac{1}{2}, b\right)$ also lies on the graph, find b.

10. Plot the graphs of $y = 3^x$ and the straight line $y = x + 3$ from $x = 0$ to $x = 2$.
    From your graph, find an approximate solution to the equation $3^x = x + 3$ in the
    given domain.

11. Draw a graph of the function $f(x) = \log_2 x$ for $0 < x \leqslant 16, x \in \mathbb{R}$.
    (Take 1, 2, 4, 8, 16 as the x-values.)

12. Find the values of a and b such that the graph of $y = a \log_2 x + b$ goes through
    the points $(8, 10)$ and $(32, 14)$.

13. The given curve is the graph of the function $y = \log_a x$.

    If the curve contains the point $(3, 1)$, find the value of a.

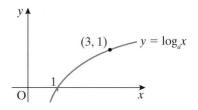

14. The diagram shows the graph of $y = f(x)$, where f is a logarithmic function.
    Which of the following represents $f(x)$?

    (a) $f(x) = \log_6 (x - 3)$ (b) $f(x) = \log_3 (x + 3)$
    (c) $f(x) = \log_3 (x - 3)$ (d) $f(x) = \log_6 (x + 3)$

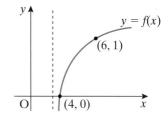

15. Which of the following graphs has equation $y = \log_5 (x - 2)$?

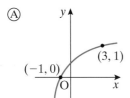 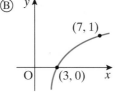 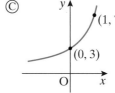 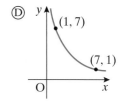

16. The diagram shows part of the graph of $y = \log_3 (x - 4)$.
    The point $(q, 2)$ lies on the graph.
    Find the value of q.

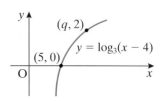

17. The temperature $T°C$ in a boiler rises exponentially over 24 hours so that, after a time t hours, $T = T_0 e^{\frac{t}{20}}$.

    (i) Given that the temperature is $165°C$ after 10 hours, find the value of T_0.
    (ii) What is the temperature after 24 hours?

18. The amount A_t, micrograms of a certain radioactive substance remaining after t years, decreases according to the formula $A_t = A_0 e^{-0.002t}$, where A_0 is the amount present initially.

    (i) If 600 micrograms are left after 1000 years, how many micrograms were present initially?
    (ii) The half-life of a substance is the time taken for the amount to decrease to half of its initial amount. What is the half-life of this substance?

19. Trees in a certain location are infected by a disease.

The number of unhealthy trees, N, was observed to change over time t (in years) as given by $N = 200 - Ae^{-\frac{t}{20}}$.

(i) If there are 91 unhealthy trees after 10 years, find the value of A.

(ii) How many unhealthy trees were there initially?

(iii) What is the limiting value of N as time increases?

20. The mass, m, of a radioactive material at a time t is given by $m = m_0 e^{-kt}$ where k and m_0 are constants.

If $m = \frac{9}{10}m_0$ when $t = 10$, find the value of k.

Also find the half-life of the material.

(The half-life is the time taken for the material to decay to half its original mass.)

Section 8.7 Related graphs

In previous sections of this chapter, we dealt with a variety of functions as well as the graphs of these functions.

In this section, we will examine how changes to the equation of a function affect the graph of the function. We will confine our discussion to four basic changes.

1. $y = f(x) \pm a$

The function $f(x) = x^2$ is shown.

The function $f(x) + 2$ represents a translation vertically upwards by 2 units.

The function $f(x) - 3$ represents a translation vertically downwards by 3 units.

> $+a$ moves the graph in the positive y-direction
> $-a$ moves the graph in the negative y-direction

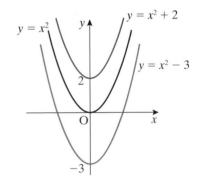

2. $y = f(x \pm a)$

The three graphs on the right show that $y = f(x + 2)$ represents a translation of the function $f(x) = x^2$ by minus 2 units parallel to the x-axis.

$f(x) = (x - 3)^2$ represents a translation of $+3$ units parallel to the x-axis.

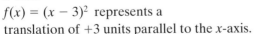

> $y = f(x + a)$ results in translating the graph parallel to the x-axis by $-a$ units
> $y = f(x - a)$ results in translating the graph parallel to the x-axis by $+a$ units

3. $y = -f(x)$

The graph of $y = -f(x)$ is a reflection in the
x-axis of the graph of $y = f(x)$.

> The graph of $y = f(-x)$ is a reflection in
the y-axis of the graph of $y = f(x)$.

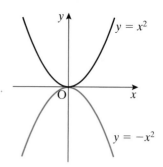

4. $y = af(x)$

The graphs of
$$f(x) = x(x - 1)(x + 2)$$
and $f(x) = 3x(x - 1)(x + 2)$
are shown.

Multiplying a function by a constant
will not change the points where the
graph intersects the x-axis but it does
have the effect of stretching the
graph up and down.

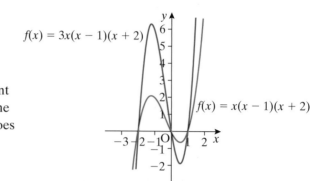

Example 1

The graph of $y = f(x)$ is shown.
Use separate diagrams to draw a sketch of

(i) $y = -f(x)$ (ii) $y = f(x) + 2$

(iii) $y = 2f(x)$ (iv) $y = f(-x)$

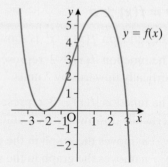

(i)

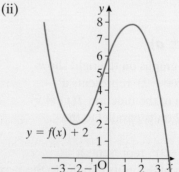

This is a reflection of
$y = f(x)$ in the x-axis.

(ii)

This is a vertical movement
(or translation) of $+2$ units
parallel to the y-axis.

(iii)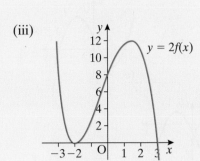

(iv)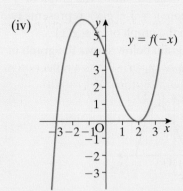

This is a stretch of $y = f(x)$
parallel to the x-axis by a
scale factor of 2.

This is a reflection of $y = f(x)$
in the y-axis.

Exercise 8.7

1. The curve with equation $y = f(x)$ is shown
   on the right.
   Sketch a separate graph of each of the
   following.
   Show where each graph intersects the
   x-axis and y-axis.

   (i) $f(x) + 3$ (iii) $-f(x)$
   (ii) $2f(x)$ (iv) $f(-x)$

2. The graph of $y = f(x)$ is shown in red.
   Write down the equations of $g(x)$ and $h(x)$ in
   terms of $f(x)$.

   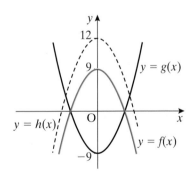

3. The graph of a function $y = f(x)$ is shown.
   Copy the diagram and on it, draw a rough sketch of
   (i) $y = f(x + 3)$ (ii) $y = f(x - 2)$.

   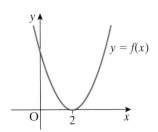

4. The given diagram shows the graph of $y = g(x)$.
   The function $y = 3 - g(x)$ represents two
   changes to the graph of $y = g(x)$.
   Which diagram below shows the graph of
   $$y = 3 - g(x)?$$

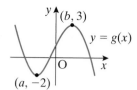

(A)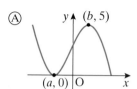

(B)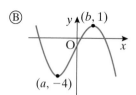

(C)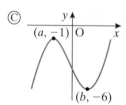

(D)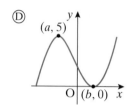

5. The given diagram shows a sketch of the
   function $y = f(x)$.

   (i) Copy the diagram and on it, sketch
       the graph of $y = -f(x)$.
   (ii) On a separate diagram, sketch the
        graph of $f(x) - 3$.

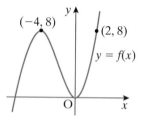

6. Which one of the following diagrams shows a parabola with equation $y = ax^2 + bx + c$,
   where both

   (i) $a > 0$ and (ii) $b^2 - 4ac > 0$?

(A)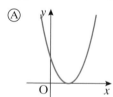

(B)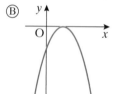

(C)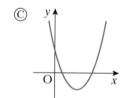

(D)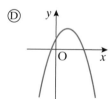

7. The diagram shows a sketch of $y = f(x)$.
   Which of the diagrams below shows a
   sketch of $y = -2 - f(x)$?

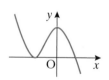

(A)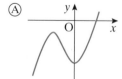

(B)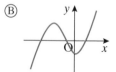

(C)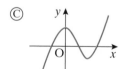

(D)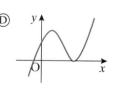

8. On the right is the graph of $y = f(x)$.

Copy this diagram and on it, draw a sketch of the curve

$$y = 4 + f(-x).$$

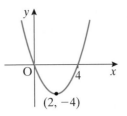

9. The given diagram shows part of the curve with equation $y = f(x)$. The curve crosses the x-axis at $(a, 0)$ and the y-axis at $(0, -b)$.

On separate diagrams, sketch

(i) $y = 2f(x)$ (ii) $y = f(-x)$.

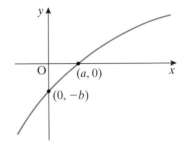

10. A function f is defined on the set of real numbers by $f(x) = (x - 2)(x^2 + 1)$.

(i) Find where the graph of $y = f(x)$ cuts:
   (a) the x-axis   (b) the y-axis.

(ii) The diagram shows the graph of $y = f(x)$.

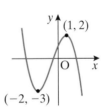

Which of the following shows the graph of

$$y = f(x + 2) - 1?$$

Ⓐ $(-4, 3)$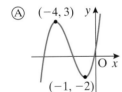
Ⓑ
Ⓒ
Ⓓ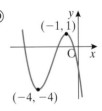

Revision Exercise 8 (Core)

1. Functions f and g are given by $f(x) = 2x - 3$ and $g(x) = x^2$.
   Find an expression for $gf(x)$ and hence solve the equation $gf(x) = 9$.

2. Which sketch graph fits which equation?
   Give reasons for your answers.

$y = 2x$

$y = x^2 - 2$

$y = 2 - x^2$

$y = x^2 + 2$

Ⓐ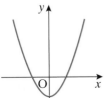
Ⓑ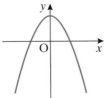
Ⓒ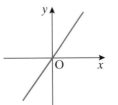

3. The domain of the function $f(x) = \dfrac{x}{x + 1}$ is $\{1, 2, 3, 4, 5\}$.

   Find the range of the function.

4. Determine the equation of the parabola
   shown on the right.

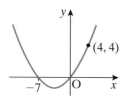

5. Given that $g(x) = 5 + \dfrac{x}{2}$, find $g^{-1}(x)$.

   Hence, find   (i) $g^{-1}(-2)$ (ii) the value of x for which $g(x) = g^{-1}(x)$.

6. Part of the graph of $y = a^x$, where $a > 0$, is shown.
   The graph cuts the y-axis at C.

   (i) Write down the coordinates of C.

   B is the point $(2, 16)$.

   (ii) Calculate the value of a.

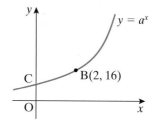

7. The graph of $f(x) = x^3 - 2x^2 - 5x + 6$
   is shown.
   Use the graph to write down

   (i) the roots of the equation $f(x) = 0$
   (ii) the roots of the equation $f(x) = -2$
   (iii) the roots of the equation
         $x^3 - 2x^2 - 5x = 0$.

   Is $y = f(x)$ a one-to-one function?
   Explain.
   Explain why $f(x)$ is a surjective function in the given range.

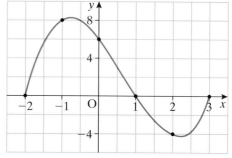

8. The diagram shows part of the graph of $y = 2m^x$.

   (i) Find the value of m.

   (ii) Write down the coordinates of P.

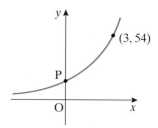

9. (i) Show that $f(x) = x^3 + ax^2 + b$ has a stationary point at $x = 0$ for all values of a and b.

   (ii) Given that $f(x)$ has a second stationary point at $(-2, 6)$, find the values of a and b
        and the nature of both stationary points.

10. Express $x^2 + 2x$ in the form $(x + h)^2 + k$, where $h, k \in \mathbb{Z}$.
Hence, write down the coordinates of the turning point of the graph of $f(x) = x^2 + 2x$.
Now draw a sketch of the graph of $f(x)$.

11. (i) State the domain and range for the relations represented by each of the following graphs:

(a)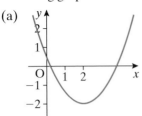

(b)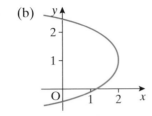

(c)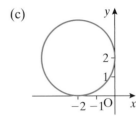

(ii) State if each of the graphs represents a function, giving a reason for your answer in each case.

12. The given diagram shows the graphs of

$y = 2^x$, $y = 5^x$, $y = \left(\frac{1}{2}\right)^x$ and $y = 3^{-x}$.

Use different values for x, and the corresponding y-values, to match each graph to its equation.

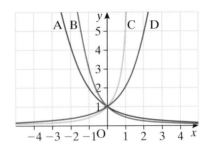

13. The displacement of a train from a point O is modelled by the equation,
$s = 0.25e^t$ metres.
Find the speed of the train, correct to one place of decimals, at $t = 0, 1, 2, 3, 4$ seconds and hence draw a sketch of the speed of the train for $0 \le t \le 4$ s.

14. Given $f(x) = 10x$ and $g(x) = x + 3$,
   (i) find $fg(x)$ and $(fg)^{-1}(x)$
   (ii) prove that if $fg(a) = b$, then $(fg)^{-1}(b) = a$.

15. $f(x) = x^2 + 3$ and $g(x) = x + 4$ define two functions.
   (a) Find expressions for $fg(x)$ and $gf(x)$.
   (b) Show that $fg(x) + gf(x) = 0$ has no real roots.

16. The functions f and g are defined as follows:

$$f(x) = x^2,\ x \in \mathbb{R} \text{ and } g(x) = \frac{1}{2x - 3},\ \text{for } x \in \mathbb{R}, x \ne \frac{3}{2}.$$

   (i) State the range of f.
   (ii) The inverse of g is g^{-1}. Find $g^{-1}(x)$.
   (iii) State the range of g^{-1}.
   (iv) Solve the equation $fg(x) = 9$.

Revision Exercise 8 (Advanced)

1. Functions $f(x) = x - 1$, $g(x) = 2x^2 - x - 1$ and $h(x) = \log_3 x$ define three functions on suitable domains.

   (i) Find expressions for $hf(x)$ and $hg(x)$.

   (ii) Hence solve the equation $hg(x) - hf(x) = 2$.

2. The equations of four functions and their graphs are given below.
   Associate each function with its graph.

   (a) $y = \frac{1}{3}(x + 4)(8 - x)$ (b) $y = x^2 - x + 2$

   (c) $y = -10 + 2(x - 1)^2$ (d) $y = \frac{1}{2}(9 - x^2)$

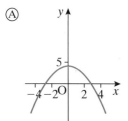
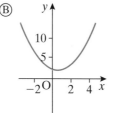
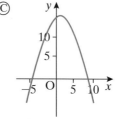
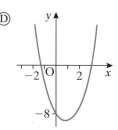

3. (i) The line m shown contains the point $(5, 3)$.
   Copy the diagram and draw a sketch of
   the line n, where the equation of n is
   the inverse of the equation of m.

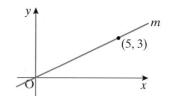

   (ii) A function f is given by $f(x) = +\sqrt{16 - x^2}$.
   Write down a suitable domain of f.
   What is the range of f?

4. Express $x^2 - 4x + 12$ in the form $(x - h)^2 + k$.
   Hence, write down the coordinates of the turning point and draw a sketch of the curve.

5. A rectangular piece of cardboard has
   dimensions 18 cm by 24 cm. Four corners,
   x cm by x cm, are cut from each corner.
   An open box is formed by folding up
   the flaps.
   Find a function for the volume, V, of the
   box in terms of x.
   State the domain of the function.

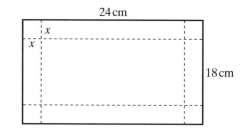

6. (i) The graph of $y = a.b^x$ is given.
   Use the graph to find the values
   of a and b.

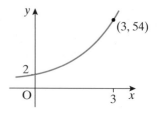

(ii) A function and its graph are shown.

    (a) For what value of x is the function discontinuous?

    (b) Write down the domain of the function.

    (c) Write down the range.

    (d) Is the function injective for $y > 0$? Explain.

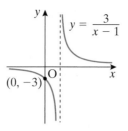

7. A canvas wind-shelter has two square ends, each of side x metres, and a rectangular back of length ℓ metres. The area of canvas is $9\,\text{m}^2$.

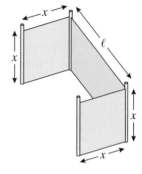

    (i) Show that $\ell = \dfrac{9}{x} - 2x$, and hence show that the enclosed volume, $V\,\text{m}^3$, is $9x - 2x^3$.

    (ii) Plot the graph of V against x for $0 \leqslant x \leqslant 3$.

    (iii) (a) Use your graph to find the value of x that gives the largest possible volume.

        (b) From your graph, what is this largest volume?

8. Functions f and g are defined by $f: x \to 3x - 1$ for $\{x \in \mathbb{R}\}$ and $g: x \to x^2 + 1$ for $\{x \in \mathbb{R}\}$.

    (a) Find the range of g.

    (b) Determine the values of x for which $gf(x) = fg(x)$.

    (c) Determine the values of x for which $|f(x)| = 8$.

    (d) Function $h: x \to x^2 + 3x$ for $\{x \in \mathbb{R}, x \geqslant q\}$ is one-to-one. Find the least value of q and sketch the graph of this function.

9. (i) The diagram shows the graph with equation $y = k(x - 1)^2(x + t)$. What are the values of k and t?

    (ii) Write down the equation of the image of the image of the curve in (a) the x-axis

        (b) y-axis

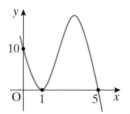

10. (i) The domain of the function $f(x) = +\sqrt{25 - x^2}$ is a subset of $\mathbb{R}$. Write down the largest possible set that is a suitable domain. What is the corresponding range?

    (ii) The diagram shows a sketch of the curve $y = 3^x$.

        (a) Write down the coordinates of the point where the curve cuts the y-axis.

        (b) Copy the diagram and add sketches of the curves

$$y = 3^{-x} \text{ and } y = 2(3^x).$$

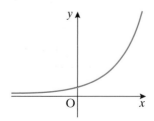

11. The population, P, of a certain organism grows exponentially over time t (days) according to $P = Ae^{\frac{t}{20}}$.

Use the table below to find the value of A and then complete the table.

Draw the graph of P against t.

t	0	5	10	15	20
P	5				

Calculate how long it takes for the population to double its initial size.

12. (i) Find the domain of values of x for which the function $f(x) = \sqrt{x^2 - 7x + 12}$ exists.

(ii) This is the graph of $y = \sin x$.

(a) Explain why $y = \sin x$ is a function.

(b) Is it a one-to-one (injective) function?

(c) Is it a surjective function in the domain $0 \leqslant x \leqslant 2\pi$?

(d) Suggest a restricted domain in which the function is injective.

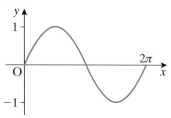

13. Which one of the following diagrams represents the graph with equation $\log_3 y = x$?

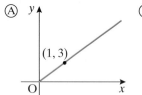   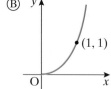   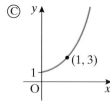   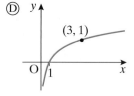

14. A population of birds, P, on an island is a function of the number of predators, n. The equation for the population is $P(n) = n^3 - 12n^2 - 60n + 850$, where $n > 0$.

(i) Explain why $n > 0$ is a necessary condition.

(ii) Find the minimum size of the population of birds on the island and the number of predators when this happens.

(iii) Sketch a graph of the function

Revision Exercise 8 (Extended Response Questions)

1. (a) For the equation $x^2 + 4x - 2 \equiv (x + a)^2 + b$, find the values of a and b. Hence, write down the coordinates of the turning point.

(b) Sketch the graph of $y = x^2 + 4x - 2$, indicating clearly the coordinates of any intersections with the coordinate axes.

(c) Find the value of the discriminant of $x^2 + 4x - 2$. Explain how the sign of the discriminant relates to your sketch in part (b).

(d) The equation $x^2 + 4x + k = 0$, where k is a constant, has no real roots. Find the set of possible values of k.

2. An arch is constructed as shown.

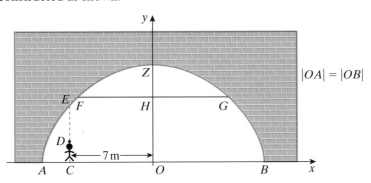

The height of the arch is 9 metres ($|OZ| = 9$ m).
The width of the arch is 20 metres ($|AB| = 20$ m).
The equation of the curve is of the form $y = ax^2 + b$, taking axes as shown.

(a) Find values of a and b.
(b) A man of height 1.8 m stands at C ($|OC| = 7$ m).
How far above his head is the point E on the arch? (That is, find the distance $|DE|$.)
(c) A horizontal bar $[FG]$ is placed across the arch as shown.
The height, $|OH|$, of the bar above the ground is 6.3 m. Find the length of the bar.

3. (a) Find the values of a and b such that the graph of $y = a \log_2 (x - b)$ passes through the points $(5, 2)$ and $(7, 4)$.

(b) Which one of the following statements is not true of the graph of the function

$$f: R^+ \to R, f(x) = \log_5 x \, ?$$

(i) The domain is R^+.
(ii) The range is R.
(iii) It passes through the point $(5, 0)$.
(iv) It has a vertical asymptote with equation $x = 0$.
(v) The slope of the tangent at any point on the graph is positive.

4. (a) The diagram on the right shows part of the graph of a function with equation $y = f(x)$.

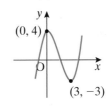

Which of the following diagrams shows the graph with equation $y = -f(x - 2)$?

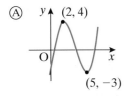 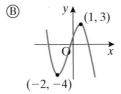 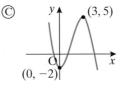 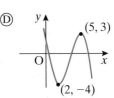

(b) The number of people, N, who have a particular disease at time t years is given by $N = N_0 e^{kt}$.

   (i) If the number initially is 20 000, and the number decreases by 20% each year, find:

      (a) the value of N_0 (b) the value of k

   (ii) How long does it take for 5000 people to be infected?

5. The functions f and g are defined with their respective domains by

$$f(x) = x^3, \qquad \text{for all real values of } x$$

$$g(x) = \frac{1}{x-3}, \quad \text{for real values of } x, x \neq 3$$

(a) State the range of f.

(b) (i) Find $fg(x)$.
    (ii) Solve the equation $fg(x) = 64$.

(c) (i) The inverse of g is g^{-1}. Find $g^{-1}(x)$.
    (ii) State the range of g^{-1}.
    (iii) Express in terms of x, $gg^{-1}(x)$.
    (iv) State the value of x at which the graph of $y = g^{-1}(x)$ is not continuous.

6. The value €M of a particular house in a certain area during the period 2006 to 2012 can be modelled by the equation $M = Ae^{-pt}$, where t is the time in years after 1 January 2006.
The value of the house on 1 January 2006 was €130 000 and its value on 1 January 2007 was €122 000.

  (i) State the value of A.
  (ii) Calculate the value of p, correct to two significant figures.
  (iii) What was the value of the house at the end of 2011?
     Give your answer to the nearest €100.

7. (a) Which of the following graphs has equation $y = \log_5(x - 2)$?

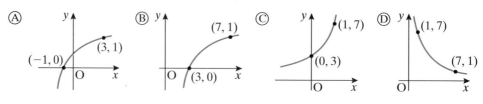

(b) The diagram shows the curves with equations

$y = 4^x$ and $y = 3^{2-x}$.

The graphs intersect at the point T.

(i) Show that the x-coordinate of T can be written in the form $\dfrac{\log_a p}{\log_a q}$, for all $a > 1$.

(ii) Calculate the y-coordinate of T.

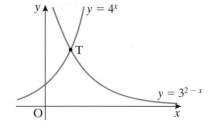

8. The equation of a function is $y = x^2 - 4x + 5$, $x \in \mathbb{R}$.

(a) Express $x^2 - 4x + 5$ in the form $(x + h)^2 + k$, where $h, k \in \mathbb{Z}$.
Hence, write down the coordinates of the turning point of the function and draw a rough sketch of the graph.

(b) Use the result in (a) to find the inverse function of $y = x^2 - 4x + 5$.

(c) Using the inverse function found in part (b), or otherwise, add a sketch of this inverse function to the sketch drawn in (a) above.

9. A farmer accidentally spread a dangerous chemical on a paddock. The concentration of the chemical in the soil was initially measured at 5 kg/ha. One year later, the concentration was found to be 2.8 kg/ha.

It is known that the concentration, C, is given by

$$C = C_0 e^{-kt}$$

where C_0 and k are constants, and t is measured in years.

(i) Evaluate C_0 and k.

(ii) It is safe to use the paddock when the concentration is below 0.2 kg/ha?
How long must the farmer wait after the accident before the paddock can be used?
Give your answer in years, correct to one decimal place.

Statistics 2

Key words

scatter diagram   correlation   causal relationship   causality
correlation coefficient   line of best fit   normal distribution   normal curve
Empirical Rule   standard scores (z-scores)   margin of error
confidence interval   hypothesis testing   null hypothesis

Section 9.1 Scatter diagrams

A **scatter graph** or **scatter diagram** is a graph consisting of points plotted on an x–y plane. Each point represents the values of two different variables such as the heights and weights of different individuals. Such data connecting two variables is called **bivariate data**.

After plotting the points on a scatter graph, we look for a pattern, particularly a **linear** pattern. If the points on a scatter graph lie approximately on a straight line, we say that there is a linear relationship between the two sets of data. The closer the points are to a straight line, the stronger the relationship will be.

The table below shows the average temperature and the number of ice-creams sold by a shop over a 12-day period.

Average temperature (°C)	10	12	16	20	13	16	14	17	19	20	21	16
No. of ice-creams sold	1	5	20	50	15	25	14	30	32	42	50	30

Using the horizontal axis for the temperature and the vertical axis for the numbers of ice-creams sold, we get the following scatter graph.

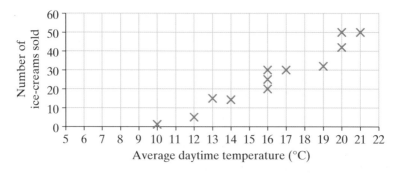

The scatter graph shows that the number of ice-creams sold increases as the temperature increases. Since the points lie close to a straight line, we say that there is a linear relationship between the two sets of data.

Correlation

Correlation is the strength of a relationship between two variables, say x and y. We say x and y are correlated if a scatter graph shows a linear pattern to the plotted points (x, y). If no pattern exists, the variables are not correlated.

The three diagrams below illustrate **positive correlation**, **negative correlation** and **no correlation**.

The variables x and y have a **positive correlation** if y increases as x increases.

The variables x and y have a **negative correlation** if y decreases as x increases.

The variables x and y show no linear pattern.

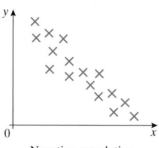

Positive correlation   Negative correlation

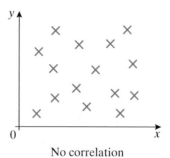

No correlation

The correlation is **high** if the points are close to a straight line.
The correlation is **low** if the points are more spread out.

It is possible to have strong and weak positive correlations as well as strong and weak negative correlations.
The scatter diagrams below illustrate these possibilities:

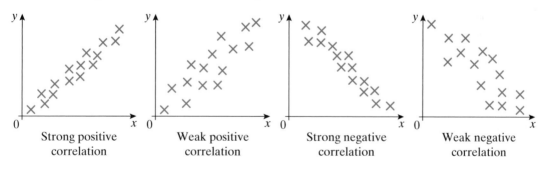

Strong positive correlation   Weak positive correlation   Strong negative correlation   Weak negative correlation

---

Example 1

The table shows the weights and heights of 12 people.

Height (cm)	150	152	155	158	158	160	163	165	170	175	178	180
Weight (kg)	57	62	63	64	58	62	65	66	65	70	66	67

(i) Draw a scatter graph to show this data.
(ii) Describe the strength and type of correlation between these heights and weights.

(i) We draw two axes at right angles.
We put the heights on the horizontal axis.
We start with 140 cm and go up to 180 cm.
We put the weights on the vertical axis, starting at 55 kg and going up to 70 kg.
We then plot the points (150, 57), (152, 62), ... etc.
The scatter graph is shown below.

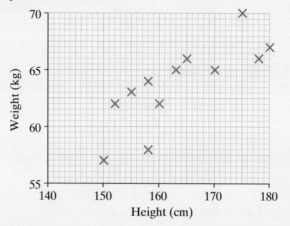

(ii) The correlation is weak positive as the points do not lie very close to a
straight line. The correlation is positive because the weight generally
increases as the height increases.

Causal relationships and correlation

The price of a used car depends, among other things, on the age of the car. The age of the car
causes the price of the car to decrease. We say that there is a **causal relationship** between the
age of the car and the price of the car.

Definition | When a change in one variable causes a change in another variable, we say that there is a causal relationship between them.

The scatter graph shows the relationship
between the sales of iced drinks and
temperature. The correlation is strong
and positive. You would expect this as
a rise in temperature would tend to
result in an increase in the sales of
iced drinks.

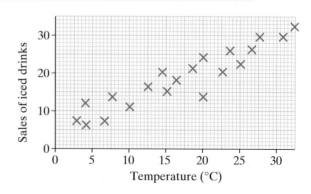

It would therefore be reasonable to conclude that there is a **causal relationship** between the increase in temperature and the sales of ice creams.

The scatter diagram below shows the number of iPads and the number of fridges sold by an electrical shop over a ten-month period.

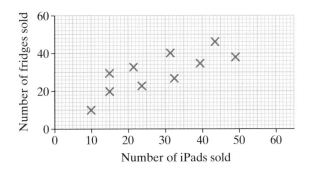

The graph shows that there is a reasonably strong positive correlation between the number of iPads sold and the number of fridges sold. However, this does not mean that there is a causal relationship between them; buying an iPad does not cause you to buy a fridge.

> Correlation does not necessarily mean that there is a causal relationship.

Exercise 9.1

1. Here are sketches of six scatter graphs:

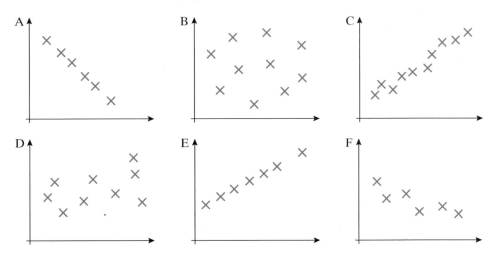

Which diagram(s) show
  (i) positive correlation   (ii) negative correlation
(iii) no correlation   (iv) strong negative correlation?
Describe the correlation in graph F.

2. Four scatter graphs are shown below.

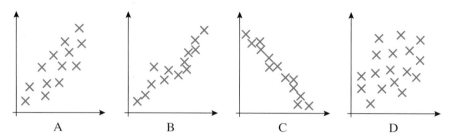

| A | B | C | D |

   (i) Which of these graphs shows the strongest positive correlation?
  (ii) Which of these graphs shows negative correlation?
 (iii) Which of these graphs shows the weakest correlation?

3. The examination marks of a sample number of
students in both their mock and final examinations
are shown in the given scatter graph.

   (i) Describe the correlation shown in the graph.
  (ii) What can you say about the relationship
between the mock and final marks of the
students?

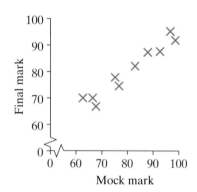

4. Brian recorded the percentages achieved in Statistics and Mathematics exams by
ten students.

| Statistics % | 78 | 82 | 74 | 75 | 93 | 70 | 66 | 62 | 77 | 89 |
| Mathematics % | 70 | 76 | 61 | 70 | 89 | 65 | 59 | 58 | 73 | 82 |

   (i) Draw a scatter diagram of this data.
  (ii) Describe the correlation shown.
 (iii) Describe the relationship between the percentages achieved in Statistics and
Mathematics for these students.

5. Describe the type of correlation – positive, negative or no correlation – that you would
expect between these variables:
   (i) the age of a boat and its second-hand selling price
  (ii) the heights of children and their ages
 (iii) the shoe sizes of children and the distances they travel to school
 (iv) time spent watching television and time spent studying
  (v) the number of cars on the road and the number of accidents.

6.

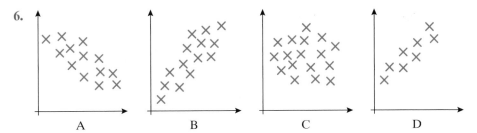

A   B   C   D

Four scatter graphs are shown above. For each of the following situations, choose the most appropriate of the scatter graphs. Explain your choice in each case.

  (i)   Boys' heights and their shoe sizes.
  (ii) Men's weights and the times taken by them to complete a crossword puzzle.
  (iii) Ages of cars and their selling prices.
  (iv) Marks achieved in Maths Paper 1 and Maths Paper 2.

7. The scatter graph below shows the relationship between the ages and prices of used motorcycles.

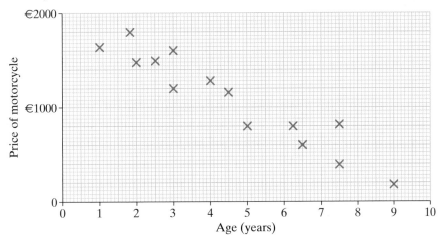

  (i)   Describe the correlation shown in this scatter graph.
  (ii) Is there a causal relationship between the variables? Explain your answer.

8. A small electrical shop recorded the yearly sales of radio sets and television sets over a period of ten years. The results are shown in the table below.

Year	1	2	3	4	5	6	7	8	9	10
No. of televisions sold	60	68	73	80	85	88	90	96	105	110
No. of radios sold	80	60	72	65	60	55	52	44	42	36

  (i)   Using scales going from 50 to 120 for the sales of televisions and 30 to 90 for the sales of radios, draw a scatter graph.
  (ii) What sort of correlation does the scatter graph suggest?
  (iii) Is there a causal relationship between the television sales and radio sales? Explain your answer.

Section 9.2 Measuring correlation – Line of best fit ———

1. Calculating the correlation coefficient

Correlation is the strength of a relationship between two sets of data.

The numerical measure of this property is called the **correlation coefficient** and is denoted by the letter r.

The value of r will always lie between -1 and 1.

   $r = 0$ indicates no correlation.
   $r = 1$ indicates **perfect positive** linear correlation.
$r = -1$ indicates **perfect negative** linear correlation.

Here are some examples of the value of r:

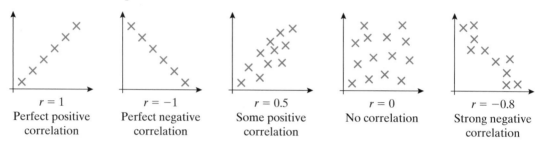

| $r = 1$ | $r = -1$ | $r = 0.5$ | $r = 0$ | $r = -0.8$ |
| Perfect positive correlation | Perfect negative correlation | Some positive correlation | No correlation | Strong negative correlation |

The nearer the value of r is to 1 or -1, the closer the points on the scatter diagram are to a straight line.

There are several methods of calculating a correlation coefficient.

The method selected for our course is called the **product–moment correlation coefficient, r.**
The formula that is used to find this coefficient involves a lot of tedious calculations.

For our course, it is recommended that we use the electronic calculator to find the value of r.

The steps involved in the input of data and finding the value of r are given in *Appendix 1* at the end of the book.

2. The line of best fit

We have already stated that when points on a scatter diagram lie on, or close to, a straight line a strong correlation exists.

To draw the line that fits best through the points you should aim to have the points evenly spread on either side of the line.

This scatter diagram shows the average daytime temperature plotted against the number of ice-creams sold.

A line that is drawn to pass as close as possible to all the plotted points on a scatter diagram is called the **line of best fit**.

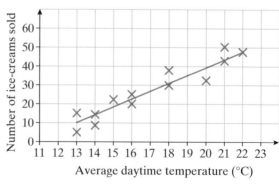

The line drawn is called **the line of best fit**.

It can go through some, all or none of the points.

This line shows the general trend of the relationship between the two sets of data. The line can be used to estimate other values. However, estimating values where the line has been extended beyond the existing points is less reliable.

Example 1

The table below shows the number of hours of sunshine and the maximum temperature in ten Irish towns on a particular day.

Maximum temperature (°C)	12	13	14	15	16	17	18	19	20	21
Hours of sunshine		9.6	11.6	10.2	13.25	11.8	13.6		15.4	15.2	15

   (i) Plot a scatter diagram and draw a line of best fit for the data.
  (ii) Use your line of best fit to estimate the number of hours of sunshine when the maximum temperature was 18°C.
 (iii) Describe the correlation shown in your diagram.
 (iv) Use your calculator to find the correlation coefficient.

   (i) The scatter diagram and line of best fit are shown below:

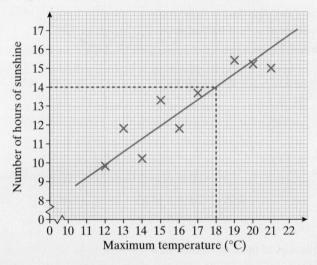

  (ii) The dotted lines on the diagram show that there are 14 hours of sunshine when the temperature is 18°C.
 (iii) The diagram shows that there is strong positive correlation between the two sets of data.
 (iv) The correlation coefficient, by calculator, is 0.9176.

3. Finding the equation of the line of best fit

From our knowledge of coordinate geometry, we should be familiar with the equation of a line in the form $y = mx + c$.

In statistics it is more usual to use the form (in the calculator), $y = A + Bx$

The equation, $y = A + Bx$ has a gradient (slope) of B and its intercept on the y axis is $(0, A)$

Thus to find the equation of a line of best fit drawn by eye,
   (i)   find two points on the line and use these points to find the slope of the line.
  (ii) Use the slope found and one of the points to find the equation of the line using

$$y - y_1 = m(x - x_1).$$

 (iii) Express the equation in the form $y = A + Bx$.

Example 2

This scatter diagram shows the results of a scientific experiment involving two variables x and y.
  (i) Find the equation of the line of best fit.
 (ii) Assuming that this line is valid for larger values of x, find the value of y when $x = 52$.

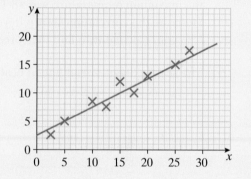

 (i) (15, 10) and (25, 15) are two points on the line.

Slope $m = \dfrac{15 - 10}{25 - 15} = \dfrac{5}{10} = \dfrac{1}{2}$

Equation of line: $y - y_1 = m(x - x_1)$
                     $y - 10 = \frac{1}{2}(x - 15)$ ... (15, 10) is a point on the line
           $\Rightarrow 2y - 20 = x - 15$
          $\Rightarrow$ $y = \frac{1}{2}x + \frac{5}{2}$

The equation of the line of best fit is $y = \frac{1}{2}x + \frac{5}{2}$.

 (ii) We use the equation $y = \frac{1}{2}x + \frac{5}{2}$ to find the value of y when $x = 52$.

$x = 52 \Rightarrow y = \frac{1}{2}(52) + \frac{5}{2}$, i.e., $y = 28\frac{1}{2}$

Thus $y = 28\frac{1}{2}$ when $x = 52$.

Example 3

The table below shows the weights and heights of 12 pupils.

Height (cm)	150	152	155	158	158	160	163	165	170	175	178	180
Weight (kg)	57	62	63	64	58	62	65	66	66.5	70	66	67

  (i) Draw a scatter diagram to show this data.

 (ii) Describe the strength and type of correlation between these heights and weights.

(iii) Draw a line of best fit on your scatter diagram.

 (iv) Tony is 162 cm tall.

       Use your line of best fit to estimate his height.

  (v) Use your calculator to find the correlation coefficient, correct to two decimal places.

 (vi) Find the equation of the line of best fit in the form $y = ax + b$.

  (i) The scatter diagram and line of best fit are shown below:

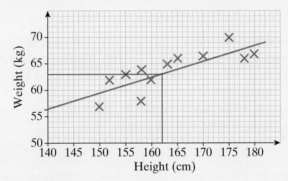

 (ii) Strong positive correlation.

 (iv) Draw a line from 162 cm on the height axis to meet your line of best fit.
Now draw a horizontal line and read off the value where it meets the weight axis.

       Tony's probable weight is about 63 kg.

  (v) By calculator, the correlation coefficient is 0.8.

 (vi) Two points on the line are (175, 67) and (155, 61)

$$\text{Slope of the line} = \frac{67 - 61}{175 - 155} = \frac{6}{20} = \frac{3}{10}$$

Equation of the line: $y - y_1 = m(x - x_1)$

$$y - 61 = \frac{3}{10}(x - 155)$$
$$y = \frac{3}{10}x - \frac{3 \times 155}{10} + 61$$
$$y = \frac{3}{10}x + \frac{29}{2}$$

Exercise 9.2

1. Four scatter graphs A, B, C and D are shown below.

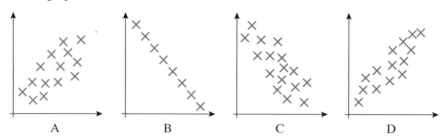

A   B   C   D

Match one of the following numbers with each of the graphs above so that it best represents the correlation:

$$0.1, \quad -0.4, \quad 1, \quad -1, \quad 0.6, \quad -0.8, \quad 0.8$$

2. Match one of these correlation coefficients to each of the descriptions below:

$$0.9, \quad -0.1, \quad -1, \quad -0.8, \quad 0, \quad 0.2$$

  (i)   Strong positive correlation   (ii) Strong negative correlation
(iii) No correlation   (iv) Perfect negative correlation
  (v) Very weak negative correlation   (vi) Very weak positive correlation

3. The scatter diagram below shows the heights and weights of a group of children. A line is drawn through some of these points.

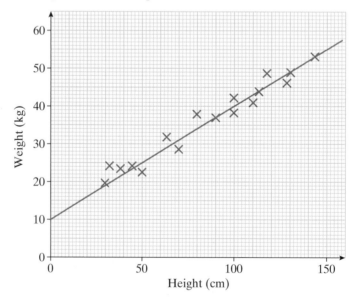

   (i) What is the name given to this line?
  (ii) Explain why this is a suitable line of best fit.
 (iii) Use the line to find the likely weight of a child who is 150 cm in height.
 (iv) Describe the correlation between the two sets of data.

4. Use your calculator to show that the correlation coefficient of the following set of data is 0.86.

x	1	1	1	2	2	2	3	3	3	9
y	1	2	3	1	2	3	1	2	3	8

5. The following table shows the marks of ten candidates in Physics and Mathematics. Use your calculator to find the correlation coefficient, correct to two decimal places.

Mark in Physics (x)	18	20	30	40	46	54	60	80	88	92
Mark in Mathematics (y)	42	54	60	54	62	68	80	66	80	100

6. The number of forest fires and the annual rainfall (in cm) were recorded over an 8-year period.
The results are given in the table below:

Rainfall (cm)	19	23	24	7	22	27	20	16
No. of fires	24	9	12	32	18	10	21	20

  (i) Plot the data on a scatter diagram.
 (ii) Construct a line of best fit by eye.
(iii) Calculate the value of r, the correlation coefficient.
(iv) Find the equation of the line of best fit.
 (v) Use your equation to predict the number of fires in a year with a rainfall of 25 cm.

7. The table below shows the pairs of scores obtained by eight pupils on two types of tests.

Test A	21	6	43	48	8	31	29	14
Test B	58	94	28	18	84	41	54	71

  (i) Draw a scatter diagram for these results.
 (ii) Describe the correlation between the two sets of scores.
(iii) Draw a line of best fit on your scatter diagram.
(iv) Find the equation of this line.
 (v) Another pupil sat Test A and was given a score of 18, but was absent for Test B. Use your line of best fit to estimate the score on Test B for this pupil.

8. The table below shows the heights of five fathers and their sons.

Height of father (cm)	163	185	185	193	197
Height of son (cm)	167	180	187	188	182

Use your calculator to find the correlation coefficient, r, correct to two decimal places.

9. Ten students were selected at random from those visiting the tuck shop at mid-morning break. The students were asked their age and for how many hours they watched television each week.

The results are shown in the table.

Student	1	2	3	4	5	6	7	8	9	10
Age, x (years)	17	16	18	13	10	$11\frac{1}{2}$	14	11	15	12
Hours of TV watching, y	12	15	20	10	2	2.25	10.5	2.5	11	13

(i) Draw a scatter diagram of this data.
(ii) Add a line of best fit by eye.
(iii) Find the equation of the line of best fit.
(iv) Use the equation of the line to find how many hours a child of $16\frac{1}{2}$ years watches television.

10. This data shows the engine size and the fuel economy of a range of petrol cars.

Engine size (litres)	1.6	1.4	3.0	1.2	1.1	1.0	2.0	1.7	1.3	4.0	3.5
Fuel economy	12	14	11	14	15	18	11	12	15	6	8

(i) Show this information on a scatter diagram.
(ii) Describe the correlation between the engine size and the fuel economy of these cars.
(iii) Calculate the correlation coefficient, r.
(iv) Draw the line of best fit and find its equation.
(v) A Lamborghini has a 5.7 litre engine.
What fuel economy would you expect from this car, using the equation of the line of best fit?
Explain why this result may not be reliable.

11. The manager of a factory decided to give the workers an incentive by introducing a bonus scheme. After the scheme was introduced, the manager thought that the workers might be making more faulty products because they were rushing to make articles quickly. A study of the number of articles rejected, y, and the amount of bonus earned, €x, gave the figures shown in the table.

Employee	A	B	C	D	E	F	G	H
Bonus, x (€)	14	23	17	32	16	19	18	22
Number of rejects, y	6	14	5	16	7	12	10	14

(i) Draw a scatter diagram for this data and add a line of best fit by eye.
(ii) What sort of correlation is there between the two variables?
(iii) Calculate the correlation coefficient, r.
(iv) Calculate the equation of the line of best fit.
(v) If the maximum number of rejects acceptable is 9, what level should the maximum bonus be set at?

Section 9.3 The normal distribution

When the physical characteristics, such as height or weight, of a large number of individuals are arranged in order, from lowest to highest, in a frequency distribution, the same pattern shows up repeatedly. This pattern shows that large numbers cluster near the middle of the distribution, as illustrated by the symmetrical histogram shown below.

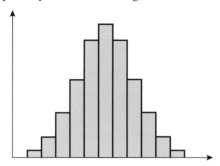

If the distribution is very large and continuous, and the class intervals become sufficiently small, the distribution forms a symmetrical bell-shaped smooth curve called **the curve of normal distribution** or simply the **normal curve** as shown on the following page:

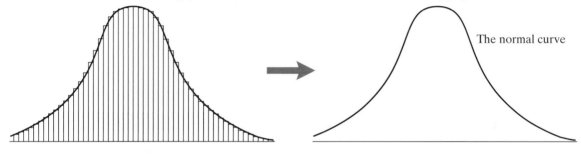

The normal curve

The normal distribution is the most important continuous distribution in statistics.

The curve on the right shows a normal distribution with mean μ.
The red line is the axis of symmetry.

The mode, median and mean are all equal.
They lie on the axis of symmetry.

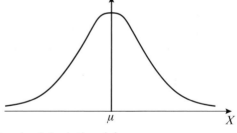

All normal distributions will have a mean (μ) and standard deviation (σ).
Different values for μ and σ will give different normal distributions.

The diagram on the right shows two normal distributions with the same mean but different standard deviations.

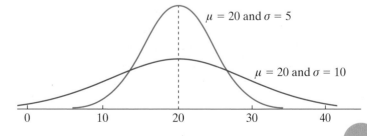

$\mu = 20$ and $\sigma = 5$

$\mu = 20$ and $\sigma = 10$

This diagram shows two normal distributions with the same standard deviation but different means.

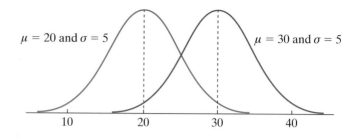

$\mu = 20$ and $\sigma = 5$ $\mu = 30$ and $\sigma = 5$

Empirical Rule

All normal distributions share some very important characteristics.

1. About 68% of all the values of any normal distribution lie within one standard deviation of the mean, i.e., in the range $[\mu - \sigma$ and $\mu + \sigma]$.

   34% lie to the right of the mean.
   34% lie to the left of the mean.

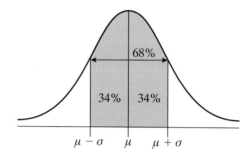

2. About 95% of all values lie within two standard deviations of the mean, i.e., in the range $[\mu - 2\sigma$ and $\mu + 2\sigma]$.

   $47\frac{1}{2}\%$ lie to the right of the mean.

   $47\frac{1}{2}\%$ lie to the left of the mean.

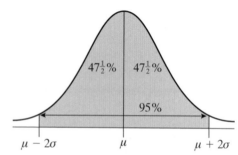

3. Almost all (99.7%) of the values lie within three standard deviations of the mean.

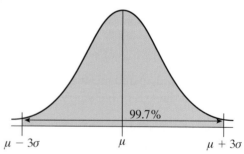

The three characteristics of the normal distribution listed above are generally known as **The Empirical Rule**.
This rule is highlighted below.

The Empirical Rule

- Approximately 68% of a normal distribution lie within one standard deviation of the mean
- 95% lie within two standard deviations of the mean
- 99.7% lie within three standard deviations of the mean.

Example 1

The marks, out of 100, in an examination are normally distributed.
The mean mark is 60 and the standard deviation is 6 marks.
  (i)   Work out the mark that is two standard deviations above the mean.
 (ii)   What percentage of the marks lie between 48 and 72 marks?
(iii)   What percentage of the marks lie between 60 and 72 marks?
(iv)   If 1000 students took the examination, how many students scored less than 54 marks?

  (i)   The mark that is two standard deviations above the mean is:

  mean + twice standard deviation = $60 + 2(6) = 72$ marks.

 (ii) $48 = 60 - 12 = \mu - 2\sigma$ and $72 = 60 + 12 = \mu + 2\sigma$
There are 95% of all values in the range $[\mu - 2\sigma$ and $\mu + 2\sigma]$.
∴ 95% of the marks lie between 48 and 72.

(iii) $60 = \mu$ and $72 = 60 + 12 = \mu + 2\sigma$
Since 95% of the marks lie between $\mu - 2\sigma$ and $\mu + 2\sigma$,
$\frac{1}{2}(95\%)$, i.e. $47\frac{1}{2}\%$, lie between μ and $\mu + 2\sigma$.
Thus, $47\frac{1}{2}\%$ lie between 60 and 72 marks.

(iv) $54 = 60 - 6 = \mu - \sigma$
From the curve, 34% of the marks lie
between μ and $\mu - \sigma$.
∴ $50\% - 34\% = 16\%$
∴ 16% are less than $\mu - \sigma$, i.e.,
less than 54 marks.
16% of 1000 = 160
Therefore 160 students scored
less than 54 marks.

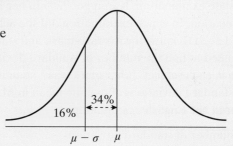

Example 2

Bottles of 300 ml shampoo are filled with the amounts in the bottles normally distributed with a mean of 300 ml and a standard deviation of 3 ml.
If 10 000 bottles are filled, how many bottles contain amounts that are
  (i)   within one standard deviation of the mean?
 (ii)   more than two standard deviations above the mean?
(iii)   If the manufacturer rejects bottles that contain amounts more than 3 standard deviations from the mean, what is the largest amount of shampoo in a bottle you would find for sale?

(i) 68% of the bottles lie within one standard deviation of the mean.
     68% of 10 000 = 6800.
     ∴ 6800 bottles lie within one standard deviation of the mean.
(ii) 95% of the bottles lie within 2 standard deviations of the mean.
     $\frac{1}{2}$ of 95%, i.e. $47\frac{1}{2}$%, lie within 2 standard deviations **above** the mean.
     ∴ 50% − $47\frac{1}{2}$%, i.e. $2\frac{1}{2}$%, lie more than two standard deviations above
     the mean.
     $2\frac{1}{2}$% of 10 000 = 250.
     250 bottles are more than 2 standard deviations above the mean.
(iii) 3 standard deviations above the mean is 300 + 3(3) = 309.
     Therefore, 309 ml is the largest amount you would find in a bottle.

Note: The Empirical Rule gives a rough approximation of percentages of data lying within
a number of standard deviations of the mean. A far more accurate method, involving
z-tables, will be seen in the next section.

Standard scores (*z*-scores)

In a state examination, Karen got 72% in her English examination and 68% in her Maths
examination. In which examination did she achieve the better result? To determine this, we
would need to know the average mark and standard deviation for each subject. We would
then need to find the number of standard deviations Karen's mark was above or below the
mean in each subject. If her mark was 1 standard deviation above the mean in English and
0.75 standard deviations above the mean in Maths, then Karen would have done relatively
better in her English examination.

The number of standard deviations
that a value lies above or below the mean
is called a **standard score** or **z-score**.

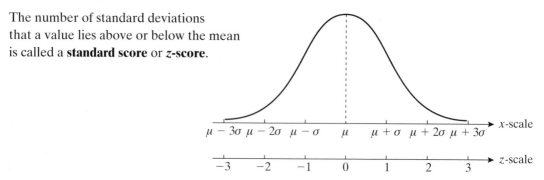

In general, if x is a measurement belonging to a set of data with mean μ and standard
deviation σ, then its value in z-units is given below:

$$z = \frac{x - \mu}{\sigma}, \text{ where } \begin{array}{l} x \text{ is the score or value} \\ \mu \text{ is the mean} \\ \sigma \text{ is the standard deviation} \end{array}$$

Standard scores are especially useful for dealing with normal distributions.

Simon and Susan did a test in French and a test in Science.
Both tests had a maximum mark of 100. The results are given in the table below:

	Susan's mark	Simon's mark	Mean mark	Standard deviation
French	75	50	60	10
Science	65	40	50	5

Work out the z-scores for each subject and comment on the performance of
Simon and Susan.

Susan: z-score in French $= \dfrac{x - \mu}{\sigma} = \dfrac{75 - 60}{10} = \dfrac{15}{10} = 1.5$

z-score in Science $= \dfrac{x - \mu}{\sigma} = \dfrac{65 - 50}{5} = \dfrac{15}{5} = 3$

Simon: z-score in French $= \dfrac{50 - 60}{10} = \dfrac{-10}{10} = -1$

z-score in Science $= \dfrac{40 - 50}{5} = \dfrac{-10}{5} = -2$

Overall, Susan did better as her standard scores were 1.5 and 3 above the mean.
Each of Simon's scores was below the mean.
The 'best' mark was Susan's Science mark because it had the highest standard score.
The 'worst' mark was Simon's Science mark because it had the lowest standard score.

Exercise 9.3

Note: In the following questions, where appropriate, use the Empirical Rule to estimate
percentages.

1. For each of the following normal curves, find the percentage of all the values that are in
the shaded area:

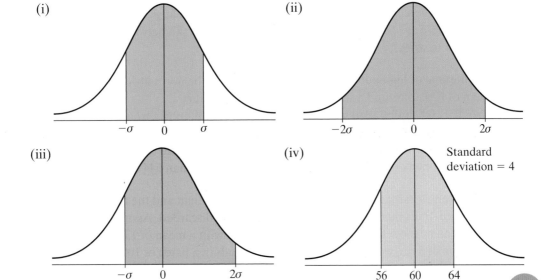

(i)

(ii)

(iii)

(iv)

Standard
deviation = 4

2. The normal distribution shown on the right represents the heights, in cm, of a group of teenagers.

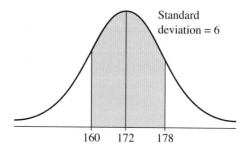

Standard deviation = 6

160   172   178

   (i) What percentage of the teenagers are between 172 cm and 178 cm in height?
   (ii) What percentage of the teenagers are taller than 178 cm?
   (iii) What percentage of the teenagers are between 160 cm and 178 cm in height?

3. The mean speed of vehicles on a road can be modelled by a normal distribution with mean 55 km/h and standard deviation 9 km/h.
   What would be the speed of a vehicle that was travelling at
   (i) one standard deviation below the mean
   (ii) two standard deviations above the mean
   (iii) three standard deviations above the mean?

4. A normal distribution has a mean $\mu = 60$ and standard deviation $\sigma = 5$.
   (i) Find the range within which 68% of the distribution lie.
   (ii) Find the range within which 95% of the distribution lie.

5. The heights of a large sample of adults are normally distributed with a mean of 170 cm and a standard deviation of 8 cm.
   Within what limits do
   (i) 68% of the heights lie
   (ii) 99.7% of the heights lie?

6. The mean time it takes factory workers to get to a factory is 35 minutes.
   The times can be modelled by a normal distribution with a standard deviation of 6 minutes.
   (i) What percentage of workers will take between 23 and 47 minutes to get to work?
   (ii) What percentage of the workers will take longer than 47 minutes?
   (iii) If there are 600 factory workers, how many will take between 23 and 47 minutes to get to work?

7. The lifetime of light bulbs were tested and found to be normally distributed with a mean of 620 hours and a standard deviation of 12 hours.
   (i) If 12 000 bulbs were manufactured, how many lifetimes would fall within one standard deviation of the mean?
   (ii) How many of the 12 000 bulbs would last between 620 and 644 hours?
   (iii) How many of the 12 000 bulbs would last longer than 644 hours?

8. To test tennis balls, they are dropped from a given height and the height they rebound is measured. Balls that rebound less than 128 cm are discarded. Assuming that the rebound height can be modelled by a normal distribution with a mean of 134 cm and a standard deviation of 3 cm, work out how many tennis balls in a batch of 1000 will be rejected.

9. Chicken portions produced for a fast-food restaurant have weights that are normally distributed with a mean of 160 g and a standard deviation of 10 g.
   (i) What percentage of the portions have weights between:
       (a) 140 and 180 g?   (b) 130 and 190 g?

   Portions are packed in boxes of 100 portions.
   (ii) How many portions in a box would you expect to weigh between 140 and 190 g?

10. In a normal distribution the mean μ is 80 and the standard deviation σ is 4.
    Use the formula $z = \dfrac{x - \mu}{\sigma}$ to convert each of these values to z-scores:
    (i) 84   (ii) 72   (iii) 86   (iv) 70

11. Explain what is meant by
    (i) a z-score of 2   (ii) a z-score of -1.5.

12. In a class test, the average mark was 70 and the standard deviation was 15. Karl received a z-score of 1.8 and Tanya received a z-score of -0.6.
    (i) Explain the meaning of each z-score in terms of the average mark and standard deviation.
    (ii) What were Karl's and Tanya's marks in the test?

13. The table shows Carmel's height and weight, alongside the mean and standard deviation for her class.

	Carmel's values	Class mean	Class standard deviation
Weight (kg)	48	44	8
Height (cm)	160	175	10

    Calculate the z-scores for Carmel's height and weight.

14. Anna's marks for Maths and History, as well as the mean and standard deviations of the marks for each subject, are given in the table below:

Subject	Anna's mark	Mean mark	Standard deviation
Maths	80	75	12
History	70	78	10

    (i) Find Anna's z-score for each subject.
    (ii) In which subject did she perform better?
         Justify your answer.
    (iii) Anna's friend Ciara got a z-score of 0.5 in History.
          What raw score did Ciara get in History?

15. Sarah-Jane received a z-score of 1.8 in a mathematics test.
    (i) What does this mean?
    (ii) If her raw score is 80 and the standard deviation of scores in the test is 12, what is the mean score?
    (iii) If Senan's score is 50 in the same test, what is his z-score?

16. The mean and standard deviation of two French papers are shown.
The marks for both papers are normally distributed.

	Mean	Standard deviation
Paper 1	45	8
Paper 2	56	12

Sarah was present for Paper 1 but absent for Paper 2.
In Paper 1, she scored 59 marks.
   (i) What was Sarah's z-score on Paper 1?
   (ii) Sarah expected to do equally well on Paper 2.
        What would be the best estimate for her mark in this paper?

17. A class of students is given a History test and Physics test.
Both the History and Physics marks are approximately normally distributed.
The mean and the standard deviation of each distribution are shown in the table.

	Mean	Standard deviation
History	52	6
Physics	60	8

The graph shows a sketch of the distribution for the History marks.

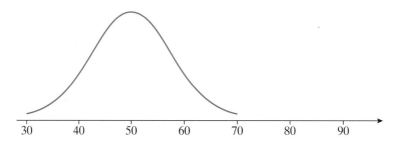

   (i) Show, on a copy of the same graph, a sketch of the distribution of the
        Physics marks.

Kelly scores 64 in the History test and 72 in the Physics test, but she claims that she is
better at History than at Physics.
   (ii) By standardizing her marks, find out whether her test results support
        her claim.

18. As part of her geography fieldwork, Alison is measuring and comparing the lengths of
pebbles on two beaches. On the first beach, the mean length is 8 mm and the standard
deviation is 1.4 mm. On the second beach, the mean length is 9 mm and the standard
deviation is 0.8 mm. She finds a pebble of length 10 mm on each beach. She claims that
this is less likely to happen on the first beach.
Use the standardised scores to test her claim.

Section 9.4 Normal Probability Distributions

A probability distribution is similar to
a frequency distribution, and also has a mean
and a standard deviation.

For a continuous random variable, X,
the probability that X lies between a and b,
i.e. $P(a \leqslant X \leqslant b)$, is given by the area under
the curve between a and b.

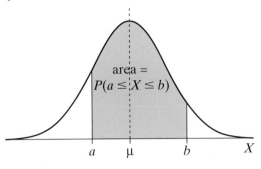

From the theory of probability the area under
the entire curve is always 1.

A probability distribution can be normally distributed, just like a frequency distribution.
A probability distribution that has the distinctive bell shape is called a **normal probability
distribution**.

Standard Normal Distribution (Z Distribution)

There are many different normal probability distributions, with different means and different
standard deviations.

The most important normal probability distribution, for many reasons, is the so-called
standard normal probability distribution. This has a mean of 0 and a standard deviation of 1.
It is also called the Z distribution.

The area between the standard normal curve and the Z-axis is 1.

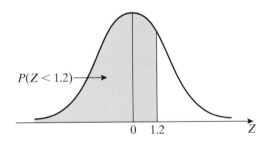

Pages (36–37) of *formulae and tables* gives the area under the curve as far as a particular
value of Z.

The shaded area in the diagram above represents the probability that $Z \leqslant 1.2$.

However, since the curve is symmetrical about the line $Z = 0$, the tables allow us to find the
area under the curve for any value of Z.

The method of finding various areas under the curve are shown below:

$P(Z \leq 1.68)$ can be read directly from the tables.

$$P(Z \leq 1.68) = 0.9535$$

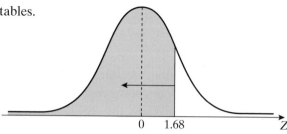

$P(Z \geq 0.85)$
To find the area to the right of 0.85
use the equation,

$$P(Z \geq 0.85) = 1 - P(Z \leq 0.85)$$
$$= 1 - 0.8023$$
$$= 0.1977$$

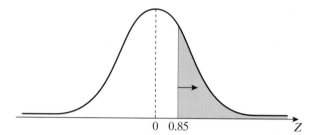

$P(Z \leq -1.23)$
To find the area left of -1.23, we use
the fact that the curve is symmetrical
and find the area to the right of 1.23

i.e. $P(Z \leq -1.23) = 1 - P(Z \leq 1.23)$
$$= 1 - 0.8907$$
$$= 0.1093$$

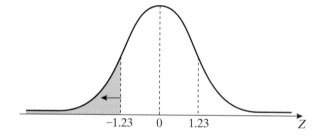

$P(-1.21 \leq Z \leq 0.93)$
To find this area
  (i) find area to the left of 0.93
  (ii) find area to the left of -1.21.

Then subtract (ii) from (i)

For example,
Area to the left of 0.93 = 0.8238

Area to the left of -1.21 $= 1 - P(Z \leq 1.21)$
$$= 1 - 0.8869 = 0.1131$$
$\Rightarrow$ area of shaded portion $= 0.8238 - 0.1131$
$$= 0.7107$$

If we are given the probability that $Z \leq k$, we can still use the tables to find the value of
Z that corresponds to k.

The following example illustrates this.

Example 1

Find a in each of the following:
  (i) $P(Z \leqslant a) = 0.7324$ (ii) $P(Z \leqslant a) = 0.1724$

  (i) The area to the left of $z = 0$ is 0.5.
       Thus $P(Z \leqslant a) = 0.7324 \Rightarrow a$ is positive
       From the tables, $0.7324 \Rightarrow a = 0.62$

 (ii) $P(Z \leqslant a) = 0.1724 \Rightarrow a$ is negative
       Thus $P(Z \leqslant -a) = 1 - P(Z \leqslant a)$
       $$= 1 - 0.1724$$
       $$= 0.8276$$
       $$\Rightarrow a = 0.94$$
       $$\Rightarrow -a = 0.94$$
       $$\Rightarrow a = -0.94$$

Other Normal Distributions

Suppose a random variable X which is normally distributed has a mean of μ and a standard deviation of σ. The standard normal tables (Z tables) can be used to find probabilities connected with X.

This is done by converting values of X into the corresponding Z values. The formula for converting from the given (x – units) into z – units is given below.

Standard scores $z = \dfrac{x - \mu}{\sigma}$

> x is the given score or variable
> μ is the given mean
> σ is the given standard deviation

Thus for example to calculate $P(X \leqslant x_1)$:
  (i) calculate $z_1 = \dfrac{x_1 - \mu}{\sigma}$, for a given x_1, μ and σ.
 (ii) then $P(X \leqslant x_1) = P(Z \leqslant z_1)$

Example 2

The mean height of all the students in a certain school is 175 cm and the standard deviation is 15 cm. If a student is selected at random, find the probability that he is less than, or equal to, 190 cm tall.

If 90% of the students are less than or equal to x cm, find the value of x, assuming that the distribution is normal.

In the given distribution, $\mu = 175$ and $\sigma = 15$

Using the formula $\qquad z_1 = \dfrac{x_1 - \mu}{\sigma}$

$x_1 = 190 \qquad \Rightarrow \qquad z_1 = \dfrac{190 - 175}{15} = 1$

$\Rightarrow P(X \leqslant 190) = P(Z \leqslant 1)$

$\qquad\qquad\qquad = 0.8413$

$\Rightarrow P(\text{student} \leqslant 190\,\text{cm}) = 0.8413$

If 90% of the students are less than or equal to x cm, we need to find the value of z_1 in the diagram on the right.

From the tables on page 36,

$\qquad P(Z \leqslant z_1) = 0.9$

$\qquad\qquad \Rightarrow z_1 = 1.28$

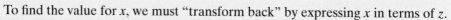

To find the value for x, we must "transform back" by expressing x in terms of z.

$z = \dfrac{x - \mu}{\sigma} \Rightarrow x = z\sigma + \mu$

$\qquad\qquad\qquad = 1.28(15) + 175 = 194.2$

Therefore 90% of the students are less than or equal to 194.2 cm.

Exercise 9.4

1. Using your *Formulae and Tables* book, find the area of the shaded region under each of the following standard normal curves:

   (i)

   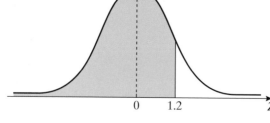

   (ii)

   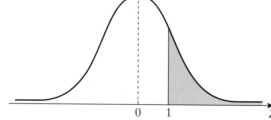

(iii)

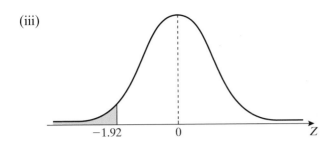

(iv)

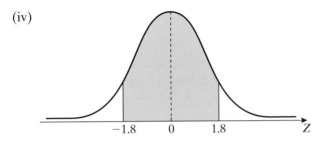

If Z is a random variable with standard normal distribution, find

2. $P(Z \leqslant 1.42)$ 3. $P(Z \leqslant 0.89)$ 4. $P(Z \leqslant 2.04)$

5. $P(Z \geqslant 2)$ 6. $P(Z \geqslant 1.25)$ 7. $P(Z \geqslant 0.75)$

8. $P(Z \leqslant -2.3)$ 9. $P(Z \leqslant -1.3)$ 10. $P(Z \leqslant -2.13)$

11. $P(Z \leqslant 0.56)$ 12. $P(-1 \leqslant Z \leqslant 1)$ 13. $P(-1.5 \leqslant Z \leqslant 1.5)$

14. $P(0.8 \leqslant Z \leqslant 2.2)$ 15. $P(-1.8 \leqslant Z \leqslant 2.3)$ 16. $P(-0.83 \leqslant Z \leqslant 1.4)$

Find the value of z_1 in each of the following if Z is a random variable with normal distribution.

17. $P(Z \leqslant z_1) = 0.8686$ 18. $P(Z \leqslant z_1) = 0.6331$

19. $P(-z_1 \leqslant Z \leqslant z_1) = 0.6368$ 20. $P(-z_1 \leqslant Z \leqslant z_1) = 0.8438$

21. If X is a random variable with normal distribution and has mean $\mu = 50$ and standard deviation $\sigma = 10$, find
     (i) $P(X \leqslant 60)$ (ii) $P(X \leqslant 55)$ (iii) $P(X \geqslant 45)$

In each of the following, X is a random variable with normal distribution with a given mean (μ) and standard deviation (σ). Find the required probability in each case.

22. $\mu = 300$, $\sigma = 25$, find   (i) $P(X \geqslant 294)$ (ii) $P(X \leqslant 312)$.

23. $\mu = 250$, $\sigma = 40$, find   (i) $P(X \geqslant 300)$ (ii) $P(X \leqslant 175)$.

24. $\mu = 50$, $\sigma = 8$, find   (i) $P(52 \leqslant X \leqslant 55)$ (ii) $P(48 \leqslant X \leqslant 54)$.

25. $\mu = 100$, $\sigma = 80$, find   (i) $P(85 \leqslant X \leqslant 112)$ (ii) $P(105 \leqslant X \leqslant 115)$.

26. $\mu = 200$, $\sigma = 20$, find   (i) $P(190 \leqslant X \leqslant 210)$ (ii) $P(185 \leqslant X \leqslant 205)$.

27. The life of a particular light bulb is normally distributed with a mean life of 210 hours and a standard deviation of 20 hours. Find
   (i) the probability that a bulb, selected at random, will last more than 240 hours
   (ii) the probability that a bulb will last less than or equal to 200 hours.

28. The chest measurements of teenage male customers for T-shirts may be modelled by a normal distribution with mean 101 cm and standard deviation 5 cm. Find the probability that a randomly-selected customer will have a chest measurement which is
   (i) less than 103 cm
   (ii) 98 cm or more
   (iii) between 95 and 100 cm.

29. The time taken by a postman to deliver letters to a certain apartment block is normally distributed with mean 12 minutes and standard deviation 2 minutes. Estimate the probability that he takes
   (i) longer than 17 minutes
   (ii) less than 10 minutes
   (iii) between 9 and 13 minutes.

30. A mobile phone company finds that its phone bills are normally distributed with a mean of €53 and a standard deviation of €15.
Find the probability that, if a mobile phone bill is chosen at random, the amount due will be between €47 and €74.

31. The heights of a large group of female students are normally distributed with a mean of 165 cm and a standard deviation of 3.5 cm. A student is selected at random from this group.
   (i) Find the probability that she is less than 160 cm in height.

The Drama teacher is looking for a student with a height between 168 cm and 174 cm for a part in a school play.
   (ii) Find the proportion of students from this group that would satisfy these conditions.

32. The mean length of 500 laurel leaves from a certain bush is 151 mm and the standard deviation is 15 mm. Assuming that the lengths are normally distributed, find how many leaves measure
   (i) greater than 185 mm
   (ii) between 120 mm and 155 mm.

33. A biscuit company knows that the weights of the packets of one of their brands are normally distributed with a mean of 300 grams and a standard deviation of 6 grams. How many of 1000 packets, selected at random, can be expected to weigh
   (i) less than 295 grams
   (ii) between 306 and 310 grams?

34. The mean percentage mark achieved by students in Geography in a state examination was 60% and the standard deviation was 10%.
  (i) What is the probability that a randomly selected student scored
    (a) below 45%
    (b) between 50% and 75%?
  (ii) Students got a special award if they obtained a mark greater than 90% of all the other students in the examination.
    What percentage mark would the student need to get a prize?

Revision Exercise 9 (Core)

1. For the given normal curve, find the percentage of the data that is in the shaded region.

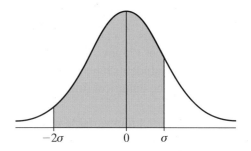

2. Four scatter diagrams are shown below:

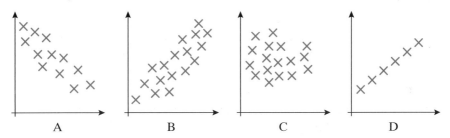

A   B   C   D

For each of the following, choose the most appropriate of the scatter diagrams above:
  (i) Number of caps of an international rugby player and number of points scored.
  (ii) Distance (north) from equator and winter daylight hours.
  (iii) Men's percentage body fat and the time taken for them to solve a Rubik's Cube.
  (iv) An example of negative correlation.
  (v) A scatter diagram showing a correlation coefficient of 0.7.

3. The heights of students in a certain university are normally distributed with a mean of 180 cm and a standard deviation of 10 cm.
  (i) Make a copy of the given normal curve and write down the values of a, b, c, d and e.
  (ii) Find the z-score that corresponds to 190 cm.
  (iii) What percentage of students have a height greater than 190 cm?

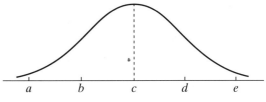

a b c d e

4. The table shows the marks of 15 students taking Paper 1 and Paper 2 of a maths exam. Both papers were marked out of 40.

Paper 1	36	34	23	24	30	40	25	35	20	15	35	34	23	35	27
Paper 2	39	36	27	20	33	35	27	32	28	20	37	35	25	33	30

   (i) Draw a scatter diagram to show this information.
   (ii) Describe the correlation shown in the scatter diagram.
   (iii) Draw a line of best fit on your scatter diagram.
   (iv) Find the equation of the line of best fit.
   (v) Joe scored 32 on Paper 1 but was absent for Paper 2.
       Use your line of best fit to estimate his score on Paper 2.

5. The heights of a large number of students can be modelled by a normal distribution with mean 175 cm.
95% of students have heights between 160 and 190 cm.
Using the empirical rule work out the standard deviation of the students' heights.

6. If Z is a random variable with standard normal distribution, use the *formulae* **and** *tables* booklet to find $P(Z > 0.93)$.

7. (i) Explain briefly what you understand by the term 'correlation'.
   (ii) The table below gives the marks, out of 20, obtained by five students in two tests:

Test 1	8	9	7	2	13
Test 2	7	10	5	4	14

     (a) Use your calculator to calculate r, the correlation coefficient.
     (b) What does this value tell us about the performance of the students in the tests?

8. The length, X, of bamboo canes sold in a garden centre can be modelled by the normal distribution shown in the diagrams below. Work out the probability of a cane chosen at random falling in the shaded area of each diagram.

(i)
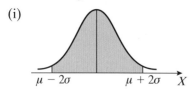

(ii)
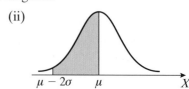

9. Simon takes French and German tests.
   The marks for both tests are normally distributed.
   In French he scores 76 and in German he scores 78.
   The French marks have a mean of 68 and a standard deviation of 10.
   The German marks have a mean of 70 and a standard deviation of 12.
   (i) Calculate Simon's z-score in French.
   (ii) Calculate Simon's z-score in German.
   (iii) Use the z-scores to compare Simon's results.

10. Explain, with the aid of an example, what is meant by the statement:

   "Correlation does not necessarily imply causality".

Revision Exercise 9 (Advanced)

1. If Z is a random variable having a standard normal distribution, use the **formulae and tables** booklet to find $P(-1 \leqslant Z \leqslant 1.24)$.

2. (i) Find $P(1 \leqslant Z \leqslant 2)$, where Z is a random variable having a normal distribution.
   (ii) If Z is a random variable with normal distribution and $P(Z \leqslant k) = 0.8686$, find k.

3. The time a mobile phone battery lasts before needing to be recharged is assumed to be normally distributed with a mean of 48 hours and a standard deviation of 8 hours.
   (i) Find the probability that a battery chosen at random will last more than 60 hours.
   (ii) Find the probability that the battery at least 35 hours.

4. If Z is a random variable having a standard normal distribution, find the value of k if $P(-k \leqslant Z \leqslant k) = 0.8438$.

5. Television tubes have a mean life of 4000 hours and a standard deviation of 500 hours. Assuming that their life can be modelled by a normal distribution, estimate:
   (i) the percentage of tubes lasting less than 3000 hours
   (ii) the **probability** that a tube will last for between 3000 and 5000 hours.
   (iii) In a batch of 10 000 tubes, after how many hours would you expect only $2\frac{1}{2}\%$ of the tubes to be still working?

6. The following table gives the number of employees and the units produced for a certain company over a 4-month period.

Month	Number of employees	Units produced
January	100	80
February	85	75
March	76	64
April	60	60

   (i) Use your calculator to find r, the correlation coefficient.
   (ii) Comment briefly on the value of r that you found.

7. Mr Cross has two very different trees in his garden. He knows that the lengths of the leaves on both trees are approximately normally distributed. For the first tree, the mean length is 5 cm and the standard deviation is 1 cm. For the second tree, the mean length is 8 cm and the standard deviation is 1.5 cm. He picks leaves which measure exactly 7 cm from both trees. He claims that this is more likely to happen on the second tree. Use the standardised scores to test his claim.

8. The table below shows the temperature of water as it cools in a freezer:

Time (minutes)	5	10	15	20	25	30
Temperature (°C)	36	29	25	20	15	8

   (i)   Use this information to draw a scatter diagram.
   (ii) What type of correlation is shown?
   (iii) Draw a line of best fit and find its equation.
   (iv) Use the equation of the line to estimate the time when the temperature of the water reaches 0°C.
   (v)   Use your calculator to calculate r, the correlation coefficient, correct to 2 decimal places.

9. The table shows the mean and the standard deviation of the heights of a sample of adult males and a sample of boys aged nine.
   The heights of both the adult males and the boys are normally distributed.

	Adult males	Boys aged nine
Mean	180 cm	135 cm
Standard deviation	18 cm	10 cm

David is a boy aged nine whose height is 120 cm.
   (i)   How many standard deviations below the mean is David's height?

It is believed that the height of a boy aged nine is a good indicator of his adult height.
   (ii) Estimate the height that David will be when he is an adult.

The diagram below shows the distribution of the heights of the boys aged nine.
   (iii) Copy the diagram and sketch the distribution of the heights of the adult males.

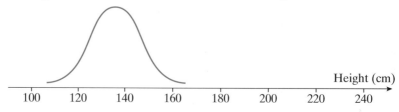

Revision Exercise 9 (Extended Response Questions)

1. The lengths of roofing nails are normally distributed with a mean of 20 mm and a standard deviation of 3 mm.
   - (i) What percentage of nails lie between
     - (a) 17 mm and 23 mm
     - (b) 14 mm and 23 mm?
   - (ii) If 10 000 nails were measured, how many would have a length between 17 mm and 26 mm?
   - (iii) What is the probability that a roofing nail, selected at random, is more than 23 mm long?

2. A class of students takes examinations in both mathematics and physics. The marks that they obtain are as follows:

Student	1	2	3	4	5	6	7	8	9	10
Mathematics	65	45	40	55	60	50	80	30	70	65
Physics	60	60	55	70	80	40	85	50	70	80

   - (i) Plot the data on a scatter diagram and draw the line of best fit by eye.
   - (ii) Find the equation of the line of best fit.
   - (iii) Determine the value of the correlation coefficient, using your calculator.
   - (iv) Interpret this value in the context of the question.

3. The height of a certain population of adult males is normally distributed with a mean of 176 cm and a standard deviation of 7 cm.
   - (i) Find the probability that the height of a randomly selected man will be greater than 190 cm.
   - (ii) If two males are selected at random, find the probability that both of their heights will exceed 190 cm.
   - (iii) If n males were selected at random from the population, write an expression for the probability that r of the males will have heights exceeding 190 cm using your answer from (i)
   - (iv) Find the probability that at least two males from a randomly selected group of 10 will have heights exceeding 190 cm.

4. The average age of a sample of Bingo players is 60 years with a standard deviation of 8 years. The distribution is found to be normally distributed.
   - (i) If the ages were standardised, what would the z-scores be for
     - (a) Abdul: 70   (b) Marie: 52   (c) George: 60   (d) Elsie: 92?
   - (ii) What percentage of people in the sample are more than 76 years old?
   - (iii) Ezra has a z-score of 2.5. How old is she?
   - (iv) Comment on the likelihood of a 40-year-old being in the sample.

5. A person's *maximum heart rate* is the highest rate at which their heart beats during certain extreme kinds of exercise. It is measured in beats per minute (bpm). It can be measured under controlled conditions. As part of a study in 2001, researchers measured the maximum heart rate of 514 adults and compared it to each person's age. A representative sample of the results are shown in the scatter diagram below.

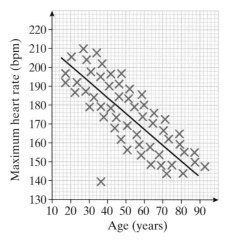

(i) From the diagram, estimate the correlation coefficient.

(ii) Circle the *outlier* on the diagram and write down the person's age and maximum heart rate.

(iii) The line of best fit is shown on the diagram.
Use the line of best fit to estimate the maximum heart rate of a 44-year-old person.

(iv) By taking suitable readings from the diagram, calculate the slope of the line of best fit.

(v) Find the equation of the line of best fit and write it in the form:
$MHR = a - b \times$ (age), where MHR is the maximum heart rate.

(vi) The researchers compared their new rule for estimating maximum heart rate to an older rule. The older rule is: $MHR = 220 -$ age. The two rules can give different estimates of a person's maximum heart rate. Describe how the level of agreement between the two rules varies according to the age of the person. Illustrate your answer with two examples.

(vii) A particular exercise programme is based on the idea that a person will get most benefit by exercising at 75% of their estimated MHR. A 65-year-old man has been following this programme, using the old rule for estimating MHR. If he learns about the researchers' new rule for estimating MHR, how should he change what he is doing?

Inferential statistics

Section 10.1 Confidence interval for population proportion

1. Margin of error and confidence intervals

When dealing with sampling in *Statistics 1*, it was stated that the purpose of sampling is to gain information about the whole population by surveying a small part of the population. If data from a sample is collected in a proper way, then the sample survey can give an accurate indication of the population characteristic that is being studied.

Before a general election, a national newspaper generally requests a market research company to survey a sample of the electorate regarding their voting intentions in the election. The number surveyed is generally about 1000.

The result of the survey might appear in the daily newspaper as follows:

40% support for **The Democratic Right**.

The **40%** support is called the **sample proportion**, that is, the part or portion of the sample who indicated that they would vote for **The Democratic Right**.
A sample proportion is used to give an estimate of the **population proportion** who intend to vote for **The Democratic Right**.

The notation $\hat{p}$ is used to denote **sample proportion**.
The notation p is used to represent **population proportion**.
Since p is generally not known, $\hat{p}$ is used as an **estimator** for the true population proportion, p.

Of course everybody knows that sample surveys are not always 100% accurate. There is generally some 'element of chance' or **error** involved.

The newspaper might add to their headline the following sentence:

The margin of error is 3%.

The **margin of error** of 3% is a way of saying that the result of the survey is 40% ± **3%**. That means that the research company is quite 'confident' that the proportion of the whole electorate who intend to vote for **The Democratic Right** could be anywhere between 37% and 43%.

The expressions for the **margin of error**, E, depend on how confident we want to be of where the population proportion lies. In the work that follows, we examine the margin of error at the 95% confidence level, i.e. the interval in which 95% of the samples will lie.

The result of the opinion poll above was given as 40% ± 3%.
That could be written as 37% $< p <$ 43%, where p is the population proportion.
37% $< p <$ 43% is called the **confidence interval**.

The 'confidence' level is pitched at 95%.
The 95% confidence implies that the interval was obtained by a method which 'works 95% of the time'.

The confidence interval, 37% $< p <$ 43%, is a way of stating that if you surveyed many samples of 1000 people on the same day, the results would be in the interval 37% to 43% in 95% of the samples.

In general, if $\hat{p}$ is a sample proportion for a population proportion, p, then the confidence interval for p is given by

$$\hat{p} - E < p < \hat{p} + E,$$

where E is the margin of error.

2. Confidence interval using the margin of error approximation

At the 95% confidence level, the margin of error, E, can be found by using the margin of error approximation:

$E = \frac{1}{\sqrt{n}}$, where n is the size of the sample.

For example, if the sample size is 1000,

then $E = \frac{1}{\sqrt{1000}} \approx 0.03 \approx 3\%$.

> Margin of Error Approximation
> $$E = \frac{1}{\sqrt{n}}$$

If the sample size(n) is increased, the margin of error, E, is reduced.

Using this expression for the margin of error, E, the 95% confidence interval for p, the population proportion, is given over.

> 95% Confidence Interval
> (using the margin of error approximation)
> $$\hat{p} - \frac{1}{\sqrt{n}} < p < \hat{p} + \frac{1}{\sqrt{n}}$$
> $$\text{or } \hat{p} \pm \frac{1}{\sqrt{n}}$$

Note: The margin of error approximation, $E = \frac{1}{\sqrt{n}}$, only applies at the 95% level of confidence. Since it can be quite inaccurate, it should only be used if requested to do so.

Note: In calculations, p, $\hat{p}$ and E are always expressed in decimal form.

E.g. if 150 television viewers are interviewed in a sample survey and 63 say they like a new talk show, then the sample proportion is $\hat{p} = \frac{63}{150} = 0.42$.

Example 1

What sample size would be required to have a margin of error of
(i) 0.05   (ii) $2\frac{1}{2}\%$?
(You may use the margin of error approximation)

(i) $\quad \frac{1}{\sqrt{n}} = 0.05$

$\quad\quad \therefore \frac{1}{n} = (0.05)^2$

$\quad\quad \therefore n = \dfrac{1}{(0.05)^2}$

$\quad\quad\quad n = 400$

(ii) $\quad \frac{1}{\sqrt{n}} = 2\frac{1}{2}\% = 0.025$

$\quad\quad \frac{1}{n} = (0.025)^2$

$\quad\quad n = \dfrac{1}{(0.025)^2}$

$\quad\quad n = 1600$

Example 2

A random sample of 400 persons are given a flu vaccine and 136 of them experienced some discomfort.
Construct a 95% confidence interval for p, the population proportion who might experience discomfort. (You may use the margin of error approximation)

The sample proportion $\hat{p} = \dfrac{136}{400} = 0.34$

The margin of error $= \dfrac{1}{\sqrt{n}} = \dfrac{1}{\sqrt{400}} = \dfrac{1}{20} = 0.05$

The confidence interval is $\quad 0.34 - 0.05 < p < 0.34 + 0.05$
$$= 0.29 < p < 0.39$$

Example 3

A survey of 100 residents of a Dublin suburb were asked if they remembered seeing an advertisement for McCain's chips on television. 60 respondents said that they had.
   (i)   Calculate the sample proportion, $\hat{p}$.
   (ii) Find the margin of error, E, using the margin of error approximation.
   (iii) Construct a 95% confidence interval for p.

(i) $\hat{p} = \dfrac{60}{100} = 0.6$

(ii) $E = \dfrac{1}{\sqrt{n}} = \dfrac{1}{\sqrt{100}} = \dfrac{1}{10} = 0.1$

(iii) Confidence interval: $\hat{p} - \dfrac{1}{\sqrt{n}} < p < \hat{p} + \dfrac{1}{\sqrt{n}}$

$$0.6 - 0.1 < p < 0.6 + 0.1$$
$$0.5 < p < 0.7$$
$$\text{or } 50\% < p < 70\%$$

Note: The confidence interval is very large here because the sample was small.
A sample of 100 has a margin of error of 10%.
A sample of 1000 has a margin of error of 3%.

3. Margin of error using the standard normal tables

If many samples of the same size are taken from a population, each sample will produce a different (but similar) proportion. All these proportions form their own distribution called the **sampling distribution of the proportion**.

The **standard error**, $\sigma_{\hat{p}}$, of this distribution is given on page 34 of *Formulae and Tables* and is shown on the right.

$$\sigma_{\hat{p}} = \sqrt{\dfrac{p(1-p)}{n}}$$

Since p, the population proportion, is generally not known,
$\hat{p}$, the sample proportion, is used as an **estimator** for the population proportion.

In this section we will use the Standard Normal Tables $\left(\text{rather than the margin of error, } \dfrac{1}{\sqrt{n}}\right)$ to get a more accurate confidence interval for a population proportion.

Since the 95% level of confidence will be used, the diagram on the right will remind us that 95% of a normal distribution lies within 1.96 standard deviations of the mean.

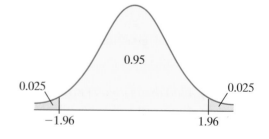

If $\hat{p}$ is the sample proportion and p is the population proportion, then the 95% confidence interval for p is given by

$$\hat{p} - 1.96\sqrt{\frac{p(1-p)}{n}} \leq p \leq \hat{p} + 1.96\sqrt{\frac{p(1-p)}{n}}$$

This can be written more concisely as $\hat{p} \pm 1.96\sqrt{\frac{p(1-p)}{n}}$.

The 95% confidence interval for a population proportion

$$\hat{p} \pm 1.96\sqrt{\frac{p(1-p)}{n}}$$

Note: An increase in confidence levels results in an increase in the interval width.

Example 4

In a survey carried out in a large city, 170 households out of a random sample of 250 owned at least one pet.
  (i) Find the standard error of the sampling distribution of the proportion at the 95% confidence level.
  (ii) Find the 95% confidence interval for the proportion of households in the city who own at least one pet.

(i) The sample proportion $\hat{p} = \dfrac{170}{250} = 0.68$

   Standard error $\sigma_{\hat{p}} = \sqrt{\dfrac{p(1-p)}{n}}$

   $\qquad = \sqrt{\dfrac{0.68(1-0.68)}{250}}$ ... using $\hat{p}$ as an estimate for p.

   $\qquad \sigma_{\hat{p}} = 0.029$

(ii) The 95% confidence interval is given by

   $\hat{p} \pm 1.96\sqrt{\dfrac{p(1-p)}{n}}$

   $= 0.68 \pm 1.96(0.029)$ ... from (i) above

   $= 0.68 \pm 0.0568$

   $= (0.6232, 0.7368)$ or about $(62\%, 74\%)$

Example 5

A random sample of 250 cars was surveyed passing a certain junction and 36 were found to have K registrations.

(i) Determine a 95% confidence interval for the proportion of cars in that area that have a K registration.

(ii) Nationally it is known that 14% of cars have a K registration.
What size of sample, n, needs to be taken so as to be 95% certain that an estimate of the proportion of K registrations is within 2% of the population proportion.

(i) The sample proportion $\hat{p} = \dfrac{36}{250} = 0.144$.

The 95% confidence interval is given by

$$\hat{p} \pm 1.96\sqrt{\dfrac{p(1-p)}{n}}$$

$$= 0.144 \pm 1.96\sqrt{\dfrac{0.144(1-0.144)}{250}} \ \dots \text{ using } \hat{p} \text{ as an estimate for } p.$$

$$= 0.144 \pm 1.96(0.0222)$$

$$= 0.144 \pm 0.0435 \ \dots \ (14.4\% \pm 4.35\%)$$

$$= 0.100, 0.1875$$

The 95% confidence interval is $(0.100, 0.1875)$.

(ii) Let n be the size of the sample. $\qquad p = 14\% = 0.14$

We require n such that $\hat{p} \pm 1.96\sqrt{\dfrac{p(1-p)}{n}} = \hat{p} \pm 0.02 \ \dots \ (0.02 = 2\%)$

$$\therefore \ 1.96\sqrt{\dfrac{0.14(1-0.14)}{n}} = 0.02$$

$$\dfrac{0.14(0.86)}{n} = \left(\dfrac{0.02}{1.96}\right)^2$$

$$0.14(0.86) \times \left(\dfrac{1.96}{0.02}\right)^2 = n = 1156.32$$

So a sample of 1157 would need to be taken.

Exercise 10.1

You may use the margin of error approximation in questions 1–8.

1. In a random sample of 500 cars, it was found that 150 of them were coloured silver.
   (i) Calculate the sample proportion, $\hat{p}$.
   (ii) At the 95% confidence level, calculate the margin of error, correct to two decimal places.
   (iii) Construct a 95% confidence interval for the proportion of all cars that are coloured silver.

2. In a random sample of 400 computer shops, it was discovered that 136 of them sold computers at below the list price recommended by the manufacturer.
   (i) Estimate the percentage of all computer shops selling below the list price.
   (ii) Construct an approximate 95% confidence interval for the proportion of shops selling below the list price.
      Briefly explain what this means.

3. The results of a survey showed that 3600 out of 10 000 families regularly purchased a specific weekly magazine.
   Construct a 95% confidence interval for the proportion of families buying the magazine.

4. A survey was undertaken to find the level of use of the internet by residents of a city. In a random sample of 150 residents, 45 said that they log on to the internet at least once a day.
   Construct a 95% confidence interval for p, the population proportion that log on to the internet once a day.

5. A college principal decides to consult the students about a proposed change in the times of lectures. She finds that, out of a random sample of 80 students, 57 of them are in favour of the change.
   Construct a 95% confidence interval for the proportion of students who are **not** in favour of the change.

6. At the 95% level of confidence, what sample size is required to have a margin of error of
   (i) 5%   (ii) 3%   (iii) 1.5%?

7. A survey was carried out in order to gauge the response to a new school "healthy eating" menu. A random sample of 200 schoolchildren was selected from different schools.
   It was found that 84 children approved of the new menu.
   Construct an approximate 95% confidence interval for the population proportion, p, who approve of the new menu.

8. A manufacturer wants to assess the proportion of defective items in a large batch produced by a particular machine. He tests a random sample of 300 items and finds that 45 items are defective.
   (i) Construct an approximate 95% confidence interval for the proportion of defective items in the batch.
   (ii) Explain what the 95% confidence interval means in the context of the question.
   (iii) If 200 such tests are performed and a 95% confidence interval constructed for each, how many would you expect to include the proportion of defective items in the batch?

In the following questions, you should use the standard error of proportion and the probabilities for the standard normal distribution (p34, 37 f&t tables) to find the margin of error.

9. A manufacturer wants to assess the proportion of defective items in a large batch produced by a particular machine.
   He tests a random sample of 300 items and finds that 45 are defective.
   Calculate a 95% confidence interval for the proportion of defective items in the complete batch.

10. In order to assess the probability of a successful outcome, an experiment is performed 200 times and the number of successful outcomes is found to be 72.
    Find a 95% confidence interval for p, the probability of a successful outcome.

11. A market researcher carries out a survey in order to determine the popularity of SUDZ washing powder in the Cork area.
    He visits every house in a large housing estate in Cork and asks the question:
    "Do you use SUDZ washing powder?"
    Of 235 people questioned, 75 answered "YES".
    Treating the sample as being random, calculate a 95% confidence interval for the proportion of households in the Cork area which use SUDZ.

12. An importer has ordered a large consignment of tomatoes.
    When it arrives, he examines a randomly chosen sample of 50 boxes and finds that 12 contain at least one bad tomato.
    Assuming that these boxes may be regarded as being a random sample from the boxes in the consignment, obtain an approximate 95% confidence interval for the proportion of boxes containing at least one bad tomato, giving your confidence limits correct to three decimal places.

13. If 400 persons, constituting a random sample, are given a flu vaccine and 136 of them experienced some discomfort, construct a 95% large-sample confidence interval for the corresponding true proportion.

14. A random sample of 120 library books is taken as they are borrowed.
    They are classified as fiction or non-fiction, and hardback or paperback.
    88 books are found to be fiction, and of these, 74 are paperback.
    Find a 95% confidence limit for:
    (i) the proportion of books borrowed that are fiction
    (ii) the proportion of fiction books borrowed that are paperback.

15. In a sample of 400 shops taken in 2012, it was discovered that 136 of them sold carpets at below the list prices which had been recommended by manufacturers.
    (i)   Estimate the percentage of all carpet-selling shops selling below list price.
    (ii) Calculate the 95% confidence limits for this estimate, and explain briefly what these mean.
    (iii) Nationally it is known that 34% of shops sold carpets at below list prices, what size sample would have to be taken locally in order to estimate the percentage to within 2% of the population proportion.

16. In a random sample of 1,200 voters interviewed nationwide, only 324 felt that the salaries of certain government officials should be raised.
    Construct a 95% confidence interval of the corresponding true proportion.

17. In a market research survey, 15 people out of a random sample of 100 from a certain area said that they used a particular brand of soap.
   (i) Calculate a 95% confidence interval for the proportion of people who use this brand of soap.
   (ii) What size of sample would need to be taken in order to estimate the percentage to within ±1.5%, given that the population proportion who used the brand was 14%? Give your answer correct to the nearest 10.

Section 10.2 Hypothesis testing for population proportion

A **hypothesis** is a statement or conjecture made about some statistic or characteristic of a population.

Here is an example of a hypothesis:

'A football team is most likely to concede a goal just after it has scored a goal'.

A **hypothesis test** is a statistical method of proving the truth or otherwise of the statement or claim.

A local council reduced the speed limit on a dangerous 8 km stretch of country road from 80 km/hr to 60 km/hr. The number of accidents on the stretch was reduced from 5 per month to 3 per month. The council claimed that the speed reduction was effective. Is the council correct in its claim?

In cases like this, a hypothesis test is set up to prove or disprove the claim.

Procedure for carrying out a hypothesis test on a population proportion

The procedure for carrying out a hypothesis test will involve the following steps:

1. Write down H_0, the **null hypothesis**, and H_1, the **alternative hypothesis**
   For example, to test if a coin is biased if we get 7 heads in 10 tosses, we could formulate the following hypothesis:
   H_0: The coin is not biased.
   H_1: The coin is biased.

2. Write down or calculate the sample proportion, $\hat{p}$.

3. Find the margin of error, E
   From Section 10.1, we note that there are two methods for calculating the margin of error:
   (i) $E = \dfrac{1}{\sqrt{n}}$
   (ii) $E = 1.96\sqrt{\dfrac{p(1-p)}{n}}$

   Unless you are asked to use method (i), the margin of error approximation, you should use the more accurate second version.

4. Write down the confidence interval for p, using

$$\hat{p} - E < p < \hat{p} + E$$

5. (i) If the value of the population proportion stated is within the confidence interval, **do not reject** the null hypothesis H_0.
    (ii) If the value of the population proportion stated is outside the confidence interval, **reject** the null hypothesis H_0 and accept H_1 (the alternative hypothesis).

Level of significance

If the population proportion, p, does not lie in the 95% confidence interval, it is said to be significant at the **5% level of significance**.

Example 1

A drugs company produced a new pain-relieving drug for migraine sufferers and claimed that the drug had a 90% success rate. A group of doctors doubted the company's claim. They prescribed the drug for a group of 150 patients. After six months, 120 of these patients said that their migraine symptoms had been relieved by the drug.
At the 5% level of significance, can the company's claim be upheld?

1. State H_0 and H_1.
    H_0: The success rate of the drug is 90%, i.e. $p = 0.9$.
    H_1: The success rate of the drug is not 90%, i.e. $p \neq 0.9$.

2. Sample proportion $\hat{p} = \dfrac{120}{150} = 0.8$

3. Margin of error $= E = 1.96\sqrt{\dfrac{(0.8)(0.2)}{150}} = 0.064$

4. Confidence interval: $\hat{p} - E < p < \hat{p} + E$
    $$0.8 - 0.064 < p < 0.8 + 0.064$$
    $$0.736 < p < 0.864$$
    $$73.6\% < p < 86.4\%$$

5. The stated population proportion, $p = 0.9(90\%)$, is not within the confidence interval.
    So we reject the null hypothesis, H_0, and accept the alternative hypothesis, H_1.
    We conclude that the success rate of the drug is not 90%.

Example 2

A coin is tossed 1000 times and heads occur 520 times.
At the 95% confidence level, does the result indicate that the coin is biased?

1. H_0: The coin is not biased
   H_1: The coin is biased

2. Sample proportion, $\hat{p} = \dfrac{520}{1000} = 0.52$

3. Margin of error, $E, = 1.96\sqrt{\dfrac{p(1-p)}{n}} = 1.96\sqrt{\dfrac{(0.5)(0.5)}{1000}} \quad \ldots (p = 0.5)$

   $= 0.03$

4. Confidence interval: $\hat{p} - E < p < \hat{p} + E$
   $\Rightarrow \quad 0.52 - 0.03 < p < 0.52 + 0.03$
   $0.49 < p < 0.55$

5. Since $P(\text{head}) = 0.5$, the population proportion $= 0.5$.
   The population proportion 0.5 is within the confidence interval found.
   We do not reject the null hypothesis, H_0, and state that the coin is not biased.

Exercise 10.2

1. In a public opinion poll, 1000 randomly-chosen electors were asked whether they would vote for the *Purple Party* at the next election and 357 replied "Yes".
   The leader of the *Purple Party* believes that the true proportion is 0.4.
   At the 5% level of significance, is the leader's belief justified?

2. A large college claims that it admits equal numbers of men and women. A random sample of 500 students gave 267 men. At the 5% level of significance, is there evidence to suggest that the college is not evenly divided between men and women?

3. A die was rolled 240 times and 52 sixes were recorded.
   (i) Write down the sample proportion, $\hat{p}$.
   (ii) What is the margin of error?
   (iii) If the dice is fair, write down the probability of throwing a 6.
   (iv) At the 95% confidence level, test the hypothesis that the dice is fair.

4. A survey in a university library revealed that 12% of returned books were overdue. After an increase in fines, a random sample of 200 returned books revealed that only 15 were overdue. The university claimed that the proportion of overdue books had changed. At the 5% level of significance, is the university's claim justified?

5. A seed company sells pansy seeds in mixed packets and claims that 20% of the resulting plants will have red flowers. A packet of seeds is sown by a gardener who finds that only 11 out of 82 plants have red flowers.
   Test the company's claim at the 95% confidence level.

6. The 'Daily Mensa' claims that at least 60% of its readers have third level degrees.
   In a random sample of 312 readers, there were 208 with third level degrees.
   At the 5% level of significance, is the paper's claim justified?

7. A coin is tossed 500 times and heads appears 267 times.
   (i) Find a 95% confidence interval for p, the population proportion of heads.
   (ii) Based on the sample above test the null hypothesis, H_0, that the coin is biased.

8. A survey proportion of 36% was obtained from a sample of size n.
   At the 95% confidence level find the value of n so that
   the margin of error is (i) 2%.   (ii) 3%

Section 10.3 Sampling distribution of the mean – The central limit theorem

The sampling distribution of the mean

If we are interested in the weights, for example, of all sixteen-year-olds in Ireland, we generally require the mean and standard deviations of these weights. We use the symbols

(i) μ to denote the **population mean**
(ii) σ to denote the **population standard deviation**.

In such a large population it would be impossible to obtain the weight of each person and so the values of μ and σ will not be known. However, if we take a random sample of this population, we can get approximate values for μ and σ. Obviously, the larger the sample, the more accurate we would expect the approximations to be.

If we take a large number of different random samples of size n, each sample will have its own mean, $\bar{x}$, and standard deviation, s.
Some of these samples are illustrated on the right.

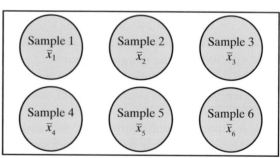

The different means of these samples are called the **sample means**.

If a large number of samples of the same size are taken, you get a correspondingly large number of means.
These means form their own distribution giving us the **distribution of sample means**.
This distribution is also called **the sampling distribution of the mean**.

The following example illustrates the shape a distribution of sample means might take when different samples (of the same size) from a population are selected.

Example 1

A population consists of five digits 2, 4, 6, 8, 10.

(i) Write down all the possible samples of 2 different digits that can occur if random samples are taken.

(ii) Find the mean of each sample and plot the distribution of the sample means.

(iii) Compare the value of the mean of the sample means with the value of the population mean.

(i) The possible samples are:

(2, 4), (2, 6), (2, 8), (2, 10), (4, 6), (4, 8), (4, 10), (6, 8), (6, 10), (8, 10)

(ii) Their means are: 3, 4, 5, 6, 5, 6, 7, 7, 8, 9

The distribution of the sample means is plotted below.

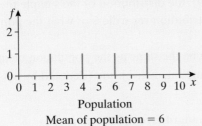

Population
Mean of population = 6

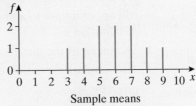

Sample means
Mean of sample means = $\frac{60}{10}$ = 6

(iii) The mean of the population is 6.

The mean of the sample means is also 6.

Thus the mean of the sample means and the population mean are equal.

If you examine the distribution of the sample means plotted on the right in the worked example above, you will notice that it begins to approximate to a normal distribution. In this case the sample size was only 2.

However, as the sample size n increases the closer the distribution will approximate to a normal distribution. Also the mean of the sampling distribution will be the same as the mean of the population.

The successive diagrams below illustrate the **shape** of the **sampling distribution of means** resulting from different-sized samples from a given population with a normal distribution.

Distribution when $n = 2, 5$ and 25.

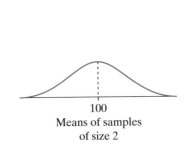

100
Means of samples
of size 2

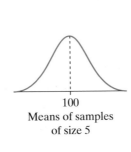

100
Means of samples
of size 5

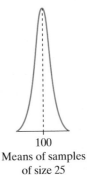

100
Means of samples
of size 25

From the diagrams, you can see that if samples are taken from a normal population, the sampling distribution of means is normal for any sample size.

As n increases, the curve representing the sampling distribution of the mean gets taller and narrower. These diagrams also show how the standard deviation decreases as n increases. The sample means will be packed tightly around the population mean. The larger the samples become, the tighter the means will be packed.

From the worked example and from the three diagrams shown above, we can see that when samples are taken from a population, the sampling distribution of the mean takes on the characteristics of a normal curve as the sample size increases. This observation leads us to one of the most important theorems in statistics that is widely used in sampling. It is called the **Central Limit Theorem** and is stated more formally below.

The Central Limit Theorem

If a random sample of size n with mean $\bar{x}$ is taken from a population with mean μ and standard deviation σ, then

> If the sample size is large ($n \geqslant 30$), the distribution of the sample means will approximate to a normal distribution regardless of what the population distribution is.

> The mean of the distribution will be the same as the population mean μ.

> The standard deviation of the sampling distribution (denoted by $\sigma_{\bar{x}}$) is given by $\dfrac{\sigma}{\sqrt{n}}$.

$\left[\dfrac{\sigma}{\sqrt{n}} \text{ is often referred to as the } \textbf{standard error of the mean.} \right]$

As n increases, the standard error gets smaller.

> If the underlying population is normal, the sampling distribution of the mean will always have a normal distribution even if the sample size is small (<30).

The diagram on the right illustrates how the distribution of the sample mean approximates to a normal distribution even when the underlying population is skewed.

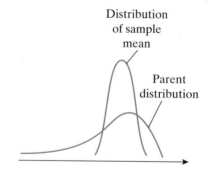

Distribution of sample mean

Parent distribution

When dealing with the sampling distribution of the mean, we convert the given units to standard units using the formula given on the right.

$$z = \frac{\bar{x} - \mu}{\sigma_{\bar{x}}} = \frac{\bar{x} - \mu}{\dfrac{\sigma}{\sqrt{n}}}$$

Example 2

A random sample of 250 is selected from a population having mean 30 and standard deviation 5.
Find the probability that the sample mean is greater than 30.5.

Since $n = 250$, the sample mean is normally distributed since $n \geqslant 30$.
Changing to standard units we get:

$$z = \frac{\bar{x} - \mu}{\frac{\sigma}{\sqrt{n}}} = \frac{30.5 - 30}{\frac{5}{\sqrt{250}}} = \frac{0.5}{0.3162} = 1.581$$

$$z = 1.581$$

Now
$$\begin{aligned} P(\bar{x} > 30.5) &= P(Z > 1.581) \\ &= 1 - P(Z \leqslant 1.581) \\ &= 1 - 0.9429 \\ &= 0.0571 \end{aligned}$$

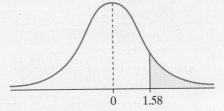

The probability that the mean is greater than 30.5 is 0.0571.

Example 3

A normal distribution has a mean of 40 and a standard deviation of 4.
If 25 items are drawn at random, find the probability that their mean lies between 38 and 40.5.

Converting the given units to standard units we get:

$$z = \frac{\bar{x} - \mu}{\frac{\sigma}{\sqrt{n}}}$$

For $\bar{x} = 38$, $\quad z = \dfrac{38 - 40}{\frac{4}{\sqrt{25}}} = \dfrac{-2}{0.8} = -2.5$

For $\bar{x} = 40.5$, $\quad z = \dfrac{40.5 - 40}{\frac{4}{\sqrt{25}}} = \dfrac{0.5}{0.8} = 0.625$

$$\begin{aligned} P(38 < \bar{x} < 40.5) &= P(-2.5 < Z < 0.625) \\ &= P(Z < 0.625) - P(Z < -2.5) \\ &= P(Z \leqslant 0.625) - [1 - P(Z \leqslant 2.5)] \\ &= 0.7324 - [1 - 0.99379] \\ &= 0.7324 - [0.00621] \\ &= 0.7262 \end{aligned}$$

$\Rightarrow P(\text{mean lies between 38 and 40.5}) = 0.7262.$

Example 4

A population is normally distributed with mean 12 and standard deviation 3.
Find the sample size such that $P(\bar{x} > 12.5) = 0.05$, where $\bar{x}$ is the sample mean.

$$P(Z > z_1) = 0.05$$
$$\Rightarrow P(Z \leqslant z_1) = 0.95$$
$$\Rightarrow z_1 = 1.645$$

$$z_1 = \frac{\bar{x} - \mu}{\frac{\sigma}{\sqrt{n}}} \Rightarrow 1.645 = \frac{12.5 - 12}{\frac{3}{\sqrt{n}}}$$

$$\Rightarrow 1.645 = \frac{\sqrt{n}(12.5 - 12)}{3}$$

$$\Rightarrow \sqrt{n} = \frac{(1.645)3}{0.5}$$

$$\Rightarrow n = 97.42 \quad \text{i.e. } 98 \quad \text{... round up}$$

The required sample size is 98.

Example 5

A company installs new machines for packing peanuts.
The company claims that the machines fill packets with a mean mass of 500 g and
a standard deviation of 18 g.
To test the company's claim several samples of size 40 packets are taken and their
mean masses, $\bar{x}$ grams, are recorded.

(i) Describe the sampling distribution of $\bar{x}$ and explain your answer, referring to
the theorem you have used.

(ii) Write down the mean and standard deviation of the distribution of $\bar{x}$.

(iii) Draw a rough sketch of the sampling distribution of $\bar{x}$.

(iv) Find the probability that the mean of the distribution of $\bar{x}$ is less than 496.

(v) What sample size n is required so that $P(\bar{x} > 503) = 0.06$?

(i) The sampling distribution of $\bar{x}$ is approximately normal as the sample size of
40 is sufficiently large (i.e. $\geqslant 30$) to apply **The Central Limit Theorem**.

(ii) The mean of the distribution of the sample means is 500 g, the same as the
population mean.

The standard deviation (or standard error) is $\dfrac{\sigma}{\sqrt{n}} = \dfrac{18}{\sqrt{40}} = 2.846$

$$= 2.85$$

(iii) A sketch of the distribution of $\bar{x}$ is shown below.

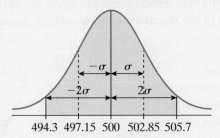

$$\mu = 500$$
$$\sigma = 2.85$$

494.3 497.15 500 502.85 505.7

(iv) Converting the given units to z-scores, we use $z = \dfrac{\bar{x} - \mu}{\dfrac{\sigma}{\sqrt{n}}}$.

For $\bar{x} = 496$, $z = \dfrac{496 - 500}{\dfrac{18}{\sqrt{40}}} = \dfrac{-4}{2.846} = -1.405$

$$
\begin{aligned}
P(\bar{x} < 496) &= P(Z < -1.405) \\
&= 1 - P(Z \leqslant 1.405) \\
&= 1 - 0.9265 \\
&= 0.0735
\end{aligned}
$$

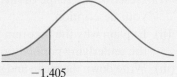

-1.405

The probability that $\bar{x} < 496 = 0.0735$ or 7.35%.

(v) $P(Z > z_1) = 0.06$
$P(Z \leqslant z_1) = 1 - 0.06 = 0.94$
$\Rightarrow z_1 = 1.56$

$$z_1 = \dfrac{\bar{x} - \mu}{\dfrac{\sigma}{\sqrt{n}}} \Rightarrow 1.56 = \dfrac{503 - 500}{\dfrac{18}{\sqrt{n}}} = \dfrac{3\sqrt{n}}{18} = \dfrac{\sqrt{n}}{6}$$

$\Rightarrow 1.56 = \dfrac{\sqrt{n}}{6}$

$\Rightarrow \sqrt{n} = 6(1.56) = 9.36$

$\Rightarrow n = (9.36)^2$

$\Rightarrow n = 87.6 = 88$ ... round up

The sample size required is 88.

Exercise 10.3

1. Fill in the correct word or symbol to complete the following statements:

   (i) When a large number of samples of size n are taken from a population, then the distribution of $\bar{x}$, the sample mean, is known as the _____ _____ of the mean.

   (ii) As the sample size increases, the standard deviation of the sampling distribution of the sample means will _____.

(iii) If the mean of the underlying population is μ, the mean of the sampling distribution of the means is _____.

(iv) If the standard deviation of a population is σ and samples of size n are taken from it, then the standard deviation of the distribution of the sample means is

_____.

2. The diagram on the right shows two curves. One of these curves represents a distribution and the other represents the distribution of the sample means of size n taken from this distribution. Which curve represents the distribution of the sample means?

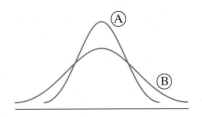

3. Samples of size 36 are taken from a population with mean 12 and standard deviation 2. The sampling distribution of the means are plotted in a curve.

   (i) Describe the shape of this curve naming the theorem you have used to support your description.
   (ii) Explain why the theorem you have mentioned can be applied when the shape of the underlying population is unknown.
   (iii) Write down the mean and standard deviation of the sampling distribution of the mean.

4. A population consists of the elements {4, 6, 8, 10}.

   (i) Write down all possible samples of size 2 (chosen without replacement) from this population.
   (ii) Give the sample mean, $\bar{x}$, for each pair.
   (iii) Show that the mean of all possible samples of size 2 equals the mean of the population.

5. The diagram on the right shows two curves Ⓐ and Ⓑ. Diagram Ⓐ represents the distribution of a population and diagram Ⓑ represents the distribution of the means from a large number of samples of size 40.

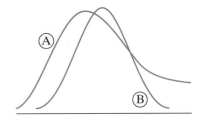

   (i) Is distribution Ⓐ skewed positively or negatively?
   (ii) Describe distribution Ⓑ.
   (iii) Explain why the *Central Limit Theorem* can be used to describe distribution Ⓑ even though the underlying population is not normally distributed.

6. A random sample of size 36 is chosen from a population with a mean of 12 and a standard deviation of 3.
   Find the probability that the sample mean is greater than 13.

7. A random sample of size 15 is taken from a normal distribution with mean 60 and standard deviation 4.
   Find the probability that the mean of the sample is less than 58.

8. Men have a mean height of 176 cm with standard deviation 11 cm.
Find the probability that the mean of a random sample of 80 men
(i) exceeds 177 cm (ii) is less than 174.8 cm.

9. At a certain college, students spend on average 4.2 hours per week at a computer terminal, with a standard deviation of 1.8 hours.
   (i) Find the standard error for a random sample of 36 students.
   (ii) Find the probability that the average time spent using a computer terminal is
       (a) greater than 4.8 hours
       (b) between 4.1 and 4.5 hours.

10. The sugar content per litre bottle of a soft drink is known to be distributed with mean 5.8 and standard deviation 1.2. A sample of 900 bottles is taken at random and the sugar content of each bottle is measured.
Estimate to 3 decimal places the probability that the mean sugar content of the 900 bottles will be less than 5.85.

11. A firm produces alternators for cars. The alternators are known to have a mean lifetime of 8 years with standard deviation 6 months.
Forty samples of 144 alternators produced by the firm are tested.
Estimate the number of samples which would be expected to have a mean lifetime of more than 8 years and 1 month.

12. A random sample of size 10 is taken from a normal distribution with mean 200 and standard deviation 10.
Find the probability that the sample mean lies outside the range 198 to 205.

13. In the given diagram, curve Ⓐ represents a normal distribution.
Curve Ⓑ represents the sampling distribution of means taken from samples of size 36.
The distribution represented by Ⓐ has mean $\mu = 80$ and standard deviation $\sigma = 8$.
The point C represents the mean of both distributions.
The point D represents the value of the variable that is two standard deviations from C in distribution Ⓐ.
The point E represents the value of the variable that is one standard error from C in distribution Ⓑ.
Write down the values of C, D and E.

14. A normal distribution has mean 75 and standard deviation 9.
A sample of size n is selected at random and the mean of this sample is $\bar{x}$.
Find n if $P(\bar{x} > 73) = 0.8708$.

15. A normal distribution has a mean of 30 and a standard deviation of $\sqrt{5}$.

   (i) Find the probability that the mean of a random sample of 40 exceeds 30.5.

   (ii) Find the value of n such that the probability that the mean of a sample of size n exceeds 30.4 is less than 0.01.

16. Free-range eggs supplied by a health food cooperative have a mean weight of 52 g with a standard deviation of 4 g.
   Assuming the weights are normally distributed find the probability that:

   (i) a randomly selected egg will weigh more than 60 g

   (ii) the mean weight of five randomly selected eggs will be between 50 g and 55 g

   (iii) the mean weight of 90 randomly selected eggs will be between 52.1 g and 52.2 g.

   Which of your answers would be unchanged if the weights are not normally distributed?

Section 10.4 Confidence interval for a population mean

In Section 10.3, the Central Limit Theorem was used to show that the sampling distribution of the mean approximates to a normal distribution for large n ($n \geqslant 30$). In this section we introduce a different way of presenting information provided by a sample mean to estimate the mean of the population from which the sample came.

If samples of size n are taken from a population, the means of the samples will vary.
To accommodate this variety, we introduce (as before for proportions) the concept of a **confidence interval** for the mean.
The endpoints of this interval are called **confidence limits**.
The **degree of confidence** is generally given as a percentage.
These percentages are generally 90%, 95% and 99%.

Note: As the confidence level increases 90%–95%–99% the **confidence interval widens**.

In the standard normal distribution, we require the values of z_1 such that 95% of the population lies in the interval $-z_1 \leqslant Z \leqslant z_1$.
The work involved in finding the value of z_1, is shown below.
We use the standard normal tables on pages 36 and 37 of *Formulae and Tables*.

From the given diagram,

$$P(Z \leqslant z_1) = 0.95 + 0.025$$
$$= 0.975$$

From the tables

$$z_1 = 1.96$$
$$\Rightarrow -z_1 = -1.96$$

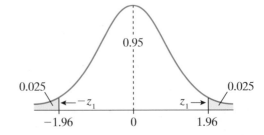

Thus in the normal distribution, 95% of the population lies within 1.96 standard deviations of the mean.

If μ is the population mean, then 95% of the sample means lie in the interval

$$\bar{x} - 1.96\sigma_{\bar{x}} < \mu < \bar{x} + 1.96\sigma_{\bar{x}}, \text{ where } \sigma_{\bar{x}} \text{ is the standard error of the mean.}$$

and $\sigma_{\bar{x}} = \dfrac{\sigma}{\sqrt{n}}$, σ being the standard deviation of the population.

$$\sigma_{\bar{x}} = \frac{\sigma}{\sqrt{n}}$$

This can be written as $\bar{x} \pm 1.96\dfrac{\sigma}{\sqrt{n}}$, which are the end-points (or confidence limits) of the mean.

Confidence Interval for Mean

If $\bar{x}$ is the mean of a random sample of size n taken from a population with a distribution with known standard deviation σ, then the end-points of the 95% confidence interval for μ, the population mean, are given by

$$\bar{x} \pm 1.96\frac{\sigma}{\sqrt{n}}$$

Note: If σ, the standard deviation of the population, is not given, use the standard deviation, s, of the sample as an approximation.

Example 1

A random sample of 400 oranges was taken from a large consignment with unknown mean μ and standard deviation 15 grams.
The mean weight of the random sample was 81.4 grams.

Find a 95% confidence interval for the mean weight of the oranges in the consignment.

The 95% confidence interval for μ is $\bar{x} \pm 1.96\dfrac{\sigma}{\sqrt{n}}$.

$$\bar{x} \pm 1.96\frac{\sigma}{\sqrt{n}} = 81.4 \pm 1.96\left(\frac{15}{\sqrt{400}}\right) \quad \dots \sigma = 15 \text{ and } n = 400$$

$$= 81.4 \pm 1.96(0.75)$$

$$= 81.4 \pm 1.47$$

$$= 79.93, 82.87$$

$$\Rightarrow 79.93 < \mu < 82.87$$

The mean of the consignment lies between 79.93 g and 82.87 g.

Example 2

A certain type of tennis ball is known to have a height of bounce which is normally distributed with standard deviation 2 cm.

A sample of 60 such tennis balls is tested and the mean height of the bounce of the sample is 140 cm.

  (i) Find a 95% confidence interval for the mean height of the bounce of this type of tennis ball.

 (ii) Explain what is meant by a "95% confidence interval".

  (i) The 95% confidence interval is given by

$$\bar{x} \pm 1.96 \frac{\sigma}{\sqrt{n}}$$

$$= 140 \pm 1.96 \left(\frac{2}{\sqrt{60}}\right)$$

$$= 140 \pm 1.96(0.258)$$

$$= 140 \pm 0.506$$

$$= 140.506 \text{ cm}, 139.494 \text{ cm}$$

The 95% confidence interval is $140.506 \text{ cm} < \mu < 139.494 \text{ cm}$.

 (ii) A "95% confidence interval", means that on 95 occasions out of 100 the interval will contain the true population mean.

Example 3

The heights of people have a standard deviation of 11.5 cm.

It is required to estimate the mean height of people, with 95% confidence, to within ±0.4 cm.

What sample size should be taken in order to achieve this estimate?

Let μ be the mean height of people.

The 95% confidence limits for μ are $\bar{x} \pm 1.96 \frac{\sigma}{\sqrt{n}}$.

$$\Rightarrow \pm 1.96 \frac{\sigma}{\sqrt{n}} = \pm 0.4 \dots \text{ standard error is } \pm 0.4 \text{ cm}$$

$$\Rightarrow 1.96 \left(\frac{11.5}{\sqrt{n}}\right) = 0.4$$

$$\Rightarrow \sqrt{n} = \frac{11.5(1.96)}{0.4}$$

$$\Rightarrow \sqrt{n} = 56.35$$

$$\Rightarrow n = (56.35)^2 = 3175.3$$

Therefore, a sample of at least 3176 should be taken.

> **Example 4**
>
> On the basis of the results obtained from a random sample of 100 men from a particular district, the 95% confidence interval for the mean height of the men in the district is found to be (177.22 cm, 179.18 cm).
> Find the value of $\bar{x}$, the mean of the sample, and σ, the standard deviation of the normal population from which the sample is drawn.
>
> The 95% confidence interval is given by
>
> $$\bar{x} \pm 1.96 \frac{\sigma}{\sqrt{n}} = (177.22, 179.18)$$
>
> $$\Rightarrow \bar{x} + 1.96 \frac{\sigma}{10} = 179.18 \ldots \text{①}$$
>
> $$\text{and} \quad \bar{x} - 1.96 \frac{\sigma}{10} = 177.22 \ldots \text{②}$$
>
> Adding ① and ②: $\quad 2\bar{x} = 356.4$
> $$\bar{x} = 178.2$$
>
> Subtracting ① and ②:
>
> $$2(1.96) \frac{\sigma}{10} = 1.96$$
>
> $$\frac{2\sigma}{10} = 1 \Rightarrow \sigma = 5$$
>
> The sample mean $\bar{x} = 178.2$ cm.
> The population standard deviation is 5 cm.

Exercise 10.4

1. A population has mean μ and standard deviation 12.
   A random sample of 800 from this population has mean 63.
   Find a 95% confidence interval for μ.

2. The weights of dairy cows are known to have a standard deviation of 42 kg.
   A random sample of 280 dairy cows has a mean weight of 284 kg.
   Find a 95% confidence limit for the mean weight of all the cows.

3. Seventy packs of butter, selected at random from a large batch delivered to a supermarket, are weighed. The mean weight is found to be 227 g and the standard deviation is found to be 7.5 g.
   (i) Calculate a 95% confidence interval for the mean weight of all packs in the batch.
   (ii) If one pack is selected at random from the seventy packs, find the probability that its weight is not in the given interval.

4. In a random sample of 100 students taking a state examination, it was found that the mean mark was 62.7 with a standard deviation of 9.2 marks.
   Find the 95% confidence limits for the mean score of all the students who took the examination.

5. The weight of vitamin E in a capsule manufactured by a drug company is normally distributed with standard deviation 0.04 mg.
   A random sample of 12 capsules was analysed and the mean weight of vitamin E was found to be 5.12 mg.
   (i) Calculate a 95% confidence interval for the population mean weight of vitamin E per capsule.
   (ii) Give the values of the end-points of the interval, correct to three significant figures.
   (iii) Explain what is meant by "95% confidence"?

6. A bank selected a random sample of 400 customers and found that they had a mean credit of €280 with a standard deviation of €105 in their accounts.
   Calculate a 95% confidence interval for the mean credit of all the bank's customers.

7. Shoe shop staff routinely measure the lengths of their customers' feet. Measurements of the length of one foot (without shoes) from each of 180 adult male customers yielded a mean length of 29.2 cm and a standard deviation of 1.47 cm.
   (i) Calculate a 95% confidence interval for the mean length of male feet.
   (ii) Why was it not necessary to assume that the lengths of feet are normally distributed in order to calculate the confidence interval in (i) above?

8. A random sample of 64 sweets is selected from a large batch.
   The sweets are found to have a mean weight of 0.932 grams and a standard deviation of 0.1 grams.
   (i) Calculate the standard error of the mean.
   (ii) What is the best estimate for μ, the mean of the large batch?
   (iii) Construct a 95% confidence interval for μ.
   (iv) What would happen if a sample size of 100 was selected rather than a sample of 64?
   (v) What conclusion can you draw from your result in part (iv)?

9. A random sample of 240 cars had a mean age of 4.6 years with a standard deviation of 2.5 years.
   (i) Give a 95% confidence interval for the mean age of all cars.
   (ii) What size of sample would be needed to estimate the mean age, with 95% confidence, to within ±0.2 years?

10. 150 boxes of cereal of a certain brand are weighed and the mean weight is 748 grams with standard deviation 3.6 grams.
    (i) Find a 95% confidence interval for the mean weight of all boxes of cereal of that brand.
    (ii) What size of sample would be needed to estimate the mean weight, with 95% confidence, to within ±1.5 grams?

11. Eighty people were asked to measure their pulse rates when they woke up in the morning. The mean was 69 beats per minute and the standard deviation 4 beats.
    (i) Find a 95% confidence interval for the population mean.
    (ii) What size of sample would be needed to estimate the mean number of beats, with 95% confidence, to within ±1.5 beats?

12. The weights of pebbles on a beach are distributed with mean 48.6 g and standard deviation 8.5 g.

A random sample of 50 pebbles is chosen.
   (i) Find the probability that the mean weight will be less than 49 g.
   (ii) Find the limits within which the central 95% of such sample means would lie.
   (iii) How large a sample would be needed in order that the central 95% of sample means would lie in an interval of width at most 4 g?

13. The 95% confidence interval for the mean mark of a group of students is (54.09, 60.71). This interval is based on the results from a random sample of 80 students.
   (i) Find $\bar{x}$, the mean of the sample.
   (ii) Find σ, the standard deviation of the normal population from which the sample is taken.

Section 10.5 Hypothesis testing for a population mean

Hypothesis testing

In Sections 10.1 and 10.4 we dealt with confidence intervals, one of the two most common types of statistical inference.

As we have seen in Section 10.2 the second type of statistical inference is **hypothesis testing**.

The procedure for performing a hypothesis test on a population mean (μ) is similar to the procedure for performing a hypothesis test on a population proportion (p) (Section 10.2).

It has already been shown that in any normal distribution 95% of the population lies within 1.96 standard deviations of the mean, that is, 95% of the population will be in the interval $\mu \pm 1.96\sigma$.

If we are dealing with a normal distribution and an experiment produces a result which is outside the interval $\mu \pm 1.96\sigma$, we would be inclined to suspect that factors other than chance are involved in the result.

To test the result we start with the assumption, or hypothesis, that the result is not biased. This assumption is called the **null hypothesis**, denoted by **H_0**.
Usually the null hypothesis is a statement of "**no** difference", "**no** effect" or "**no** change".
An hypothesis test is then carried out to **reject** or **not reject** the null hypothesis.
In this test, we speak of rejecting the null hypothesis 'at a certain level'.
This 'certain level' is called the **level of significance**.
The 5% level of significance creates a 95% confidence interval.
The 5% level of significance means that the result obtained is likely to occur on only 5 occasions out of 100.

At the 5% level of significance, the set of values, $z > 1.96$ or $z < -1.96$, is known as the **critical region** and the boundaries of the critical region are called the **critical values**.

If the values of z are in the critical region (i.e. $z > 1.96$ or $z < -1.96$), we reject the null hypothesis and conclude that factors other than chance are involved.

The critical regions at the 5% level of significance are shown below.

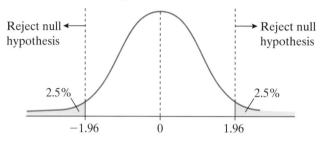

Hypothesis Testing

At the 5% level of significance, the null hypothesis is rejected if

$$z < -1.96 \quad \text{or} \quad z > 1.96$$

Hypothesis testing for a population mean

When a population is very large, it is generally not practical to find the true mean and standard deviation of the total population. However, assumptions are often made about these values and their validity is tested based on observations made from random samples taken from the population.

Take, for example, machines designed to produce batteries which last for 120 hours with a standard deviation 4 hours. What conclusions can we come to about one of these machines if a random sample of 50 batteries produced by it had a mean life of 121 hours?

We now begin the process of investigating whether these machines are producing the type of battery they were designed to produce. This process is called hypothesis testing.

Here are the basic steps of a hypothesis test:

1. Write down H_0, the **null hypothesis**, and H_1, the **alternative hypothesis**.

   H_0: The mean life of a battery is 120 hours.
   H_1: The mean life of a battery is **not** 120 hours.

2. State the **significance level, α**.
   The significance level on our course is 5% ($\alpha = 0.05$).
   This means that if $z < -1.96$ or $z > 1.96$, we **reject** the null hypothesis and **accept** the alternative hypothesis.

3. Calculate the value of the **test statistic**.
   This involves converting the given units to z-units.

To convert the given units to standard units we use

$$z = \frac{\bar{x} - \mu}{\frac{\sigma}{\sqrt{n}}}, \text{ where}$$

$\bar{x}$ = the sample mean
μ = population mean
σ = population standard deviation
n = size of sample

For the machine mentioned above,

$$z = \frac{\bar{x} - \mu}{\frac{\sigma}{\sqrt{n}}} = \frac{121 - 120}{\frac{4}{\sqrt{50}}} = \frac{1}{0.566} = 1.767$$

The test statistic is $z = 1.767$.

4. Come to a **conclusion**.
   Since $z = 1.767$ does not lie outside the range $-1.96 < z < 1.96$ it is **not** in the **critical region**. So we do **not reject** the null hypothesis and states that the mean life of a battery is 120 hours.

Note: If σ, the standard deviation of the population is not given, use s the standard deviation of the sample instead.

Example 1

Over the years, a market gardener found that the mean yield from his tomato plants was 1.83 kg per plant with a standard deviation of 0.35 kg per plant. One year he planted 600 of a new variety and these yielded 1.87 kg per plant. At the 5% level of significance, test whether the mean yield from the new plants is different from his normal variety.

1. H_0: The mean μ is 1.83.
   H_1: The mean μ is **not** 1.83.

2. The level of significance is 5%.
   The critical region is $z < -1.96$ or $z > 1.96$.

3. Calculate the test statistic by converting to standard units.

$$z = \frac{\bar{x} - \mu}{\frac{\sigma}{\sqrt{n}}} \ldots \qquad \begin{array}{ll} \bar{x} = 1.87 & \mu = 1.83 \\ n = 600 & \sigma = 0.35 \end{array}$$

$$= \frac{1.87 - 1.83}{\left(\frac{0.35}{\sqrt{600}}\right)} = \frac{0.04}{0.0143} = 2.797$$

$$z = 2.797$$

4. Since $z = 2.797$ and $2.797 > 1.96$, we reject the null hypothesis and conclude that the new variety is different from the normal variety.

Using p-values

Suppose we carry out an hypothesis test and find the test statistic to be $z = 2.16$.
Since 2.16 is greater than 1.96, we reject the null hypothesis at the 5% level of significance
($\alpha = 0.05$).

Instead of comparing $z = 2.16$ with $z = 1.96$ (and $z = -1.96$), we could compare the total
area of the two coloured regions below with the specific level of significance, $\alpha = 0.05$.

We use pages 36 and 37 of *Formulae and Tables* to find the probability that $z \leqslant -2.16$ or $z \geqslant 2.16$.

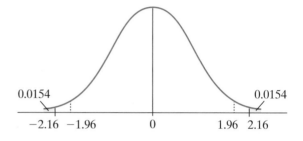

$$P(Z \leqslant -2.16) + P(Z \geqslant 2.16)$$
$$= 2P(Z \geqslant 2.16)$$
$$= 2[1 - P(Z \leqslant 2.16)]$$
$$= 2[1 - 0.9846]$$
$$= 2[0.0154]$$
$$= 0.0308$$

The shaded areas above are referred to as the **p-value**, or probability-value corresponding to
the observed value of the test statistic.
The value 0.0308 found above is the *p*-value that corresponds to the test statistic $z = 2.16$.
The *p*-value 0.0308 is interpreted as the **lowest level of significance** at which the null
hypothesis could have been rejected.

With a test statistic of $z = 2.16$ (*p*-value = 0.0308), we would certainly have rejected the null
hypothesis at the specified level of significance ($\alpha = 0.05$).
The *p*-value of 0.0308 gives us a **specific** or more precise level of significance.
The **smaller** the *p*-value is, the **stronger** is the evidence against H_0 provided by the data.

The p-value of a Test Statistic

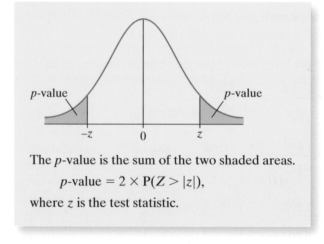

The *p*-value is the sum of the two shaded areas.
$$p\text{-value} = 2 \times P(Z > |z|),$$
where z is the test statistic.

Example 2

Calculate the *p*-value for the sample statistic $z = -2.08$.

Sample statistic is $z = -2.08$.
The sum of the probabilities that

$$z > 2.08 \quad \text{and} \quad z < -2.08$$

is the *p*-value.

$$
\begin{aligned}
p\text{-value} &= 2 \times P(Z > |2.08|) \\
&= 2 \times [1 - P(Z \leqslant 2.08)] \\
&= 2 \times [1 - 0.9812] \\
&= 2(0.0188) \\
p\text{-value} &= 0.0376
\end{aligned}
$$

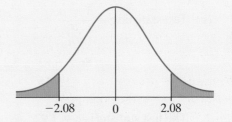

$-2.08 \qquad 0 \qquad 2.08$

Steps involved in a test of significance using a *p*-value

1. Write down the **null hypothesis H_0** and the **alternative hypothesis H_1**.

2. State the **significance level** α. (On our course $\alpha = 0.05$.)

3. Calculate the **test statistic**.

4. Find the *p*-value that corresponds to the test statistic.

5. If the *p*-value > 0.05, the result is not significant and we do **not** reject the null hypothesis H_0.

   If the *p*-value $\leqslant 0.05$, we reject the null hypothesis H_0 in favour of the alternative hypothesis H_1.

Example 3

A random sample of 36 observations is to be taken from a distribution with standard deviation 10. In the past, the distribution has had a mean of 83, but it is believed that the mean may have changed.
When the sample was taken it was found to have a mean of 86.2.

(i) State H_0 and H_1.

(ii) Calculate the value of the test statistic.

(iii) Calculate the *p*-value for the test statistic.

(iv) Use the *p*-value to state if the result is significant at the 5% level of significance.
Explain your conclusion.

(i) H_0: Mean $\mu = 83$
H_1: Mean $\mu \neq 83$

(ii) Test statistic $z = \dfrac{\bar{x} - \mu}{\dfrac{\sigma}{\sqrt{n}}}$

$$z = \frac{86.2 - 83}{\dfrac{10}{\sqrt{36}}} = \frac{3.2 \times \sqrt{36}}{10} = 1.92$$

The test statistic is $z = 1.92$

(iii) The p-value $= 2 \times P(Z > 1.92)$
$$= 2 \times [1 - P(Z \leqslant 1.92)]$$
$$= 2 \times [1 - 0.9726]$$
$$= 2(0.0274) = 0.0548$$

(iv) As the p-value is not less than or equal to 0.05, the result is not significant; we do not reject the null hypothesis.

Exercise 10.5

1. A normal distribution is thought to have a mean of 50.
   A random sample of 100 gave a mean of 52.4 and a standard deviation of 14.3.
   Is there evidence to suggest that the true mean is different from the assumed mean at the 5% level of significance?

2. Over a long period the scores obtained in a particular intelligence test were normally distributed with mean score 70 and standard deviation 6.
   When a test was taken by a random sample of 64 students, the mean score was 68.
   Is there sufficient evidence, at the 5% level of significance, that these students differ from the normal students?

3. The management of a large hospital states that the mean age of its patients is 45 years.
   The HSE statistics department decides to test this claim about the mean age of the patients.
   It took a random sample of 100 patients and found that the mean age was 48.4 years with a standard deviation of 18 years.
   (i) What is the null hypothesis?
   (ii) State the alternative hypothesis.
   (iii) Work out the test statistic for the sample mean.
   (iv) At the 5% level of significance, is there evidence to show that the mean age of the patients is not 45 years?
   Give a reason for your conclusion.

4. A particular machine produces metal rods whose lengths are normally distributed with a mean length of 210 cm and with a standard deviation of 6 cm.
   The machine is serviced and a sample is taken to investigate if the mean length has changed.
   The sample of 100 rods gave a mean length of 211.5 cm.
   (i) What is the null hypothesis?
   (ii) What is the alternative hypothesis?
   (iii) Work out the test statistic for the sample mean.
   (iv) At the 5% level of significance, is there evidence of a change in the mean length of rods produced by the machine?
   Explain your conclusion.

5. Mice kept under laboratory conditions have a mean lifespan of 258 days and a standard deviation of 45 days.
   64 of these mice, selected at random, were each given a measured dose of a certain drug each day, and the mean lifespan for this group was 269 days.
   At the 5% level of significance, is there evidence to suggest that the drug has altered the mean lifespan of the mice?

6. In 1970 the average number of children per family in a certain town was 3.8 with a standard deviation of 0.6. In 1980 a random sample of 40 families had a total of 144 children.
   At the 5% level of significance, is there evidence to conclude that the mean number of children per family had changed?

7. The mean mark for all students taking a certain Leaving Certificate subject was 48.7. In a particular town, 120 students took this examination.
   The mean mark of these students was 46.5 with a standard deviation of 9.5.
   At the 5% level of significance, is there evidence to suggest that the mean mark of the students of this town differs from the rest of the population?

8. In each of the following, the z-score for a sample mean is given.
   Work out the corresponding p-value for each test statistic.
   (i) $z = 1.73$ (ii) $z = -1.91$ (iii) $z = -1.65$ (iv) $z = -2.06$

9. 'Standard' batteries have a mean lifetime of 85 hours with a standard deviation 12 hours. A sample of 200 'long-life' batteries had a mean lifetime of 86.5 hours.
   (i) Calculate the sample statistic for this sample.
   (ii) Work out the corresponding p-value for this sample statistic.
   (iii) Is the result significant at the 5% level of significance?

10. Experience has shown that the scores obtained in a particular test are normally distributed with mean score 70 and standard deviation 6.
    When the test is taken by a random sample of 36 students, the mean is 68.5.

   (i) Calculate the sample statistic for this sample.

   (ii) Calculate the *p*-value for this sample statistic.

   (iii) Use the *p*-value you have found to investigate if the mean score of the sample differs from the mean score of the population at the 5% level of significance.

11. The security department of a warehouse wants to know whether the average time required by the night watchman to walk his round is 12.0 minutes.
    In a random sample of 36 rounds, the night watchman averaged 12.3 minutes with a standard deviation of 1.2 minutes.

   (i) Calculate the test statistic for this sample.

   (ii) Can we reject the null hypothesis that $\mu = 12.0$ minutes at the 5% level of significance?

   (iii) Work out the *p*-value that corresponds to the test statistic found in (i) above.

   (iv) If this *p*-value is used, do you reach the same conclusion with regard to significance at the 5% level?

12. The lengths of metal bars produced by a particular machine are normally distributed with mean length 420 cm and standard deviation 12 cm.
    The machine is serviced, after which a sample of 100 bars gives a mean length of 423 cm.

   (i) Calculate the sample statistic for this sample.

   (ii) Work out the *p*-value for this sample statistic.

   (iii) Use this *p*-value to determine if there is evidence, at the 5% level, of a change in the mean length of the bars produced by the machine, assuming that the standard deviation remains the same.

13. A machine is designed to produce screws with a stated mean length of 5 mm.
    A random sample of 400 screws produced by the machine is found to have a mean length of 5.008 mm and a standard deviation of 0.072 mm.
    Estimate the standard error of the mean, and obtain an approximate 95% confidence interval for the mean of the whole output of this machine.

    Investigate if the mean of the sample differs significantly from the stated mean at the 5% level of significance.

Revision Exercise 10 (Core)

1. The weights of a large collection of bags of potatoes have a mean of 25 kg and a standard deviation of $\sqrt{5}$ kg.
   Estimate, to 2 decimal places, the probability that a random sample of 50 bags will have a mean weight of between 24.5 kg and 25.5 kg.

2. A random sample of size 20 is taken from a population of size 80.
   Find the mean and standard error of the sampling distribution if the population is normally distributed with mean 2.85 and standard deviation 0.07.

3. The pulse-rate of a sample of 32 people was measured.
   The mean was found to be 26.2 with standard deviation $s = 5.15$.
   Calculate the 95% confidence interval for the population mean.

4. A machine is regulated to dispense liquid into cartons in such a way that the amount of liquid dispensed on each occasion is normally distributed with a standard deviation of 20 ml.

   Find the confidence limits for the mean amount of liquid dispensed if a random sample of 40 cartons had an average content of 266 ml.

5. Among the first 150 customers at a new snack bar, 90 order coffee.
   Assuming that this is a random sample from the population of future customers, estimate a 95% confidence interval for the proportion of future customers who will order coffee.

6. A sample poll of 100 voters chosen at random from all voters in a given constituency indicated that 55% of them were in favour of candidate A.
   Find the 95% confidence interval for the proportion of all the voters in the district in favour of this candidate.

7. Irish third-level students are known to have a mean height of 176 cm with a standard deviation 11 cm.
   A random sample of 60 equivalent German students had a mean height of 179 cm.
   Does this suggest that the mean height of German students differs from that of Irish students at the 95% confidence level?

8. Jars of honey are filled by a machine.
   It has been found that the quantity of honey in a jar has a mean of 460.3 g with a standard deviation of 3.2 g.
   It is believed that the machine controls have been altered in such a way that, although the standard deviation is unaltered, the mean quantity may have changed.
   A random sample of 60 jars is taken and the mean quantity of honey per jar is found to be 461.2 g.
   (i)   State the null and alternative hypotheses.
   (ii) Calculate the sample statistic for the mean.
   (iii) Is there evidence, at the 5% level of significance, that the sample mean is different from the population mean?

9. A firm produces batteries which are known to have a mean lifetime of 96 hours.
   Forty samples of 36 batteries each are tested.
   (i)   Describe the sampling distribution of the means of these samples, mentioning the theorem you have used to justify your answer.
   (ii) Explain why the theorem you have mentioned can be applied when the shape of the underlying population is not known.
   (iii) Estimate the number of samples in which the average lifetime of the 36 batteries is greater than 98 hours if the standard deviation of the batteries is 6 hours.

10. Draw a rough sketch of the normal curve showing the critical regions, at the 5% level of significance, of a hypothesis test.

   (i) Clearly indicate the rejection regions.

   (ii) What are the critical z-values for the limits of these rejection regions?

   (iii) For a z-value of 1.6, estimate the corresponding p-value for this statistic.

11. In a survey of 250 households in a large city, 170 households owned at least one pet.

   (i) At the 95% confidence level, calculate the margin of error, correct to two decimal places. (You may use the margin of error approximation)

   (ii) Find an approximate 95% confidence interval for the proportion of households in the city that own at least one pet.

Revision Exercise 10 (Advanced)

1. A large number of random samples of size n are taken from a normal distribution with a mean of 74 and a standard deviation of 6.
   The means, $\bar{x}$, of these samples are calculated.
   Find the sample size n required to ensure that the probability of $\bar{x} > 72$ is 0.854.

2. The weights of bags of fertiliser may be modelled by a normal distribution with mean 12.1 kg and standard deviation 0.4 kg.
   Find the probability that:

   (i) a randomly selected bag will weigh less than 12.0 kg,

   (ii) the mean weight of four bags selected at random will weigh more than 12.0 kg,

   (iii) the mean weight of 100 bags will be between 12.0 and 12.1 kg.

   How would your answer to (iii) be affected if the normal distribution was not a good model for the weights of the bags?
   Explain your answer.

3. A plant produces steel sheets whose weights are known to be normally distributed with a standard deviation of 2.4 kg.
   A random sample of 36 sheets had a mean weight of 31.4 kg.
   Find a 95% confidence interval for the mean weight of sheets produced by the plant.

4. The residents of a rural area are being asked for their views on a plan to build a wind farm in their area.
   Environmental campaigners claim that 20% of the residents are against the plan.

   (i) State one reason why surveying a random sample of 30 residents will allow reliable conclusions to be drawn.

   (ii) Using a 5% significance level, calculate a 95% confidence interval for the population proportion against the plan.

5. (i) Explain briefly what is meant by the term "95% confidence interval".

   (ii) A car manufacturing company tested a random sample of 150 cars of the same model to estimate the mean number of kilometres travelled per litre of petrol consumption for all cars of that model.
   The sample mean of kilometres travelled per litre consumed was 13.52 and the standard deviation was 2.23.

   Form a 95% confidence interval for the mean number of kilometres travelled per litre of petrol consumed for all cars of that make.
   Give all calculations correct to two places of decimal.

6. A neurologist wants to test the effect a new drug has on response times. 100 rats are injected with a unit dose of this drug and the response times are recorded.
   The neurologist knows that the mean response time for rats not injected with the drug is 1.2 seconds.
   The mean response time of the 100 rats injected with the drug is 1.05 seconds with a sample standard deviation of 0.5 seconds.

   (i) State the null and alternative hypotheses for this test.

   (ii) Determine the critical region at the 5% level of significance and illustrate your answer with a sketch.

   (iii) Calculate the test statistic and answer the question "Do you think that the drug has an effect on the response time at the 5% level of significance?"

   (iv) Calculate the p-value for the test statistic and interpret this value.

7. A school of motoring claims that 80% of its clients are successful in their first driving test. A person who did not believe this claim took a random sample of 72 clients and found that 50 of these had been successful in their first driving test.

   (i) Using $\frac{1}{\sqrt{n}}$, write down the margin of error.

   (ii) Calculate the sample proportion as a decimal correct to two decimal places.

   (iii) Write down the confidence interval, at the 95% level of confidence, in terms of $\hat{p}$ and n.

   (iv) Can the school's claim be upheld at the 95% level of confidence?

8. A market gardener sells carrots in 25 kg sacks.
   The wholesaler suspects that the true mean weight is not 25 kg.
   He weighs a random sample of 50 sacks and finds that the mean weight is 24.5 kg with a standard deviation of 1.5 kg.

   (i) State the null and alternative hypotheses.

   (ii) Calculate the sample statistic for the sample.

   (iii) Calculate the p-value for this statistic.

(iv) Is the wholesaler's suspicion justified at the 5% level of significance?

(v) Complete the following sentence:

"The p-value is the _____ level of significance at which the null hypothesis could have been _____".

9. The weights of male students at a large university are normally distributed with a mean of 68 kg and a standard deviation of 3 kg.
Eighty samples of 25 students are picked at random (with replacement).

(i) Find the mean and standard error of the resulting sampling distribution.

(ii) In how many of the samples would you expect the sample mean to be less than 67.5 kg?

10. In an opinion poll, 2000 people were interviewed and 527 said they preferred white chocolate to milk chocolate.

(i) Calculate the margin of error at the 95% confidence level. (You may use the margin of error approximation)

(ii) Calculate the 95% confidence interval for the proportion of the population who prefer white chocolate.

11. A survey is conducted of voters' opinions on several different issues.

(i) What is the overall margin of error of the survey, at 95% confidence, if it is based on a simple random sample of 1111 voters? (You may use the margin of error approximation)

(ii) A political party had claimed that it has the support of 23% of the electorate. Of the voters in the sample above, 234 stated that they support the party.
Is this sufficient evidence to reject the party's claim, at the 95% confidence level?

12. A company states that 20% of the visitors to its website purchase at least one of its products. A sample of 400 people who visited the site is checked and the number who purchased a product is found to be 64.

(i) Calculate the margin of error in this case.

(ii) Based on this sample, should the company's claim be accepted?
Explain your reasoning.

13. The NCCB believed that 70% of maths teachers were in favour of a syllabus change in maths. A questionnaire was sent to a large number of maths teachers asking for their opinions. Of the 180 replies received, 134 were in favour of the change.
Investigate if the NCCB's beliefs were borne out at the 5% level of significance.

14. The owner of a large apple-orchard states that 10% of the apples on the trees in his orchard have been attacked by birds. A random sample of 2500 apples is picked and 274 apples are found to have been attacked by birds.

(i) At the 95% level of confidence, what is the margin of error?

(ii) Calculate $\hat{p}$, the sample proportion.

(iii) Investigate if the orchard owner's claim is justified at the 5% level of significance.

Revision Exercise 10 (Extended Response Questions)

1. A company instals a new machine in a factory.
    The company claims that the machine will fill bags with wholemeal flour having a mean weight of 500 g and a standard deviation of 18 g.
    36 bags are checked in a random sample to test this claim.
    Their mean weight is 505 g.
    (i)   State the null and the alternative hypotheses.
    (ii) Calculate the test statistic for the sample mean.
    (iii) Find the p-value that corresponds to the test statistic.
    (iv) Is the result significant at the 5% level of significance?
          Explain your answer.

2. Among 80 fish caught in a certain lake, 28 were inedible as a result of the chemical pollution of their environment.
    (i) Work out the standard error for this proportion.
    (ii) Construct a 95% confidence interval for the true proportion of fish in this lake which are inedible as a result of chemical pollution.

3. The 95% confidence interval for the mean weight, in grams, of a consignment of oranges is (79.93, 82.87). This result is based on a random sample of 400 oranges.
    Using this confidence interval, find
    (i) $\bar{x}$, the mean of the sample
    (ii) σ, the standard deviation of the normal population from which the sample is taken.

4. The masses of loaves from a certain bakery are normally distributed with mean 500 grams and standard deviation 20 grams.
    (i)   Determine what percentage of the output would fall below 475 grams and what percentage would be above 530 grams.
    (ii) A sample of 40 loaves yielded a mean mass of 495 grams.
          Calculate the sample statistic for the mean.
    (iii) Calculate the p-value for this sample statistic.
    (iv) Does the p-value found above provide evidence that the mean weight of loaves from this sample is different from the mean of 500 g at the 5% level of significance?

5. (a) Write down the mean and standard deviation of the distribution of the means of all possible samples of size n taken from an infinite population having mean μ and standard deviation σ.

    Describe the shape of this distribution of sample means when
    (i) n is large
    (ii) the distribution of the population is normal.
    Explain briefly how the Central Limit Theorem can be applied to (i) and (ii) above.

(b) The standard deviation of all till receipts at a supermarket during 2013 was €8.50 and the mean of the receipts was €37.

    (i) Find the probability that the mean of a random sample of 100 till receipts is greater than €37.50.

    (ii) Find the value of *n* such that the probability that the mean of the sample of size *n* exceeds €37.50 is less than 0.06.

6. The distribution of the hourly earnings of all employees in Ireland in October 2009 is shown in the diagram. It can be seen that the distribution is positively skewed.

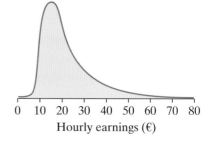

The mean is €22.05.
The median is €17.82.
The standard deviation is €10.64.
The lower quartile is €12.80.
The upper quartile is €26.05.

    (i) If an employee is selected at random from this population, what is the probability that the employee earns more than €12.80?

    (ii) If six employees are selected at random from this population, what is the probability that exactly four of them had hourly earnings of more than €12.80?

In a computer simulation, random samples of size 200 are repeatedly selected from this population and the mean of each sample is recorded. A thousand such sample means are recorded.

    (iii) Describe the expected distribution of these sample means. Your description should refer to the shape of the distribution and to its mean and standard deviation.

    (iv) How many of the sample means would you expect to be greater than €23?

7. The contents of a bag of oats are normally distributed with mean 3.05 kg and standard deviation 0.08 kg.

    (i) What proportion of bags contains less than 3.11 kg?

    (ii) What proportion of bags contains between 3.00 kg and 3.15 kg?

    (iii) Without using tables, write down the weight that is exceeded by 97.5% of the bags. (Use the Empirical Rule.)

    (iv) If 6 bags are selected at random, what is the probability that the mean weight of the contents will be between 3.00 kg and 3.15 kg?

8. A gas supplier maintains a team of engineers who are available to deal with leaks reported by customers. Most reported leaks can be dealt with quickly, but some require a long time. The time (excluding travelling time) taken to deal with reported leaks is found to have a mean of 65 minutes and a standard deviation of 60 minutes.

(a) Assuming that the times may be modelled by a normal distribution, estimate the probability that:

  (i) it will take more than 185 minutes to deal with a reported leak,

  (ii) it will take between 50 minutes and 125 minutes to deal with a reported leak,

  (iii) the mean time to deal with a random sample of 90 reported leaks is less than 70 minutes.

(b) A statistician, consulted by the gas supplier, stated that, as the times had a mean of 65 minutes and a standard deviation of 60 minutes, the normal distribution would not provide an adequate model.

  (i) Explain the reason for the statistician's statement.

  (ii) Give a reason why, despite the statistician's statement, your answer to (a) (iii) is still valid.

9. Hens' eggs have masses which may be said to have a normal distribution about a mean mass of 60 g and a standard deviation of 15 g.
Eggs of mass less than 45 g are classified as *small*. The remainder are classified into two further divisions called *standard* and *large*.

  (i) If an egg is picked at random from the batch, find the probability that it is *small*.

  (ii) A sample of 50 eggs are selected at random.
  Find the probability that the mean of the sample is less than 58 g.

  (iii) It is desired that the *standard* and *large* classes should have about the same number of eggs in each. Estimate the mass at which the division should be made. Give your answer to the nearest gram.

10. A large supermarket chain commissioned a survey to find out whether people favoured extended opening hours at the weekend. Four hundred people were surveyed in Cork and 88% said that they were in favour of extended opening hours.
At the 95% confidence level,
  (i) calculate the margin of error
  (ii) calculate the confidence interval.

In Dublin, 1000 people were surveyed and 810 said that they were in favour of the extended opening hours.
The company claimed that there was no difference in opinion between the Cork and Dublin samples.
Is the company's claim justified at the 5% level of significance.
Justify your answer.

Answers

Chapter 1: Complex Numbers

Exercise 1.1

1. (i) $3\sqrt{2}$ (ii) $2\sqrt{3}$ (iii) $3\sqrt{5}$ (iv) $2\sqrt{7}$
2. (i) $8\sqrt{2}$ (ii) $11\sqrt{3}$
3. (i) $Z\backslash N = \{-3, -5\}$
   (ii) $Q\backslash Z = \{\frac{2}{3}, -\frac{7}{8}\}$
   (iii) $R\backslash Q = \{\sqrt{2}, \pi\}$
4. (i) Z is the set of positive and negative whole numbers including zero.
   (ii) $Q\backslash Z$ is the set of rational numbers (fractions) that cannot be simplified to an integer
   (iii) $Q\backslash N$ is the set of rational numbers (fractions) that cannot be simplified to an natural number
   (iv) $R\backslash Z$ is the set of all real numbers except integers
   (v) $R\backslash Q$ is the set of all real numbers except rational numbers, i.e. irrational numbers
5. (i) $3\sqrt{5}$ (ii) $-\sqrt{2}$ (iii) $11\sqrt{2}$ (iv) $-3\sqrt{3}$
6. Constructions
7. $3\sqrt{2}$, construction
8. $2\sqrt{3}$, construction
9. Construction
10. $9\sqrt{5}$
11. $\sqrt{3}, \pi, e, \sqrt[5]{2}$
12. $\sqrt{2}, \sqrt{3}, 2, \sqrt{5}, \sqrt{6}, \sqrt{7}, \sqrt{8}$; Length of c is rational.
13. $4\sqrt{2}, 2(\sqrt{6} - \sqrt{2})$
14. (i) $x = -1$
   (ii) Any value of x for which $3 - x$ is a perfect square

Exercise 1.2

1. (i) $2i$ (ii) $6i$ (iii) $3\sqrt{3}i$ (iv) $2\sqrt{5}i$
2. (i) $\pm 3i$ (ii) $\pm 2\sqrt{3}i$
3. (i) $8 + i$ (ii) $10 - 6i$ (iii) $3 + 0i$
   (iv) $-5 + 5i$ (v) $0 + 3i$ (vi) $3 - 2i$
4. (i) $1 + 2i$ (ii) $1 - 9i$ (iii) $5 - 10i$
   (iv) $2 - 4i$ (v) $3 - 10i$ (vi) $-7 + 5i$
5. (i) $0 + 13i$ (ii) $17 - 17i$ (iii) $5 - 31i$
   (iv) $25 + 0i$ (v) $26 - 0i$ (vi) $5 - 12i$

6. (i) $6 + 12i$ (ii) $7 - 3i$ (iii) $7 + 7i$
   (iv) $-9 + 3i$ (v) $10 + 10i$ (vi) $10 - 10i$
   (vii) $2 + 4i$ (viii) $2 + 16i$
7. (i) $1 + 4i, 1 - 4i$ (ii) $2 + 3i, 2 - 3i$
   (iii) $5 + i, 5 - i$ (iv) $4 + 6i, 4 - 6i$
8. $2 + \frac{\sqrt{2}}{2}i, 2 - \frac{\sqrt{2}}{2}i$
9. $i^3 = -i, i^4 = 1, i^5 = i, i^6 = -1$
   Since $i^4 = i^8 = i^{12} = \dots 1$, divide power of i by 4 and find the remainder,
   i.e. $i^{29} = i^{4.7+1} = (i^4)^7 i^1 = i^1$
10. (i) -1 (ii) $-i$ (iii) $-i$
    (iv) i (v) 1
11. (i) -2 (ii) 0
12. (i) i (ii) -24 (iii) $8i$
13. $3i$

Exercise 1.3

1. (i) $3 - 4i$ (ii) $2 + 6i$
   (iii) $-5 + 2i$ (iv) $-8 - 3i$
2. (i) $2 - 5i$ (ii) $-3 + 4i$
   (iii) $1 - 7i$ (iv) $-5 - i$
3. (i) $\frac{5}{17} + \frac{14}{17}i$ (ii) $\frac{23}{26} + \frac{11}{26}i$
   (iii) $1 - 2i$ (iv) $\frac{4}{13} - \frac{19}{13}i$
4. (i) $40 + 0i$ (ii) $4 + 0i$
   (iii) $0 + 12i$ (iv) $-32 + 24i$
5. (i) $\frac{15}{17} + \frac{25}{17}i$ (ii) $-\frac{9}{4} - \frac{7}{4}i$
   (iii) $\frac{12}{5} - \frac{6}{5}i$ (iv) $3 + 2i$
   (v) $\frac{3}{10} - \frac{11}{10}i$ (vi) $\frac{43}{85} - \frac{49}{85}i$
6. (i) $x = 4, y = -2$ (ii) $x = 8, y = -1$
   (iii) $\frac{13}{5} + \frac{9}{5}i$ (iv) $x = -5, y = -12$
7. (i) $a = -11, b = 22$ (ii) $a = -10, b = -5$
8. $x = \frac{2}{3}, y = 1$
9. $p = -1, q = -2$
10. $2 + i, -2 - i$
11. $x = 3, y = -1$ and $x = -3, y = 1$
12. (i) $2 - 4i, -2 + 4i$ (ii) $1 + 4i, -1 - 4i$
    (iii) $5 - 4i, -5 + 4i$
13. (i) $1 + 2i$ (ii) $13 + 13i$

Exercise 1.4

1. Plot
2. (iii) $2 - i$ (iv) $-4 - 3i$
   (v) $-2 + 4i$ (vi) $6 - 2i$
   (vii) $-11 + 2i$ (viii) $-\frac{1}{5} - \frac{2}{5}i$
3. (i) 10   (ii) $6 + 0i$
   (iii) $\frac{3}{10} + \frac{1}{10}i$ (iv) $10 + 10i$
4. (c) Vertices join up to form a parallelogram
5. Adding z to each, translates each point
6. (i) $-2 + 3i$ (ii) $-3 - 2i$ (iii) $2 - 3i$
7. (i) $\sqrt{29}$ (ii) $2\sqrt{5}$ (iii) $2\sqrt{5}$ (iv) $\sqrt{10}$
8. $-2 + 5i, -2 - 5i, 5 + 2i$
9. (i) $\sqrt{\frac{10}{13}}$ (ii) $10\sqrt{2}$ (iii) $\frac{\sqrt{34}}{34}$
10. True
11. $\frac{7}{2} + \frac{1}{2}i$
12. $2\sqrt{5}, 4\sqrt{5}, 6\sqrt{5}$, yes
13. Yes
14. (i) $s = \pm 6$ (ii) $t = \pm 4\sqrt{21}$
15. $\frac{1}{\sqrt{2}}$
16. Circle, centre $(1, 0)$, radius $= 1$
17. z_1 and z_2 must be both real or both imaginary numbers or $z_2 = az_1$, i.e. z_2 and z_1 must be on the same line from the origin

Exercise 1.5

1. Plot
2. Collinear points
3. (i) Translation $-3 - 4i$
   (ii) Plot
   (iii) Rotation of (i^2) followed by a translation ($+3$)
4. Plot
5. $z_2 = 2 + 6i, z_3 = -6 + 2i$
6. (i) $a = 3$
   (ii) $b = i$
   (iii) $c = i^2 = -1$
7. Plot
8. (i) Translation of the plane
   (ii) Stretching by a factor of k
   (iii) Stretching and rotating
9. Plot
10. (i) Stretching by a factor of 3
    (ii) Contracting by a factor of $\frac{1}{2}$

Exercise 1.6

1. $-2 - 4i$
2. (i) $1 \pm 4i$ (ii) $-2 \pm \sqrt{3}i$

3. (i) $z^2 - 2z + 10 = 0$ (ii) $z^2 + 4z + 5 = 0$
   (iii) $z^2 - 8z + 20 = 0$ (iv) $z^2 + 25 = 0$
4. Proof
5. $-2 - 2i, 1$
6. $2 - 3i, \frac{1}{2}$
7. Coefficients are not real
8. $a = 5, b = 6$
9. $a = 1, b = 1$. Roots are $1, -\frac{1}{2} \pm \frac{\sqrt{3}}{2}i$
10. $z^2 + 4z + 5 = 0, 3, -2 \pm i$
11. $z^2 + 6z + 13 = 0: z^3 + 4z^2 + z - 26 = 0$
12. $z^3 - 2z - 4 = 0$
13. $\alpha = -\frac{1}{2} + \frac{\sqrt{3}}{2}i, \beta = -\frac{1}{2} - \frac{\sqrt{3}}{2}i$

Exercise 1.7

1. (i) $0 + 4i$ (ii) $-\sqrt{3} + i$
   (iii) $-1 + i$ (iv) $1 + \sqrt{3}i$
2. (i) $2\sqrt{2}, \frac{\pi}{4}$ (ii) $3, -\frac{\pi}{2}$
   (iii) $4, 0°$ (iv) $2, \frac{5\pi}{6}$
3. (i) $\sqrt{2}\left(\cos \frac{\pi}{4} + i \sin \frac{\pi}{4}\right)$
   (ii) $2\left(\cos \frac{\pi}{6} + i \sin \frac{\pi}{6}\right)$
   (iii) $\sqrt{6}(\cos 144.7° + i \sin 144.7°)$
   (iv) $\sqrt{6}(\cos(-144.7°) + i \sin(-144.7°))$
   (v) $4\left(\cos \frac{\pi}{2} + i \sin \frac{\pi}{2}\right)$
   (vi) $5(\cos \pi + i \sin \pi)$
   (vii) $3\left(\cos\left(-\frac{\pi}{2}\right) + i \sin\left(-\frac{\pi}{2}\right)\right)$
   (viii) $1\left(\cos\left(-\frac{\pi}{3}\right) + i \sin\left(-\frac{\pi}{3}\right)\right)$
4. (i) $4\left(\cos \frac{2\pi}{3} + i \sin \frac{2\pi}{3}\right)$
   (ii) $1\left(\cos \frac{\pi}{6} + i \sin \frac{\pi}{6}\right)$
5. (i) $-\sqrt{3} + i$ (ii) $-1 - \sqrt{3}i$
   (iii) $\sqrt{3} - i$
   (i) $\frac{\pi}{3}$ (ii) $\frac{5\pi}{6}$ (iii) $\frac{4\pi}{3}$
   (iv) $\frac{11\pi}{6}$, rotation of $90°$
6. (i) $2\left(\cos \frac{\pi}{2} + i \sin \frac{\pi}{2}\right)$
   (ii) $2\sqrt{3}\left(\cos\left(-\frac{5\pi}{6}\right) + i \sin\left(-\frac{5\pi}{6}\right)\right)$
   (iii) $\sqrt{2}\left(\cos\left(-\frac{3\pi}{4}\right) + i \sin\left(-\frac{3\pi}{4}\right)\right)$

7. $\sqrt{2}\left(\cos \dfrac{\pi}{4} + i \sin \dfrac{\pi}{4}\right),$

$\qquad \sqrt{2}\left(\cos\left(-\dfrac{\pi}{4}\right) + i \sin\left(-\dfrac{\pi}{4}\right)\right)$

8. $t = -8$

Exercise 1.8

1. (i) $8(\cos \pi + i \sin \pi)$

(ii) $2\left(\cos \dfrac{\pi}{2} + i \sin \dfrac{\pi}{2}\right)$

2. $4\left(\cos \dfrac{2\pi}{3} + i \sin \dfrac{2\pi}{3}\right)$

3. (i) $3, \dfrac{\pi}{2}$ $\qquad$ (ii) $4, \dfrac{\pi}{3}$

$\quad$ (iii) $12, \dfrac{5\pi}{6}$ $\qquad$ (iv) $\dfrac{3}{4}, \dfrac{\pi}{6}$

4. $12\left(\cos \dfrac{\pi}{2} + i \sin \dfrac{\pi}{2}\right)$

5. $\dfrac{3}{2}\left(\cos \dfrac{\pi}{2} + i \sin \dfrac{\pi}{2}\right)$

6. $2 + 2\sqrt{3}i$

7. $\cos \pi + i \sin \pi$

8. (a) $8(\cos \pi + i \sin \pi)$

(b) $16\cos\left(\left(-\dfrac{2\pi}{3}\right) + i \sin\left(-\dfrac{2\pi}{3}\right)\right.$

$\qquad \equiv 16\cos\left(\dfrac{4\pi}{3}\right) + i \sin\left(\dfrac{4\pi}{3}\right)$

9. (i) $\dfrac{1}{3}(\cos(\pi) - i \sin(\pi))$

(ii) $-\dfrac{1}{3} + 0i$

10. $4\left(\cos \dfrac{2\pi}{3} + i \sin \dfrac{2\pi}{3}\right)$

(a) $z^2 = 16\left(\cos\left(\dfrac{4\pi}{3}\right) + i \sin\left(\dfrac{4\pi}{3}\right)\right)$

$\qquad = 16\left(\cos\left(-\dfrac{2\pi}{3}\right) + i \sin\left(-\dfrac{2\pi}{3}\right)\right)$

$\qquad = -8 - 8\sqrt{3}i$

(b) $z^3 = 64(\cos(2\pi) + i \sin(2\pi)) = 64 + 0i$

11. Proof

12. $\dfrac{1}{\sqrt{2}} + \dfrac{1}{\sqrt{2}}i$

13. Proof

Exercise 1.9

1. (i) $0 + i$ $\qquad$ (ii) $-\dfrac{\sqrt{3}}{2} - \dfrac{1}{2}i$

$\quad$ (iii) $-\dfrac{1}{2} + \dfrac{\sqrt{3}}{2}i$ $\qquad$ (iv) $1 + 0i$

$\quad$ (iv) $1 + 0i$ $\qquad$ (v) $0 + i$

$\quad$ (vi) $1 + 0i$ $\qquad$ (vii) $0 - i$

$\quad$ (viii) $0 - i$

2. $-2, -2\sqrt{3}i$

3. $0 + 243i$

4. (i) $\cos \dfrac{2\pi}{3} + i \sin \dfrac{2\pi}{3}$

(ii) $\cos \dfrac{8\pi}{3} + i \sin \dfrac{8\pi}{3}, -\dfrac{1}{2} - \dfrac{\sqrt{3}}{2}i$

5. (i) $2\left(\cos \dfrac{\pi}{6} + i \sin \dfrac{\pi}{6}\right)$

(ii) $3\left(\cos \dfrac{2\pi}{3} + i \sin \dfrac{2\pi}{3}\right)$

(iii) $2\left(\cos\left(-\dfrac{\pi}{6}\right) + i \sin\left(-\dfrac{\pi}{6}\right)\right)$

(iv) $3\left(\cos\left(-\dfrac{2\pi}{3}\right) + i \sin\left(-\dfrac{2\pi}{3}\right)\right)$

(v) $6\left(\cos \dfrac{5\pi}{6} + i \sin \dfrac{5\pi}{6}\right)$

(vi) $\dfrac{2}{3}\left(\cos\left(-\dfrac{\pi}{2}\right) + i \sin\left(-\dfrac{\pi}{2}\right)\right)$

6. (i) $-4 + 0i$ $\quad$ (ii) $-8 + 0i$ $\quad$ (iii) $-64 + 0i$

7. -4

8. $4\sqrt{2}\left(\cos\left(-\dfrac{\pi}{4}\right) + i \sin\left(-\dfrac{\pi}{4}\right)\right); -\dfrac{1}{256} + \dfrac{1}{256}i$

9. (i) $-1728 + 0i$ $\qquad$ (ii) 4096

10. $\cos\left(-\dfrac{\pi}{6}\right) + i \sin\left(-\dfrac{\pi}{6}\right); -1$

Exercise 1.10

1. (i) $-1 - 0i$ $\qquad\qquad$ (ii) $+1 + 0i$

$\quad$ (iii) $-1 + 0i$ $\qquad\qquad$ (iv) $1 + 0i$

2. (i) $\sin 2\theta = 2 \sin \theta \cos \theta$

$\quad$ (ii) $\cos 3\theta = 4 \cos^3 \theta - 3 \cos \theta$

3. Proof

4. $2, -1 + \sqrt{3}i, -1 - \sqrt{3}i$

5. $-2, 1 + \sqrt{3}i, 1 - \sqrt{3}i$

6. $4\left(\cos \dfrac{\pi}{3} + i \sin \dfrac{\pi}{3}\right); \sqrt{3} + i, -\sqrt{3} - i$

7. (a) $(\cos 2n\pi + i \sin 2n\pi), 1, -\dfrac{1}{2} + \dfrac{\sqrt{3}}{2}i,$

$\qquad -\dfrac{1}{2} - \dfrac{\sqrt{3}}{2}i$

8. $-3i, \dfrac{3\sqrt{3}}{2} + \dfrac{3}{2}i, -\dfrac{3\sqrt{3}}{2} + \dfrac{3}{2}i$

9. (i) $\dfrac{\sqrt{3}}{\sqrt{2}} + \dfrac{1}{2}i, -\dfrac{\sqrt{3}}{\sqrt{2}} - \dfrac{1}{2}i$

$\quad$ (ii) $\sqrt{3} - i, -\sqrt{3} + i$

$\quad$ (iii) $\sqrt{2} + \sqrt{2}i, -\sqrt{2} - \sqrt{2}i$

10. $\cos\left(\dfrac{2n\pi}{5}\right) + i \sin\left(\dfrac{2n\pi}{5}\right),$

$\qquad n \in \{0, 1, 2, 3, 4\}.$ Proof

Revision Exercise 1 (Core)

1. $2\sqrt{5}$
2. $x = 5, y = 4$
3. $z = -1 + 0i$ or $z = -3 + 0i$
4. $24 + 10i$, proof
5. (i) $-2 - 2\sqrt{3}i$ (ii) $p = 2$
6. $\sqrt{2}\left(\cos\dfrac{\pi}{4} + i\sin\dfrac{\pi}{4}\right); z^4 = -4 + 0i$
7. $2\left(\cos\dfrac{2\pi}{3} + i\sin\dfrac{2\pi}{3}\right)$
8. $2 - 3i$
9. Yes
10. $1 - 3i$
11. i
12. $f(z) = z^2 - (1 + 7i)z - 14 + 5i$
13. (i) $1 - 2i$ (ii) $3 + 3i$ (iii) $-2 - 5i$
14. (i) Rotation of $(-90°)$ and stretching by a factor of $1\frac{1}{2}$
   (ii) Translation $(4 - i)$
   (iii) If $z = x + iy$, $z_1 = -1\frac{1}{2}i$
   (iv) $z_3 = (4 - i)$

Revision Exercise 1 (Advanced)

1. $x = \dfrac{4}{5}, y = \dfrac{3}{5}$
2. $2 - 3i, \dfrac{1}{2}$
3. $2\left(\cos\dfrac{\pi}{6} + i\sin\dfrac{\pi}{6}\right); 2^{10}(\sqrt{3} - i)$
4. $p = -5 - 4i, q = 1 + 7i$
5. $w_2 = -\dfrac{1}{2} - \dfrac{\sqrt{3}}{2}i$. Proof
6. $\bar{p} = 2\left(\cos\dfrac{\pi}{3} - i\sin\dfrac{\pi}{3}\right), \bar{p}p = 4$
7. $-\dfrac{7}{2} + \dfrac{1}{2}i$
8. $k = -\dfrac{1}{3}$
9. i
10. $2 + i$
11. $-\dfrac{1}{2} - \dfrac{\sqrt{3}}{2}i$
12. $p = 30, 1 + 3i, -3$
13. $x = 3, y = -1$ and $x = -3, y = 1$
14. $t = +\sqrt{2}, -\sqrt{2}; \sqrt{2}i, -\sqrt{2}i, 1 + 2i, 1 - 2i$
15. $2 - 3i, 2 + i$
16. $p = 4, q = -1$ or $p = -4, q = 1; z = -1$ or $z = \dfrac{1}{2} - \dfrac{5}{2}i$

Revision Exercise 1 (Extended Response Questions)

1. (i) $pq = 6\sqrt{3} - 6i$
   (ii) $|p| = 3, |q| = 4, |pq| = 12, |p + q| = 5$
2. (i) $-\dfrac{1}{2} + \dfrac{\sqrt{3}}{2}i$
   (iii) $1\left(\cos\dfrac{2\pi}{3} + i\sin\dfrac{2\pi}{3}\right)$
   (iv) Proof
3. (i) $p - 3q + (3p + q)i$
   (ii) Proof
   (iii) $p = 4, q = -2$
4. (i) 3   (ii) $\dfrac{5\pi}{12}$ (iii) 9   (iv) 1   (v) $\dfrac{\pi}{3}$ (vi) $\dfrac{\pi}{2}$
   (a) True   (b) True
5. $z^2 = 2 + 2\sqrt{3}i, z^4 = -8 + 8\sqrt{3}i, z^6 = -64$
   (iii) Rotation and a stretching (rotation of 60°)
6. $1\left(\cos\left(-\dfrac{\pi}{6}\right) + i\sin\left(-\dfrac{\pi}{6}\right)\right); -1$
7. $0, z_1, z_2$ must be collinear points
8. (i) $ac - bd = 1, ad + bc = 0$
   (ii) $b = \dfrac{-d}{c^2 + d^2}, a = \dfrac{c}{c^2 + d^2}$
   (iii) Proof
   (v) Proof
9. Proof
10. (a) (i) $2\left(\cos\dfrac{2\pi}{3} + i\sin\dfrac{2\pi}{3}\right)$
     (ii) $z = \left(\dfrac{\sqrt{2}}{2} + i\dfrac{\sqrt{6}}{2}\right), \left(-\dfrac{\sqrt{2}}{2} - i\dfrac{\sqrt{6}}{2}\right)$
   (b) (i)

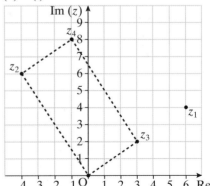

     (ii) $k = \dfrac{1}{2}$
     (iii) $z_3 = kz_1$. This represents a stretch along a line through the origin, i.e. z_3 and z_1 are the only collinear points with the origin

11. (a) (i) $\sqrt{2}\left(\cos\left(-\dfrac{\pi}{4}\right) + i\sin\left(-\dfrac{\pi}{4}\right)\right)$

(ii) $16 - 16i$

(b) (i)

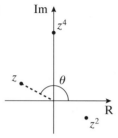

(ii) $\theta = 150° \left(\dfrac{5\pi}{6}\right)$

(iii) If $|z| > 1$
then $|z^2| > |z|$
and $|z^3| > |z^2|$ i.e. the points spiral
way from the origin

(c) (i) $z^2 = 2a^2i$, $z^4 = -4a^4$, $z^6 = -8a^6i$

(ii) The points spiral way from the
origin and are restricted to the real
and imaginary axes

12. (i) $z^k = (\cos k\theta + i\sin k\theta)$

(ii) Proof

(iii) $\cos k\theta = \dfrac{1}{2}(z^k + z^{-k})$,

$\sin k\theta = \dfrac{1}{2i}(z^k + z^{-k})$

(iv) Proof

(v) $\cos^2\theta\sin^2\theta = \dfrac{1}{8} - \dfrac{1}{8}\cos 4\theta$, $a = \dfrac{1}{8}$, $b = -\dfrac{1}{8}$

Chapter 2: Geometry 2: Enlargements and Constructions

Exercise 2.1

1. (i) 2   (ii) $x = 6\,\text{cm}$, $y = 18\,\text{cm}$

2. (i) 8   (ii) 12   (iii) 5; $7\frac{1}{2}$ sq. units

3. (i) 2   (iii) $(-2, 3)$ (iv) 120 sq. units

4. (i) 12   (ii) 6   (iii) 6; 45 sq. units

6. (i) 4   (ii) 16.4 cm   (iii) 3 cm

(iv) 1 : 3   (v) 4 cm²

7. (i) $2\frac{1}{2}$ (ii) 10   (iii) 2 : 5

(iv) 100 sq. units

8. 9 cm²

9. 1100 cm²

10. 2; $\sqrt{2}$

11. 12 cm²

12. (i) 104 mm   (ii) 42 mm

13. 10 200 m²

14. (i) 1.5 m²   (ii) 272 cm²

15. (i) 1 : 500   (ii) 60 m

(iii) 1 : 2000   (iv) 50 cm

Exercise 2.2

2. 105°

4. Circumcentre is the midpoint of the
hypotenuse; yes

5. Triangle contains obtuse angle

6. School should be built at the circumcentre
of the triangle

9. (i) $\dfrac{1}{2}ar$

13. (i) 5 cm

14. Result will hold for all obtuse-angled
triangles

16. Point of intersection of the perpendicular
bisectors of the two chords is the centre of the
circle.

Revision Exercise 2 (Core)

1. $2\frac{2}{3}$ cm

2. 10.8 m

3. (ii) $x = 3.6$, $y = 3$

4. (i) $k = 1.5$, $k = 0.5$; 6   (ii) 1.5, 13.5

5. (i) $x = 135°$, $y = 90°$

6. (i) False   (ii) False   (iii) True

(iv) False

7. (i) Point of intersection of perpendicular
bisectors of [AB] and [BC]

(ii) 125°

(iii) Yes

8. (i) 2.5   (ii) 6   (iii) 2 : 5

10. (i) 16 cm   (ii) 12 cm

Revision Exercise 2 (Advanced)

1. $x = 13.5$, $y = 27$

2. (i) 8 cm   (ii) 6 cm   (iii) scale factor $= 2$

3. 9 cm²; 22.5 cm²

4. (i) 1.2   (ii) $a = 5.4$ cm, $b = 6$ cm

(iii) scale factor $= \dfrac{4}{5}$

5. (i) 24 cm   (ii) 40.5 cm

6. $2\sqrt{21}$ cm

7. (i) $x = 28°$, $y = 56°$, $z = 34°$

8. (i) $5r$ (ii) 250 cm²

9. (ii) 18 cm

Revision Exercise 2 (Extended Response Questions)

1. Proof / Construction
2. (i) $\angle$JKM = $\angle$KLM, $\angle JKM = \angle KML$ ‖,
   $\angle MJK = \angle LKM$ (3rd angles of triangle)
   (ii) 4.9 cm
   (iii) 80 m
3. (i) (a) 4:9　　　(b) 8:27
   (ii) 8 cm　　(iii) 121.5 cm² 　(iv) 32 cm³
4. (i) 60°　　　(ii) 60°　　　(iii) 55°
5. (i) (a) 150°　　(c) 30°
   (ii) 50.23 m; 7.8 m
6. (a) (i) $2\sqrt{7}$ cm　　(ii) $4\sqrt{7}$ cm
   (iii) 6 cm　　　(iv) $24\sqrt{7}$ cm²
   (b) Proof
7. (ii) $x + z = 10$; $y + z = 26$; $x = 4$, $y = 20$,
   $z = 6$
   (iii) 4 cm
8. (i) (b) 26°　(ii) 21 cm　(iii) Proof

Chapter 3: Integration

Exercise 3.1

1. (i) $\frac{x^2}{2} + c$　　　(ii) $\frac{x^3}{3} + c$
   (iii) $x^3 + 2x^2 + c$　(iv) $-\frac{2x^3}{3} + c$
   (v) $3x + c$　　　(vi) $-\frac{x^3}{3} + 3x + c$
   (vii) $x^4 + 3x^2 + c$　(viii) $\frac{2x^3}{3} - \frac{3x^2}{2} - x + c$
   (ix) $4y^3 + c$
2. (i) $-\frac{1}{x} + c$　　　(ii) $-\frac{1}{x^2} + c$
   (iii) $-\frac{3}{x} + c$　　　(iv) $\frac{1}{x^2} + c$
   (v) $\frac{2}{3}\sqrt{x^3} + c$　　(vi) $2\sqrt{x^3} + c$
   (vii) $2\sqrt{x} + c$　　(viii) $\frac{3}{4}\sqrt[3]{x^4} + c$
   (ix) $\frac{4\pi r^3}{3} + c$
3. (i) $\frac{x^4}{2} - \frac{3}{x} + c$　(ii) $-\frac{4}{x} - 2x + \frac{x^4}{4} + c$
   (iii) $\frac{8}{3}\sqrt{x^3} - 3x + c$ (iv) $\frac{2}{3}\sqrt{x^3} + 2\sqrt{x} + c$
   (v) $\frac{4}{3}\sqrt{x^3} + \frac{2}{x} + c$ (vi) $-\frac{1}{x} - \frac{2}{3}\sqrt{x^3} + c$

4. (i) $y = \frac{x^3}{3} + \frac{3x^2}{2} + c$
   (ii) $\frac{3x^4}{2} - \frac{4x^3}{3} + \frac{x^2}{2} - 5x + c$
5. (i) $\frac{x^3}{3} - 3x^2 + 9x + c$
   (ii) $\frac{x^3}{3} - 2x - \frac{1}{x} + c$
   (iii) $\frac{2}{5}\sqrt{x^5} - 2\sqrt{x^3} + c$
6. (i) $\frac{x^4}{4} - x^3 + 4x + c$
   (ii) $\frac{3x^2}{2} - x - \frac{6}{x} + c$
   (iii) $\frac{2}{5}x^{\frac{5}{2}} - \frac{4}{3}x^{\frac{3}{2}} + 12x^{\frac{1}{2}} + c$
7. $f(x) = x^2 + 3$
8. $f(x) = x^2 - 5x + 11$
9. $c = -3$
10. $c = -3$
11. (i) $y = \frac{x^3}{3} + x^2 + 2$　　(ii) $y = 3x - \frac{x^3}{3} + 2$
12. (i) $V = \frac{t^3}{3} - \frac{t^2}{2} + 4\frac{1}{2}$　(ii) $287\frac{5}{6}$
13. (i) $k = 8$　　　　(ii) $(0, 7)$
14. $m = 2$;　(i) $k = -4$　　(ii) $y = x^2 - 4x + 9$

Exercise 3.2

1. (i) $\frac{e^{2x}}{2} + c$　　　(ii) $3e^x + c$
   (iii) $\frac{e^{4x}}{2} + c$　　(iv) $-\frac{e^{-3x}}{3} + c$
2. (i) $\frac{e^{3x}}{3} + 4x + c$　(ii) $8e^{\frac{1}{2}x} + c$
   (iii) $\frac{e^{4x}}{4} - \frac{e^{-4x}}{4} + c$
3. $\frac{dy}{dx} = 2xe^{x^2}$; $e^{x^2} + c$
4. (i) $\frac{\sin 3x}{3} + c$　　(ii) $-\frac{\cos 4x}{4} + c$
   (iii) $\frac{\cos 5x}{5} + c$　(iv) $\frac{\sin kx}{k} + c$
5. (i) $\frac{\sin 6x}{2} + c$　　(ii) $\frac{\sin 2x}{2} + \frac{\cos 5x}{5} + c$
   (iii) $-\frac{\sin(-9x)}{3} + c$
6. $3e^x + 4\cos 3x + 6x + c$
7. (i) $2e^{2x} - \frac{4\cos 3x}{3} + c$
   (ii) $3\sin x - \frac{\sin 4x}{2} + c$
8. $\frac{dy}{dx} = -8x \sin 4x^2$; $\cos 4x^2 + c$

9. (i) $e^x - \dfrac{4}{e^x} + c$

   (ii) $xe^2 - \dfrac{3}{e^x} + c$

   (iii) $-\dfrac{1}{2}e^{-2x} - 3e^{-x} + c$

10. (i) $\dfrac{1}{2}e^{2x} - \dfrac{1}{2}e^{-2x} - 2x + c$

   (ii) $7x - \dfrac{3}{e^x} + 2e^x + c$

11. $x = \dfrac{\ln y}{\ln 7}$;   (i) $\dfrac{dy}{dx} = \dfrac{1}{\ln 7} \cdot \dfrac{1}{y}$ (ii) $7^x \ln 7$

12. $y = \dfrac{-3}{e^x} + 2x$

13. Gradient $= e^2$;

   (i) $k = 2$ (ii) $y = \dfrac{1}{2}e^{2x} + \dfrac{1}{2}e^2$

14. (i) $f'(x) = 2e^x + 2xe^x$

   (ii) $2xe^x - 2e^x + c$

15. $f'(x) = \sin x + x\cos x$; $x\sin x + \cos x + c$

16. (i) $f'(x) = 4e^{2x} + 8xe^{2x}$

   (ii) $4xe^{2x} - 2e^{2x} + c$

17. $\dfrac{dy}{dx} = 2e^{3x} + 6xe^{3x} - \sin x$; $2xe^{3x} - \dfrac{2}{3}e^{3x} + c$

Exercise 3.3

1. (i) $s = \dfrac{5t^2}{2} + 4t$ (ii) $56\,\text{m}$

2. (i) $6\,\text{m/sec}^2$

   (ii) $s = \dfrac{t^3}{3} - 2t^2 + 3t + 4$

   (iii) $5\dfrac{1}{3}\,\text{m}$

3. (i) $v = 3t^2 - 12t + 9$

   (ii) $s = t^3 - 6t^2 + 9t + 6$

   (iii) $t = 1$ or $t = 3$

4. (i) $v = t^2 - 3t + 3$; $s = \dfrac{t^3}{3} - \dfrac{3t^2}{2} + 3t + 2$

   (ii) $v = 1\,\text{m/sec}$; $s = 4\dfrac{2}{3}\,\text{m}$

5. (i) $(-10t + 25)\,\text{m/sec}$ (ii) $(-5t^2 + 25t)\,\text{m}$

   (iii) $\dfrac{5}{2}\,\text{sec}$ (iv) $\dfrac{125}{4}\,\text{m}$

   (v) $5\,\text{sec}$

6. (i) $N = 4e^t + 10t + c$

   (ii) $N = 4e^5 + 56 = 650$

7. (i) $s = 0.3t^2 - \dfrac{0.004t^3}{3}$

   (ii) $2250\,\text{m}$

8. (i) $h = t^2 - 3t + 4$ (ii) $\quad t = 7.4\,\text{secs}$

Exercise 3.4

1. 9   **2.** 18   **3.** 51

4. $6\dfrac{3}{4}$ **5.** $6\dfrac{2}{3}$ **6.** -12

7. $\dfrac{3}{4}$ **8.** $17\dfrac{1}{3}$ **9.** $\dfrac{1}{4}$

10. 2   **11.** $6\dfrac{2}{3}$ **12.** $\dfrac{5}{6}$

13. $-\dfrac{3}{4}$ **14.** -9 **15.** $6\dfrac{2}{3}$

17. $\dfrac{x-4}{2}$; $-1\dfrac{3}{4}$ **18.** $k = 1$ or 3

19. $k = \dfrac{9}{2}$ **20.** $14\dfrac{2}{3}$ **21.** $n = 3$

22. (i) $\dfrac{1}{2}$ (ii) $\dfrac{1}{3}$ (iii) $\dfrac{5}{2}$ (iv) $2 + \dfrac{\pi}{2}$

23. (i) $\dfrac{1}{4}[e^8 - 1]$ (ii) $e^4 - e^2$

   (iii) $2e^{\frac{1}{2}} - 2$ (iv) $\dfrac{1}{2}\left(3 - \dfrac{1}{e^2}\right)$

24. (i) $6e^{\frac{1}{3}} - 4$ (ii) $e^2 - \dfrac{1}{e^2}$

   (iii) $\dfrac{120}{\ln 5}$ (iv) $\dfrac{7^e}{\ln 7} - \dfrac{1}{\ln 7}$

25. 1

26. $\sin 3x + 3x\cos 3x$; $\dfrac{\pi}{6} - \dfrac{1}{3}$

Exercise 3.5

1. 8 sq. units   **2.** $4\dfrac{2}{3}$ sq. units   **3.** $4\dfrac{1}{2}$ sq. units

4. $10\dfrac{2}{3}$ sq. units **5.** 8 sq. units   **6.** $4\dfrac{2}{3}$ sq. units

7. $8\dfrac{1}{6}$ sq. units **8.** $\dfrac{2}{15}$ sq. units

9. $A = (4, 0)$, $B = (-1, 0)$; $20\dfrac{5}{6}$ sq. units

10. $(0, 3)$ and $(0, -3)$; 36 sq. units

11. $\dfrac{31}{6}$ sq. units

12. $\dfrac{1}{6}$ sq. units

13. (i) $P = (2, 4)$ (ii) $1\dfrac{1}{3}$ sq. units

14. $1\dfrac{1}{3}$ sq. units

15. (i) $A = (1, 0)$, $B = (-1, 2)$

   (ii) $1\dfrac{1}{3}$ sq. units

16. $(0, 0)$ and $(2, 4)$; $1\dfrac{1}{3}$ sq. units

17. (i) $(4, 4)$ (ii) $5\dfrac{1}{3}$ sq. units

18. (i) $P = (4, -8)$, $Q = (2, 0)$

   (ii) $10\dfrac{2}{3}$ sq. units

19. (i) $C = (-2, 6)$, $D = (2, 6)$

   (ii) $10\dfrac{2}{3}$ sq. units

20. (i) $P = (2, 4)$ (ii) $2\dfrac{2}{3}$ sq. units

21. $k = \sqrt{6}$

22. (i) $52.6\,\text{m}^2$ (ii) $736\,\text{m}^3$

23. (i) $(-1, 7)$ and $(5, 37)$ (ii) 36 sq. units

24. (i) $P = 1$ sq. unit

    (ii) $Q = \left(e + \dfrac{1}{e} - 2\right)$ sq. units

Exercise 3.6

1. (i) 11   (ii) 12
    (iii) (ii) gives the exact estimate

2. (i) 3   (ii) $\dfrac{1}{3}$ (iii) $\dfrac{2}{3}$

3. 16

4. $6\dfrac{1}{3}$

5. (i) $\dfrac{2}{\pi}$ (ii) 0

    (iii) $\dfrac{1}{3}(e^3 - 1)$ (iv) $\dfrac{e^8}{8} - \dfrac{1}{8}$

6. $k = 12$

7. $k = 4$

8. (i) $\dfrac{1}{5}$ (ii) 0

9. $\dfrac{85\pi}{6}$ cm^3

10. $\dfrac{147}{10}$ m/sec

11. (i) 9 m/sec   (ii) 12 m/sec^2

12. (i) 2 m/sec   (ii) $t = (3 \pm \sqrt{3})$ sec

13. 4.5 newtons

14. (i) $\dfrac{14}{9}$ (ii) 2 sq. units

15. 8

16. 20 m/sec

Revision Exercise 3 (Core)

1. (i) $x^2 + 5x + c$ (ii) $x^3 - x^2 + 4x + c$

    (iii) $\dfrac{x^3}{3} - \dfrac{1}{x} + c$

2. (i) $-\dfrac{\cos 3x}{3} + c$ (ii) $\dfrac{\sin 5x}{5} + c$

    (iii) $-2 \cos x + \dfrac{3}{2} \sin 2x + c$

3. (i) $\dfrac{e^{5x}}{5} + c$ (ii) $\dfrac{e^{2x}}{2} - e^{-x} + c$

    (iii) $4x + \dfrac{e^{3x}}{3} + c$

4. $\dfrac{x^3}{3} - \dfrac{3x^2}{2} + 2x + c$

5. (i) $\dfrac{x^2}{2} + \dfrac{2}{x} + c$ (ii) $\dfrac{2}{3}x^{\frac{3}{2}} - 3x + c$

    (iii) $\dfrac{x^2}{2} + 4x^{\frac{3}{2}} + 9x + c$

6. (i) 3   (ii) $\dfrac{1}{2}$ (iii) $\dfrac{2}{3}$

8. (i) $\dfrac{1}{2}e^6 + 2\dfrac{1}{2}$ (ii) $-\dfrac{1}{e^4} + 1$

    (iii) $\dfrac{1}{2}e^4 - \dfrac{1}{2}e^2 + 2$

9. $3\dfrac{1}{12}$ sq. units

10. $f(x) = 5x^3 - 6x^2 + 4$

11. $8\dfrac{2}{3}$

12. $y = \dfrac{1}{2}e^{2x} - \dfrac{x^2}{2} + 4\dfrac{1}{2}$

13. (i) $A = (1, 0), B = (4, 0)$

    (ii) $6\dfrac{1}{3}$ sq. units

14. (i) 22 m/sec   (ii) 78 m/sec^2

15. $f'(x) = \sin 2x + 2x \cos 2x \; ; x \sin 2x + \dfrac{\cos 2x}{2} + c$

Revision Exercise 3 (Advanced)

1. (i) 62   (ii) $a = \dfrac{2}{3}$

2. $8\dfrac{2}{3}$

3. (i) $P = (3, 9), Q = \left(7\dfrac{1}{2}, 0\right)$

    (ii) 29.25 sq. units

4. 48π cm^3

5. $A = (0, 5); \dfrac{27}{4}$ sq. units

6. $y = 9 - 2e^{-2}$

7. (i) 5 sq. units   (ii) $P = \dfrac{20}{7}$

8. $71466\dfrac{2}{3}$ m^3

9. (i) $2x \ln 3x + x$ (ii) $x^2 \ln 3x - \dfrac{x^2}{2} + c$

10. (i) $A = \left(\dfrac{1}{2}, 2\right); B = (2, 2)$

    (ii) $\dfrac{9}{8}$ sq. units

11. 95 joules

12. (i) 125 m/sec   (ii) $s = t^3 + 5t^2 + 3$
    (iii) 75 m   (iv) 46 m/sec

13. (i) $A = (0, 3), B = (1, 0)$
    (ii) 2 sq. units

14. (i) (a) $a = 2, b = 4$ (b) $k = \dfrac{3}{4}$

    (ii) $y = \dfrac{1}{4}x^3 - \dfrac{9}{4}x^2 + 6x + 6$

15. $y = x^2 + \dfrac{2}{x} - 3$

Revision Exercise 3 (Extended Response Questions)

1. (a) $5x - 4y - 3 = 0$ (b) $\left(\dfrac{3}{5}, 0\right)$

    (c) $(1, 0)$ (d) $\dfrac{9}{40}$ sq. units

    (e) $9 : 49$

2. (a) $6\dfrac{3}{4}$ sq. units

    (c) $(2, 1)$

    (d) 5 sq. units

3. (a) $\dfrac{\pi}{6}$ (b) $\dfrac{1}{2}$ sq. unit

4. (a) At $t = 6$ mins or $t = 20$ mins

    (b) $V = 120t + 13t^2 - \dfrac{t^3}{3}$

    (c) 800 litres

6. (a) (i) 4 m   (ii) 16 m

    (b) (i) 0.7   (ii) -0.8

    (c) (i) $\dfrac{100}{3}$ (ii) $\dfrac{500}{27}$ m

    (d) $\dfrac{3125}{6}$ m²

    (e) (i) $(15 + 5\sqrt{33},\, 12)$

         (ii) $a = 20, b = 15 + 5\sqrt{33}; R = 60\sqrt{33} - 60$

7. (a) $2 + e^x + e^{-x}$

    (b) $y = -\dfrac{3}{e^x} - e^x + 8$

    (c) $\dfrac{e^4}{2} + \dfrac{1}{e^2} - \dfrac{3}{2}$

Chapter 4: Applications of Differential Calculus

Exercise 4.1

1. (i) -1 (ii) -3

2. $8x - y - 23 = 0$

3. $2x + y + 4 = 0$

4. $4x - 2y - 1 = 0$

5. $k = 5$

6. $(1, 3)$

7. $(-3, 3)$

8. $4x - 5y + 12 = 0$

9. $(2, -12)$ and $(-2, 20)$

10. $a = 1, b = -6$

11. $a = \dfrac{3}{4}, b = -5$

12. $2x - y - 3 = 0$

13. $3x - y + 1 = 0$

14. $(3, -5)$ and $(-1, 11)$

15. (i) 250 m   (ii) 76°

16. (i) Positive   (ii) Negative

    (a) $x < \dfrac{1}{2}$ (b) $-4 < x < 0$

17. (i) $8x + 4$

    (ii) (a) $x > -\dfrac{1}{2}$ (b) $x < -\dfrac{1}{2}$

18. (i) $x < \dfrac{2}{3}$ (ii) $x > -\dfrac{4}{3}$ (iii) $x < 2$ or $x > 3$

19. (i) $x > 0.3$ (ii) $x > -1$ (iii) $-1 < x < 2$

22. (i) $2x - y - 11 = 0$ (ii) $Q = (4, -3)$

23. (i) 0.12 and -0.15

    (ii) $x = 2, y = 2.16$; height $= 2.16$ km

24. (a) $A = (-2, 0), B = (0, \sqrt{2})$

    (b) $\dfrac{1}{2\sqrt{x + 2}}$

    (c) (i) $\dfrac{1}{2}$ (ii) $2y - x = 3$ (iii) $\dfrac{3\sqrt{5}}{2}$

    (d) $x > -\dfrac{7}{4}$

Exercise 4.2

1. $(2, 5)$

2. $(-2, 12)$

3. $(1, 1)$; minimum

4. $(5, -23)$, minimum; $(1, 9)$, maximum

5. (i) $(2, -15)$, minimum; $(-1, 12)$, maximum

    (ii) $(0, 0)$, minimum; $(-4, -8)$, maximum

6. $(1, 8)$, minimum; $(-1, -8)$, maximum

7. $(5, 75)$, minimum

8. $\left(\dfrac{1}{4}, -\dfrac{1}{4}\right)$, minimum

9. (i) $(-1, 3)$ (ii) $(2, 4)$

11. $a = 2, b = 3, c = 4$

12. $\dfrac{-4}{(x - 3)^2} \neq 0$

13. (ii) $\left(\dfrac{1}{2}, \dfrac{1}{2} + \ln 2\right)$, minimum point

14. (i) $(0, 1)$ (ii) minimum point

15. (a) $(2, 0)$, maximum; $(4, -4)$, minimum

16. (ii) minimum

17. $a = 2, b = -6, c = 0, d = 4$

19. (i) $a = 16$

    (ii) $g''(x) = 8 > 0 \Rightarrow$ no maximum turning point

20. (i) 70 km/hr (ii) $\dfrac{2800}{v^3}$ (iii) €40

Exercise 4.3

1. (ii)

2. (i) and (iii)

3. (i) Positive slope

    (ii) $x < -2$ or $x > 3$

    (iii) $-2 < x < 3$

    (iv) $-2, 3$

4. (i) Positive slope for $x < -1$

    (ii) Turning point at $x = -1$ (slope = 0)

    (iii) Negative slope for $x > 1$

    (The slope function of a quadratic curve is always linear.)

5. Ⓒ

6. Ⓑ

7. (i) $-2 < x < 1$ (ii) $x < -2$ or $x > 1$

    (iii) $x = -2, 1$

9. (i) (a) $x = -3$ (b) $x = 4$

    (ii) (a) $x < -3$ (b) $x > 4$

10. (i) (a) $x = -1, 3$ (b) $x = -4.5, 1$

    (ii) (a) $x < -1$ or $x > 3$

        (b) $-4.5 < x < 1$

11. C

13. (i) $a = 2, b = 4$ (ii) $k = \frac{3}{4}$

Exercise 4.4

1. 32

2. (i) $x = 12$ (ii) $P = 212$

3. $y = 50 - x$; $625\,m^2$

4. (i) $(8 - x)\,cm$ (ii) $8\,cm^2$

5. (i) $h = \dfrac{108}{x^2}$ (iii) 6 m by 6 m by 3 m

6. (i) $V = 4x^3 - 48x^2 + 144x$

7. (i) $h = \dfrac{27 - x^2}{2x}$

    (ii) Volume $= \dfrac{27x - x^3}{2}$

    (iii) $x = 3$; Volume $= 27\,cm^3$

8. (i) $P = \left(x, \dfrac{12 - 3x}{4} \right)$

    (ii) $\dfrac{x}{4}(12 - 3x)$

    (iii) $x = 2$; 3 square units

9. $V = \pi r(12 - r^2)$;

    $r = 2$

10. (i) $h = (20 - r)\,cm$

    (ii) $r = \dfrac{40}{3}\,cm$

11. (i) $\theta = \dfrac{8}{r} - 2$ (ii) Area $= 4r - r^2$

    (iii) For $r = 2$ m, maximum area $= 4\,m^2$

12. (a) (i) $|ST| = \sqrt{200}$ m

    (b) Length $= 5\sqrt{2}$ m; breadth $= \dfrac{5\sqrt{2}}{2}$ m

13. $r = \sqrt{9 - h^2}$; Volume $= 12\pi\sqrt{3}\,cm^3$

14. (a) (i) $|PS| = 6 - x$; $|RS| = 12 - \dfrac{8}{x}$

    (b) Max. $A = 32$ at $x = 2$ and min.
    $A = 20$ at $x = 1$ or $x = 4$

15. (i) $P = (x, -x^2 + 6x)$

    (ii) $\dfrac{1}{2}(x^3 - 12x^2 + 36x)$

    (iii) 16 sq. units

16. (i) $y = 60 - x$ (ii) $S = 5x^2(60 - x)$
    (iii) $0 < x < 60$ (iv) $x = 40, y = 20$
    (v) 74005

Exercise 4.5

1. 97

2. (i) 17   (ii) $x = 2$

3. (i) $10\pi\,cm^2$ per cm

    (ii) $20\pi\,cm^2$ per cm

4. $V = x^3$;

    (i) $300\,cm^3$ per cm   (ii) $75\,cm^3$

5. -50 people per year; the population is declining by 50 people per year after 3 years

6. (i) $1200t - 200t^2$

    (ii) €1800 per month

    (iii) At $t = 0$ and $t = 6$

7. (i) 35 m/sec   (ii) 20 m/sec^2

8. (i) 7 m/sec

    (ii) -2 m/sec^2

    (iii) After $\dfrac{2}{3}$ and 2 seconds

9. (i) 60 secs   (ii) 18 km

10. (i) 8 m

    (ii) When $t = 0$ or $t = 1\dfrac{1}{3}$ secs

11. (i) $t = \dfrac{2}{3}$, acceleration $= -2$;

    $t = 1$, acceleration $= 2$

    (ii) $t = \dfrac{5}{6}$, velocity $= -\dfrac{1}{6}$

12. (i) 3 cm to the left of O moving to the right at 24 cm/sec

    (ii) $v = 3t^2 - 22t + 24$

    (iii) After $\dfrac{4}{3}$ sec and 6 sec

    (iv) $11\dfrac{22}{27}$ cm to the right of O and 39 cm to the left of O

    (v) $4\dfrac{2}{3}$ sec

    (vi) $a = 6t - 22$

    (vii) When $t = \dfrac{11}{3}$ sec and the particle is $13\dfrac{16}{27}$ cm left of O moving to the left at $16\dfrac{1}{3}$ cm/sec

13. (i) $t = 0, n = 5$; $t = 10, n = 37$

    (ii) 3.2 per unit of time

    (iii) e (2.72)

Exercise 4.6

1. (i) $\dfrac{dr}{dt}$ (ii) $\dfrac{dt}{dr}$ (iii) $\dfrac{ds}{dt}$

2. (i) 2   (ii) 4

3. 20

4. 10π

5. $54\pi\,cm^2$/sec

6. $100\,cm^2$/sec

7. 2000

8. $\dfrac{1}{6\pi}$ cm/sec

9. $\dfrac{1}{6}$ cm/sec

10. (i) $(20x - x^2)\,cm^2$ (ii) $7\,cm^2$/sec

11. $5\sqrt{2}$

12. (i) $160,000\pi$ cm³/sec

(ii) 0.16 cm/sec

(iii) 640π cm²/sec

13. $\frac{4}{3}$ m/sec

14. $V = 4\pi r^3$; $\frac{dV}{dr} = 12\pi r^2$; 216π cm³/sec

15. $\frac{2}{3}$ cm/sec

Revision Exercise 4 (Core)

1. $7x - y - 15 = 0$

2. $(-2, 21)$, maximum; $(2, -11)$, minimum

3. $b = 3$

4. $-3 < x < 1$

5. (i) $x = 2$ (ii) $12x - y - 8 = 0$

6. (i) 72 m/sec   (ii) 2 secs

7. $\frac{\sqrt{3}}{2} - \frac{\pi}{3}$

8. Max. $P = 2500$

9. 12°C

10. $\frac{4}{25}$ cm/sec

11. $(-2, -4)$; $x > 2$

12. (i) $a = 3, b = 10, c = -8$

(ii) $\left(\frac{2}{3}, 0\right)$ and $(-4, 0)$

(iii) $\left(-1\frac{2}{3}, -16\frac{1}{3}\right)$

13. $\frac{1}{10}$ cm/sec

14. 20 secs; 1960 m

15. ⓒ, as the graph ⓒ is above the x-axis to illustrate that the slope of the given function is always positive

Revision Exercise 4 (Advanced)

1. $2x - y - 3 = 0$

2. $\left(\frac{1}{2}, \frac{1}{4} - \ln 2\right), (1, 1)$

3. (i) $\frac{2}{25\pi}$ m/min

(ii) 1.6 m²/min

4. (a) $(1, 3), (3, -3)$ (b) A$(1, 3)$

5. (ii) $x = 10$ cm, $h = 5$ cm;
minimum area $= 300$ cm²

6. (i) €$5\frac{13}{16}$ per hour   (ii) €5

7. $\frac{dy}{dx} = e^x(1 + x); \left(-1, -\frac{1}{e}\right)$; minimum

8. $(A, 2), (B, 4), (C, 1), (D, 3)$

9. $a = -3, b = -9, c = 12$

10. $\dfrac{800}{4 + \pi}$

11. A $= \left(\dfrac{-m - 2}{m}, 0\right)$, B $= (0, m + 2)$

(ii) 4 sq. units

12. D (both are correct)

13. $(0, 32)$ and $(-2k, 4k^3 + 32)$; $k = -2$

14. 2.7 m

15. (i)

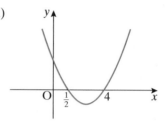

(ii)

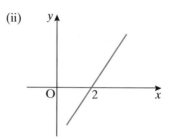

In the graph of $y = f(x)$, there is a point of inflection at $x = 2$, and at this point, $f''(x) = 0$

Revision exercise 4 (Extended Response Questions)

1. (a) 0.003 cm/sec

(b) 0.566 cm³/sec $\left(\text{based on } \dfrac{dx}{dt} = 0.003\right)$

or 0.48 cm³/sec $\left(\text{based on } \dfrac{dx}{dt} = \dfrac{0.008}{\pi}\right)$

2. (a) $h = 5 - 4x$

(c) $0 < x < \frac{5}{4}$

(d) $\dfrac{dV}{dx} = 30x - 36x^2$

(e) $\left(0, \frac{5}{6}\right)$; maximum volume $= 3\frac{17}{36}$ cm³

3. (i) (a) 20 m/sec   (b) 15 m/sec

(ii) $t = 4$ seconds

(iii) 82 m

(iv) -20 m/sec (it is descending)

(v) 40 m/sec

(vi) -40.5 m/sec when $t = 8.05$ seconds

4. (a) (i) $r = \sqrt{1 - x^2}$ (ii) $h = 1 + x$

(c) $0 < x < 1$

(d) (i) $\dfrac{dV}{dx} = \dfrac{\pi}{3}(1 - 2x - 3x^2)$

(ii) $\dfrac{1}{3}$

(iii) $\dfrac{32\pi}{81}\,\text{m}^3$

5. (i) $|AP| = \sqrt{x^2 + 36}\ \text{km};\ |PB| = (10 - x)\,\text{km}$
   (ii) 2.5 km
   (iii) 1 hr 53 mins

6. (a) $P = 10\,000$

   (b) $0 \leqslant x \leqslant 1 + \dfrac{\sqrt{6}}{2}$

   (d) $\dfrac{dP}{dr} = 40 - 40r$

   (e) $20, 0, -40$
   (f) $r = 1$; Population $= 30\,000$ people

7. (a) $h = 100\,\text{cm}$
   (b) $t = 400$ secs

   (c) $\dfrac{dV}{dt} = 680\,\text{cm}^3/\text{sec}$

   (d) Speed $= 216.32\,\text{cm/sec}$
   (e) Speed $= 27.04\sqrt{h}\,\text{cm/sec}$
   (f) $c = 0.6$

8. (a) $V = \dfrac{1}{3}\pi r^2 h$

   (b) $r = \dfrac{h}{10}$

   (c) $V = \dfrac{\pi h^3}{300}$

   (d) $\dfrac{dV}{dt} = 0.1\,\text{cm}^3/\text{sec}$

   (e) $\dfrac{dh}{dt} = \dfrac{2}{5\pi}\,\text{cm/sec}$

   (f) $\dfrac{dA}{dt} = \dfrac{1}{25}\,\text{cm}^2/\text{sec}$

9. (b) 2 and 7.83
   (c) $294\,\text{cm}^3$
   (d)

	Cups in part (b)		Cup in part (c)
radius (r)	8.77 cm	4.44 cm	7.35 cm
height (h)	2 cm	7.83 cm	5.20 cm
capacity (V)	161 cm³	161 cm³	294 cm³

   (e) Middle one: $r = 4.44\,\text{cm}$, $h = 7.83\,\text{cm}$
       Others are either too wide or too shallow
   (f) $178°$

10. (a) 450 birds
    (b) -9.098 birds per year
    (c) 150 birds
    (d) $t = 35.8$ years, i.e. in the 36th year

Chapter 5: Financial Maths

Exercise 5.1

1. €4031.75
2. €6092.01, €1092.01
3. $r = (1 + i)^{\frac{1}{12}} - 1$
4. (i) 0.49%   (ii) 0.21%   (iii) 0.33%
5. 4.5%
6.

Y	P	i
1	15 000	525
2	15 525	543.83
3	16 068.38	562.39
4	16 630.77	582.07
5	17 212.85	602.45

7. 1.98%
8. €27 830.10
9. (i) €14 375.34   (ii) €15 892.57
   (iii) €17 220.86
10. €6627.09
11. €16 822.61
12. 20.15 years
13. €422 049.95
14. 20.01 years
15. 0.4868%; €56.46; 4
16. €15 203.66

Exercise 5.2

1. (i) €13 311.16   (ii) €5906.23
2. €400.82
3. (i) €25 432   (ii) €15 618.43
4. (i) €57 344   (ii) €28 688.075
   (iii) €151 540.50   (iv) €65 508.43
5. $t = 5$ years
6. 6166 kg
7. (i) 7.8%   (ii) 13.53 years
8. (i) €300   (ii) €446.27
9. (i) €12 182.4   (ii) €4547.06
   (iii) €2357.19
10. (i) 36%   (iii) -1600
    (iv) (4.2, 1300)   (v) €845.66

Exercise 5.3

1. €790.66; €70.66
2. (i) 0.33%   (ii) €1148.55
3. €11 265.95
4. Proof

5. Proof

6. $P(1.09) + P(1.09)^2 + \ldots P(1.09)^5$; $A = €1000$

7. (i) i=0.7207%   (ii) €5257.31

8. €1017.23

9. €371.49

10. Proof

11. (i) €14 978.13   (ii) €23 768.41

Exercise 5.4

1. €1178.66

2. €103 800

3. €614; €565; €536; €72 394; €94 455; €117 798

4. Plan B

5. €17 738.11

6. The second offer is better

7. €13 068.78

Revision Exercise 5 (Core)

1. €6335.93   **2.** €36 778.58

3. €1024   **4.** €20 344.37

5. 16.1%; 34.5%

6. $200(1.0075) + 200(1.0075)^2 + 200(1.0075)^3 + \ldots$

$a = 200(1.0075)$, $r = (1.0075)$

$S_5 = 200(1.0075)\left[\dfrac{1.0075^5 - 1}{0.0075}\right]$

7. €9560.51

8. (i) €33 385.22   (ii) €19 000.13

(iii) €33 385.22

Revision Exercise 5 (Advanced)

1. (i) €211 205.4   (ii) €32 910.04

2. €100 000 gives €964 629.32; €1000 gives

€919 857.37

3. $i = 5\%$; €3571

4. €74 734

5. $i = 8.75\%$

6.

Pension fund	Interest
127 953	3838.59
116 791.59	3503.75
105 295.38	3158.86
93 454.24	2803.63
81 257.87	2437.74
68 695.61	2060.87
55 756.48	1672.69
42 429.17	1272.88
28 702.01	861.06
14 563.07	436.89

Revision Exercise 5 (Extended Response Questions)

1. €87 422.1; €11 954.75

2. (i) €673 292.26   (ii) €7173.3

(iii) €13 435.36

3. (i) $€P = \dfrac{€M(i)(1 + i)^n}{(1 + i)^n - 1}$

(ii) $i = 0.72\%$ monthly

(iii) 321

(iv) 26 years 9 months

4. (i) €140 254.1   (ii) 324 months

(iii) 135 months

5. (i) $A + A(1.04) + A(1.04)^2 + A(1.04)^3$

(ii) $S_{26} = A\left(\dfrac{(1.04)^{26} - 1}{1.04 - 1}\right)$

(iii) €485 199.00

(iv) Payment 1: €485 199;

Payment 3: €524 791.00

(v) Payment 2: €481 587;

Payment 4: €474 443.85

(vi) $\dfrac{485\,199(1.04)^n}{(1.0478)^n}$

(vii) €11 508, 316

(viii) 31%

Chapter 6: Length – Area – Volume

Exercise 6.1

1. (i) $\dfrac{a}{2 + a}$ (ii) $a = 8$

2. (i) $10x^2$ (ii) $5x^2$ (iii) $2:1$

3. Base = 13 cm, height = 8 cm

4. 9 cm, 40 cm

5. 12 m

6. 30°, 45°, 105°

7. (i) Parallelogram

(ii) $(|AD| + |BC|) \times h$

(iii) The area of the trapezium is half the area of the rectangle:

$\text{Area} = \dfrac{(|AD| + |BC|)}{2} \times h$

8. 15 cm, 21 cm

9. (i)   (ii)

(iii)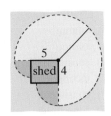

(iv) has the largest area

10. 30 cm²

11. (i) 19.99 cm

(ii) $h = 9.31$ cm, area $= 50.04$ cm²: also area
$= \frac{1}{2}(10.75)(10.75) \sin 60° = 50.04$ cm²

12. 38.605 m²

13. (i) $\angle EOD = 60°$

(ii) $\angle ODE = 60°$

(iii) 64.95 cm²

14. (i) $\alpha = 135°$, $\beta = 150°$, $\theta = 120°$

(ii) 134.8 cm²

15. (i) $x = 15.8$ cm (ii) $y = 4.65$ cm

16. Proof

Exercise 6.2

1. (i) 29.7 cm   (ii) 35.6 cm²

2. (i) 73 cm²   (ii) 38 cm

3. (a) $\dfrac{\pi r^2}{2}$ (b) $\pi(R^2 - r^2)$

(c) $(x + 2a)^2 - \pi a^2$ (d) $\dfrac{\pi a^2}{4} + ab$

(e) $\dfrac{a}{2}\sqrt{x^2 - \dfrac{a^2}{4}}$ (f) $\dfrac{\sqrt{3}a^2}{4}$

4. $r = \dfrac{P}{2 + \theta}$

5. 6.8 cm

6. (i) $2r^2$ (ii) $\dfrac{r^2}{4}(\pi - 2)$

7. Radius $= \dfrac{40}{\pi} \cong 12.73$ m,

Area $= \dfrac{1600}{\pi} \approx 509.30$ m² because we use an

approximation for π

8. (i) $1:2$ (ii) $4:1$

9. $\dfrac{42\sqrt{2}}{\pi}$

10. (i) $\dfrac{\pi}{3}$ radians   (ii) $6 + \dfrac{4\pi}{3}$ cm

(iii) $\dfrac{4\pi}{3} + \sqrt{3}$ cm²   (iv) $\dfrac{2\pi - 3\sqrt{3}}{3}$

11. Area $= \dfrac{r^2}{2}(\theta - \sin\theta); 3\pi + 2 : \pi - 2$

12. 153.71 cm²

13. $r = 6$ cm or 8 cm

14. 170 m²

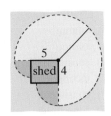

Exercise 6.3

1. (i) (a) 10.5 m²   (b) 18.5 m²

(c) 2771.3 cm²   (d) 560 cm²

(e) 336 cm²   (f) 749.4 cm²

(ii) (a) 2.1 m³   (b) 4.3 m³

(c) 7542.3 cm³   (d) 800 cm³

(e) 254 cm³   (f) 1128.5 cm³

2. (i) f: 2427 mm², d: 2121 mm², $b\backslash a$: 1257 mm²,
e: 905 mm², g: 805 mm², h: 720 mm²,
c: 283 mm², i: 195 mm²

(ii) f: 7238 mm², d: 7069 mm², a: 4189 mm²,
b: 2962 mm², e: 1810 mm², g: 1257 mm²,
h: 1056 mm², c: 339 mm², i: 144 mm²

3. (i) 4.92 m³

(ii) option 2 (€30 per 100 kg): €390

(iii) $V = \dfrac{h\tan\theta + 2a}{2}.h.w$

(iv) bottom $= 1.5$ m, top $= 2.7$ m

4. (i) $x = 2.5$ cm

(ii)  , triangular prism

(iii) 24 cm³

(iv)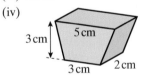

5. (i) 476.4 cm³   (ii) 1481.0 cm³

6. (i) 3 hr 23 min   (ii) 4 hr 46 min

7.   532 cm²

8. Volume = 422 cm³, Area = 484.16 cm²

9. (a) area   (b) length

(c) area   (d) length

(e) area + length

(f) length + area

(g) volume

(h) volume

10. (i) consistent   (ii) inconsistent

   (iii) inconsistent   (iv) consistent

   (v) consistent   (vi) inconsistent

   (vii) consistent

11. (i) 0.01%   (ii) 485012.5 ±9795.625 cm³

12. 130.425km; 138.425km

13. (i) 84 cm³   (ii) 12 cm, 148 cm²

   (iii) Volume = $\frac{m^3}{6}$, Area = $\frac{m^2}{2}(1 + \sqrt{2} + \sqrt{5})$

14. (i) (a) 2744 cm³   (b) $1437\frac{1}{3}$ cm³

   (c) 48%

   (ii) less, $33\frac{1}{3}$%

15. 496.4 cm³

Exercise 6.4

1. 0.134 ha

2. 17.61 cm²;   (i) 2.3%   (ii) 17.505 cm²

3. (i) 17.5 u^2 (ii) 17.75 u^2

4. 1.82 u^2

5. (i) 1:2.14   (ii) 2.75

6. 81 120 km²

Revision Exercise 6 (Core)

1. 2:5

2. (a) area = 1464 cm²; volume = 3589 cm³

   (b) area = 434 cm²; volume = 523 cm³

   (c) area = 25 500 cm²; volume = 225 000 cm³

3. (i) 1.28 rad (ii) 16 cm²   (iii) 1:1.391

4. Capacity = 450 m³, 750 hours

5. (i) $x = \sqrt{20}$ (ii) $x = 3.96$ cm

   (iii) $x = 0.99$ rads

6. Proof

7. No; Min possible size of envelope = 11.5 cm

   Max possible size of card = 11.6 cm

8. (i) ± 0.5 cm   (ii) 179 cm³   (iii) 14.6%

9. 74°; 72°

10. (i) (8.5±0.05)cm

   (ii) 213.72 cm³

   (iii) 1.59%

11. 28

12. (i) 10.6u^2 (ii) 16.73u^2

13. (i) $(10 + 2\sqrt{7})$ m (ii) $(4 + 2\sqrt{5} + 2\sqrt{6})$ m²

14. (i) 16π cm ≈ 50.3 cm

   (ii) 32π cm² ≈ 100.5 cm²

15. €38 186.72

16. 112.7 cm³

Revision Exercise 6 (Advanced)

1. (i) Proof   (ii) $r = 25$ (iii) $\theta = 2$ radians

2. (i) A: 2500 holes; B: 2822 holes

   (ii) A: 21.46%; B: 11.34%

3. (i) Area$_{PQO} = \frac{1}{2}r^2 \sin \theta$

   (ii) Area segment = $\frac{1}{2}r^2(\theta - \sin \theta)$

   (iii) Area$_{PQN} = \frac{1}{2}r^2(\sin (\pi - \theta))$

4. (d) Surface area = 56 077 cm²;

   volume = 133 518 cm³

   (e) Surface area = 1092 cm²;

   volume = 1767 cm³

   (f) Surface area = 332 cm²;

   volume = 436 cm³

5. (i) 4.189 cm²   (ii) 2.4567 cm²

6. (i) 1.84 rads   (ii) 80.96 m

   (iii) 26.7 m   (iv) 848 m²

7. Proof

   (i) $r = 3.0$ cm   (ii) $A = 19.95$ cm²

8. (i) $A - B$: increasing speed (accelerating)

   nearly uniformly

   $C - D$: starts to slow down

   $E - F$: Having stopped starts to move

   again

   (ii) Distance

   (iii) 5.47 km

9. Proof

10. 840 mm²

Revision Exercise 6 (Extended Response Questions)

1. (i) (a) $l = r\theta$

   (b) $A = \frac{1}{2}r^2\theta$

   (ii) $A = 2r - r^2$ ... Proof

   (iii) $A = 1 - (r - 1)^2$

   (iv)

   (v) $\theta = 2$ radians

2. (i) Areas are the same ... false
Triangle longer by 10.18% ... true
Difference of 9.24% ... true
(ii) 57.52°
(iii) No

3. (i) $A = 4h^2 - 80h + 400$
(ii) $h = \frac{20}{3}$ cm
(iii) $V = 4h^3 - 80h^2 + 400h$

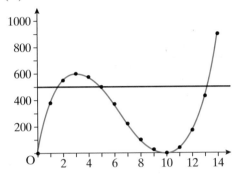

(iv) $h = 3.5$ cm
(v) $h = 2$ cm, 5 cm, 13 cm
(vi) $h > 10 \Rightarrow 20 - 2(10) = 0 \Rightarrow$ no volume

4. (i) $A = 150$ cm²
(ii) 4.8%
(iii) $a = 0.66, b = 0.87, c = 0.96$
(iv) Derivation
(v) $A = \frac{r^2}{4}(5.92) = 1.495r^2$
(vi) $A_5 = 37$ cm², $A_{10} = 149.5$ cm², $A_{15} = 336$ cm²
(vii) Since $A = \frac{\pi r^2}{2} = 1.57r^2$, the formula underestimates the area by 5.78%

5. (i) $l = 15 - h, w = 20 - 2h$, height $= h$
(ii) Volume $= 2h^3 - 50h^2 + 300h$
(iii) $h = 5$ cm
(iv) $V = 500$ cm³
(v) $h = 2.9$ cm
(vi)

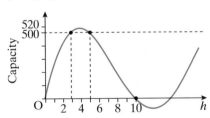

(vii) No, it is not possible, new capacity would be $500 + 50 = 550$ cm³ and no value of h would give a capacity of 550 cm³

Chapter 7: Probability 2

Exercise 7.1

1. (ii) $\frac{7}{12}$ (or $\frac{28}{48}$)

2. (ii) $\frac{13}{18}$ (iii) $\frac{5}{36}$

3. (i) $\frac{12}{35}$ (ii) $\frac{6}{35}$ (iii) $\frac{18}{35}$

4. (ii) $\frac{9}{25}$ (iii) $\frac{12}{25}$

5. (ii) $\frac{1}{3}$ (iii) $\frac{5}{18}$

6. (ii) $\frac{2}{27}$

7. (i) $\frac{7}{15}$ (ii) $\frac{8}{15}$

8. (ii) $\frac{2}{5}$ (iii) $\frac{3}{5}$

9. (ii) $\frac{13}{60}$

10. (ii) $\frac{4}{15}$

11. (i) 0.3 (or 30%) (ii) $\frac{18}{25}$

12. $\frac{35}{216}$

Exercise 7.2

1. 10 **2.** 6.5 **3.** €12.75 **4.** 4

5. −0.2 **6.** 1.43 **7.** 1.5

8. Expect to win €3$\frac{1}{3}$; not fair as mathematical expectation $\neq 0$

9. €0; yes, since expected amount is zero.

10. €22.50; loss as bet is €25

11. €190

12. (i) 0.3 (ii) 2.9

13. Lose €16.67

14. (i) $p + q = 0.4; 2p + 4q = 1$
(ii) $p = 0.3, q = 0.1$

15. (i) 0.0456 (ii) €77.84
(iii) €361.89 (iv) €427.50

16. 13$\frac{1}{3}$

17. Play dice; cards (lose €6.25); dice (lose €3.33)
Difference = €2.92

Exercise 7.3

1. $\frac{125}{1296}$

2. $\frac{25}{216}$

3. $\frac{162}{3125}$

4. 0.059

5. (i) $\frac{300}{2197}$ (ii) $\frac{27}{256}$ (iii) $\frac{1}{4}$

6. (i) Fixed number of independent trials with two outcomes that have constant probabilities

(ii) $\frac{1}{2}; \frac{1}{2}; 8$

7. (i) $\frac{5}{32}$ (ii) $\frac{5}{16}$

8. (i) $\frac{3125}{7776}$ (ii) $\frac{3125}{7776}$ (iii) $\frac{625}{3888}$

9. $\frac{560}{2187}$

10. $\frac{5}{16}$

11. (i) 0.028 (ii) 0.31

12. 0.124 $\left(\text{or } \frac{48384}{360625}\right)$

13. $\frac{1}{9}$

14. (i) $\frac{96}{625}$ (ii) $\frac{608}{625}$

15. (i) $\frac{81}{625}$ (ii) $\frac{96}{625}$ (iii) $\frac{544}{625}$

16. (i) $\frac{441}{1000}$ (ii) $\frac{189}{2500}$

17. (i) $\frac{144}{625}$ (ii) $\frac{72}{3125}$

18. (i) 750 (ii) 125 (iii) 1875

19. (ii) $\frac{1}{81}$ (iii) $\frac{1}{3}, \frac{32}{81}$

20. (i) 0.29071 (ii) 0.04845

21. (i) $\frac{3}{13}$ (ii) 0.0588

22. 0.08

23. (i) 0.27869 (ii) 0.11148

24. (i) 0.0563 (ii) 0.00309; 0.07508

Exercise 7.4

1. (i) $\frac{2}{5}$ (ii) $\frac{1}{3}$ (iii) $\frac{2}{15}$

2. (i) $\frac{1}{3}$ (ii) $\frac{1}{4}$

3. Yes; $P(A) \times P(B) = P(A \cap B)$

4. 0.1

5. 0.5

6. (i) 0.1 (ii) $P(A \cap B) \neq P(A).P(B)$

(iii) $\frac{2}{7}$

7. (i) 0.56

(ii) $P(A \cap B) = P(A) \times P(B) = 0.56$

8. (i) $\frac{2}{15}$

(ii) $P(A).P(B) = \frac{1}{15}$ and $P(A \cap B) = \frac{2}{15}$
$\Rightarrow$ not equal

9. (i) $\frac{2}{3}$ (ii) $\frac{1}{2}$

10. 0.49; No, as $0.49 \neq 0.42$

11. (i) 0.03 (ii) 0.2 (iii) 0.32

12. (ii) 0.2 (iii) 0.2

(iv) Yes, as $P(A \cap B) = P(A).P(B) = 0.15$

13. (i) $\frac{1}{15}$ (ii) $\frac{11}{15}$ (iii) $\frac{1}{5}$

14. (i) Independent events; obtaining a head when a coin is tossed

(ii) They are mutually exclusive; zero

15. (i) $P(A) = 0.48$; $P(B) = 0.3$

(ii) $P(A).P(B) \neq P(A \cap B)$

(iii) 0.36

16. $P(E \cap F) \neq 0$ and $P(A \cap B) \neq P(A).P(B)$

Exercise 7.5

1. (i) 0.025 (ii) $\frac{11}{4165}$ (or 0.00264)

(iii) $\frac{46}{833}$ (iv) $\frac{44}{4165}$

2. 330; (i) $\frac{5}{11}$ (ii) $\frac{2}{11}$ (iii) $\frac{1}{66}$

3. (i) $\frac{1}{364}$ (ii) $\frac{1}{91}$ (iii) $\frac{9}{91}$ (iv) $\frac{55}{182}$

4. (i) $\frac{16}{81}$ (ii) $\frac{1}{6}$

5. (i) $\frac{2}{3}$ (ii) $\frac{5}{42}$

6. (i) $\frac{11}{46}$ (ii) $\frac{30}{49}$

7. (i) 120 (ii) 56 (iii) $\frac{7}{15}$ (iv) $\frac{14}{15}$

8. (i) $\frac{1}{2}$ (ii) $\frac{1}{40}$ (iii) $\frac{1}{20}$ (iv) $\frac{9}{20}$

9. $\frac{20}{147}$

10. (i) $\frac{1}{56}$ (ii) $\frac{3}{28}$ (iii) $\frac{1}{14}$ (iv) $\frac{11}{56}$

Exercise 7.6

1. Allocate numbers 1 to 20 and use random number table.

2. Allocate numbers 1 to 8, giving 1 and 2 to fish; 3 to vegetarian; 4, 5, 6, 7, 8 to meat.

3. (i) 0.3125 (ii) 0.0625

4. Generate random numbers; 0 and 1 the cars turn right; 2 to 9 the cars turn left; generate using the random number key on your calculator.

5. (i) 14

6. 23 **7.** 0.52 **8.** 3

Revision Exercise 7 (Core)

1. (i) 0.2 (ii) 0.5 (iii) 0.4

2. (ii)

3. 0.4116

4. (i) 142506 (ii) 51300

(iii) $\frac{950}{2639}$ (or 0.36)

5. (i) $\frac{4}{625}$ (ii) $\frac{64}{625}$

6. (i) $\frac{256}{625}$ (ii) $\frac{64}{625}$

7. (i) $\frac{2}{5}$ (ii) $\frac{3}{10}$

8. (i) 0.5   (ii) 0.8

   (iii) 0.9; $P(E \cap F) = P(E).P(F)$; 0.5

9. 23 cent

10. $\frac{1}{2}$

Revision Exercise 7 (Advanced)

1. $\frac{20}{27}$

2. 0.75

3. (i) $\frac{1}{35}$ (ii) $\frac{11}{35}$

4. (i) $\frac{3}{8}$ (ii) $\frac{2}{13}$ (iii) $\frac{27}{110}$ (iv) $\frac{13}{25}$

5. (i) Proof   (ii) (a) $\frac{1}{6}$ (b) $\frac{1}{4}$

6. (i) 0.15   (ii) $\frac{7}{15}$ (iii) $\frac{1}{10}$

7. (i) $\frac{19}{27}$ (ii) $\frac{1}{2}$

8. Lose €5; not fair since expected payout not zero.

9. (i) 0.2 $\left(\text{or } \frac{3125}{15552}\right)$ (ii) 0.067 $\left(\text{or } \frac{3125}{46656}\right)$

10. (i) $\frac{1}{6}$

   (ii) $\frac{1}{4}$; Yes as $P(E \cap F) = P(E).P(F)$

Revision Exercise 7 (Extended Response Questions)

1. (i) ABEH, ACEH

   (ii) $\frac{3}{4}$ (iii) $\frac{3}{8}$ (iv) $\frac{1}{16}$

2. (i) 0.063   (ii) 0.309   (iii) 0.042

3. (a) (i) $\frac{1}{5}$ (ii) $\frac{5}{13}$ (iii) $\frac{17}{25}$

   (b) $\frac{1}{6}$ (independent of p)

4. (i)

	Girl	Boy	Total
Basketball	6	8	14
~~Basketball~~	9	5	14
	15	13	28

   (ii) $\frac{15}{28}$ (iii) $\frac{1}{2}$ (iv) $\frac{1}{2}$ (v) $\frac{3}{7}$

   (vi) $\frac{2}{5}$ (vii) $\frac{8}{13}$ (viii) $\frac{3}{14}$

5. (i) $\frac{1}{14}$ (ii) $\frac{97}{105}$ (iii) $\frac{37}{42}$

   (iv) $\frac{17}{21}$; no, since answers to (iii) and (iv) are different

6. (i) $\frac{3}{4}$ (ii) $\frac{8}{25}$ (iii) $\frac{44}{75}$

   (iv) No   (v) No

7. (a) (i) 0.6   (ii) $a = 0.3$, $b = 0.3$

   (b) 3 boys (9 girls)

8. (i) Spinner: $E(x) = 4$; Dice: $E(x) = 3.5$; Spinners have better chance

9. (i) $\frac{5}{16}$ (ii) 0.149

10. (i) $\frac{1}{3}$ (ii) $\frac{37}{45}$

   (iii) Yes, as $P(E \cap F) = P(E).P(F)$

   (iv) No, as $P(E \cup F) \neq P(E) + P(F)$

Chapter 8: Functions and Graphs

Exercise 8.1

1. The input 2 has two different outputs, i.e., 5 and 10

2. (i) Is a function

   (ii) Not a function, as -2 has two different outputs

   (iii) Is a function

3. (i) Yes

   (ii) No, as input a has two different outputs

   (iii) No, as input 9 has two different outputs

   (iv) Yes

4. $(-1, 6), (0, -4), (1, -2), (2, 0), (3, 2)$; Range $= \{-6, -4, -2, 0, 2\}$

5. (i) 4   (ii) -11 (iii) $3k - 2$ (iv) $6k - 5$

6. (i) 4   (ii) 36   (iii) 36

   (iv) $a^2 - 4a + 4$

7. $k = \frac{8}{9}$

8. $k = \frac{1}{3}$

9. (i) $x = \pm\sqrt{2}$ (ii) $x = 15$ (iii) $x = -1, 1\frac{1}{2}$

10. (i) $\frac{1}{2}$; 11   (ii) 2   (iii) $\frac{5}{2}$

11. (i) $-4k - 3$ (ii) $k = -4$

12. (i) $x = -\frac{8}{3}$ (ii) $x = 1$ (iii) $x = \frac{13}{18}$

13. (i) $x = -1, 3$ (ii) $x = -2, 3$ (iii) $x = 1$

14. (i) Yes   (ii) Yes   (iii) Yes

   (iv) No   (v) Yes   (vi) No

   (vii) Yes   (viii) Yes   (ix) No

15. Ⓐ and ⑤; Ⓑ and ⑥; Ⓒ and ①; Ⓓ and ②; Ⓔ and ②; Ⓕ and ④

16. (i) Domain $= \mathbb{R}$; Range $= [-2, \infty)$

   (ii) Domain $= (-\infty, 2]$; Range $= \mathbb{R}$

   (iii) Domain $= [-2, 3]$; Range $= [0, 9]$

   (iv) Domain $= [-3, 1)$; Range $= [-6, 2]$

(v) Domain = $[-4, 0]$; Range = $[0, 4]$
(vi) Domain = $\mathbb{R}$; Range = $(-\infty, 4)$

17. (i), (iii), (iv) and (vi) are functions

18. $k = 2$

19. $p = -2, q = 1; x = 1$

20. (i) $-3b + c = -9$ and $c = -3$

    (ii) $b = 2, c = -3$

    (iii) $D = (1, 0)$

Exercise 8.2

1. (i) 10   (ii) 19   (iii) 5   (iv) 26
    (v) 101   (vi) 9   (vii) 33   (viii) 1

2. (i) 7   (ii) 25   (iii) -21
    (iv) $8x + 1$; 3

3. (i) 11   (ii) 2   (iii) $2x^2 + 3$
    (iv) $4x^2 - 4x + 3$; $x = 0, 2$

4. (i) $2^{4x + 2}$ (ii) $3 + 2^{x + 1}$

5. $12x^2 + 12x + 3$; $a = -1, 0$

6. (i) $4x - 3; 4x + 3$ (ii) -9

7. (i) $c = 2$ (ii) $m = -1$

8. $s = 1, t = 2$

9. $\frac{1}{2}$

10. (i) $hf(x) = \log_2(x^2 - x + 10)$;
           $hg(x) = \log_2(5 - x)$

    (ii) $x = 3$, as $x > 0$ (log of negative number
         is undefined)

11. (i) $4x + 9$ (ii) $8x + 21$
    (iii) $16x + 45$; $f^n(x) = 2^n x + 3(2^n - 1)$

12. $-2x^2 - 1 \neq 4x^2 - 4x + 2$; composition of
    functions is not commutative

13. Yes; both equal to x

15. (i) $f(x) = x^2$ and $g(x) = 3x - 1$

    (ii) $f(x) = 5x + 3$ and $g(x) = \frac{1}{x}$

    (iii) $f(x) = x^2, g(x) = \sin x, k(x) = 3x$

    (iv) $f(x) = 2x, g(x) = \sqrt{x}, h(x) = \cos x$

16. $2^{4x + 2}$; $x = 1$

17. $f(r) = \frac{5t}{4}$;

    (i) $A(r) = \pi r^2$ (ii) $A = g(r) = \pi\left(\frac{5t}{4}\right)^2$

18. (i) This function represents 4% of sales.
    (ii) This function represents the value
         of sales in excess of €4000;
         $fg(x) = 0.04(x - 4000)$ represents
         average weekly commission; €160

Exercise 8.3

1. (a) (i) f is a function
        (ii) f is not injective
        (iii) f is not surjective

    (b) (i) g is a function
        (ii) g is injective
        (iii) g is surjective;
            There is an exact one-to-one
            correspondence between the elements
            in A and B; hence bijective

2. (i) Yes   (ii) No   (iii) No
    (iv) Not both injective and surjective

3. (a) Surjective
    (b) Injective
    (c) Bijective

4. (i) Yes   (ii) No   (iii) Yes;
         Not a one-to-one correspondence

5. (i) (a), (b), (d), (e) and (f) are functions
    (ii) Only (b) and (e) are injective functions

6. Injective because any horizontal line will
    intersect the curve at most once.
    Surjective because any horizontal line will
    intersect the curve at least once

7. (i) Yes   (ii) Yes

8. (i) $y \geqslant -1$
    (ii) $\mathbb{R}$
    (iii) Range not equal to codomain
    (iv) Codomain: $y \geqslant -1$
    (v) Line intersects the curve more than once
    (vi) $x \geqslant 3$ or $x \leqslant 3$

9. (i) No; a horizontal line will intersect the
        curve more than once
    (ii) Yes; as range and codomain are equal
    (iii) $x \geqslant 2$ or $x \leqslant 2$

10. (i) Not injective
    (ii) Is surjective; No; not both injective and
         surjective

11. A vertical line will intersect the curve more
    than once; $y \geqslant 0$ or $y \leqslant 0$

12. (i) N
    (ii) N
    (iii) All even numbers
    (iv) Codomain and range not equal
    (v) Yes
    (vi) Codomain should be the set of even
         positive numbers

13. (i) No; a horizontal line will intersect the
        graph more than once

(ii) Yes; a horizontal line will intersect the graph at least once

(iii) $\pi \leqslant x \leqslant 3\pi$

14. (i) Yes, as a horizontal line will intersect the graph at least once

(ii) No, as a horizontal line will intersect the graph more than once

(iii) $x \geqslant 0$; $y \geqslant 0$

15. (i) $y > 0$　　(ii) Yes　　(iii) Yes

(iv) Because it is both injective and surjective

Exercise 8.4

1. $f^{-1}(x) = x + 4$

2. $f^{-1}(x) = \dfrac{x + 3}{2}$

3. $f^{-1}(x) = \dfrac{x - 3}{5}$

4. $f^{-1}(x) = \dfrac{x}{3}$

5. $f^{-1}(x) = \dfrac{5x}{2}$

6. $f^{-1}(x) = \dfrac{2x + 3}{4}$

7. $f^{-1}(x) = \dfrac{-6}{x - 1}$

8. $f^{-1}(x) = \dfrac{x}{x - 3}$

9. $f^{-1}(x) = \dfrac{10 - 3x}{2}$

10. $f^{-1}(x) = \dfrac{x - 5}{4}$; Yes

11. $f^{-1}(x) = 3(x + 2)$

12. (i)

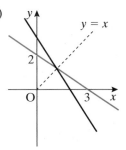

(ii)

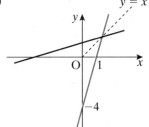

(iii)

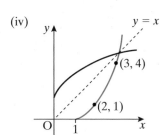

(iv)

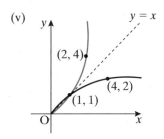

(v)

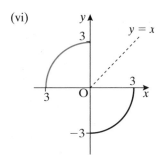

(vi)

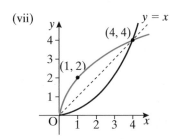

(vii)

(viii)

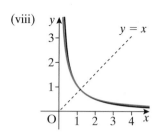

(ix)

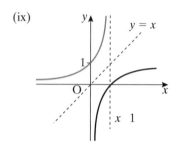

13. (i) $l: x - 3y + 4 = 0$; $m: 3x - y - 4 = 0$

14. $k = 2$

15. (i) $gf(x) = 2x - 7$; $[gf(x)]^{-1} = \dfrac{x + 7}{2}$

(ii) Yes

16. $f^{-1}(x) = 2x - 3$; Domain of $f^{-1}(x) = \left[1\tfrac{1}{2}, 4\right]$
$(= $ Range of f); Range of $f^{-1}(x) = [0, 5]$

17. (i) $f^{-1}(x) = -2 + \sqrt{x + 10}, x \geqslant -10$

(ii) $f^{-1}(x) = 1 + \sqrt{x + 6}, x \geqslant -6$

(iii) $f^{-1}(x) = 4 + \sqrt{x + 19}, x \geqslant -19$

(iv) $f^{-1}(x) = -4 + \sqrt{x - 4}, x \geqslant 4$

18. $f^{-1}(x) = 3 - 2x$; Domain of $f^{-1}(x) =$
$\left[-\tfrac{1}{2}, 2\right]$; Range of $f^{-1}(x) = [-1, 4]$

19. $A \leqslant 3$ $[$or $(-\infty, 3]]$

20. $b = 0$; $g^{-1}(x) = \sqrt{1 - x}, x \leqslant 1$;
Domain of $g(x) = (1, -3)$ or $(-3, 1)$

Exercise 8.5

1.

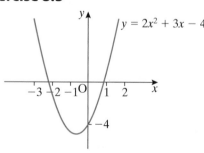

$y = 2x^2 + 3x - 4$

2. (i) $(0, 0)$ and $(4, 0)$

(ii) $(-2, 0)$ and $(4, 0)$

(iii) $(-1, 0)$ and $(3, 0)$

(i)

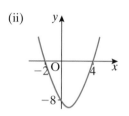

(ii)

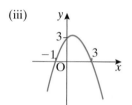

(iii)

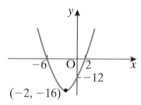

3. (i) $(x - 2)^2 - 2$

(ii) $(x - 6)^2$

(iii) $-(x - 4)^2 + 4$

4. $(x + 2)^2 - 16$; Intersects x-axis at $(-6, 0)$
and $(2, 0)$; Turning point $= (-2, -16)$

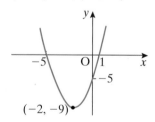

5. x-axis at $(1, 0)$ and $(-5, 0)$; y-axis at $(0, -5)$;
$(x + 2)^2 - 9$; $(-2, -9)$

6. $\left(x + \frac{3}{2}\right)^2 - \frac{49}{4}; \left(-\frac{3}{2}, -\frac{49}{4}\right);$ x-axis at $(-5, 0)$
and $(2, 0)$; y-axis at $(0, -10)$

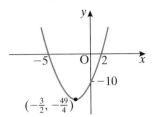

7. $a = -4, c = 8$

8. (i) $y = x^2$
(ii) $y = x^2 - 4x + 3$
(iii) $y = -\frac{5}{4}(x + 3)(x - 1)$

9. Graph Ⓑ

10. Graph Ⓓ

11. $y = (x + 1)^2 + 3$, i.e. $y = x^2 + 2x + 4$

12. (a) Intersects x-axis at $(-1, 0), (-2, 0)$ and $(3, 0)$; y-axis at $(0, -6)$
(b) Intersects x-axis at $(-3, 0), (0, 0)$ and $(6, 0)$; y-axis at $(0, 0)$
(c) Intersects x-axis at $(-2, 0)$ and $(1, 0)$; y-axis at $(0, -4)$
(d) Intersects x-axis at $(0, 0), (-3, 0)$ and $(3, 0)$; y-axis at $(0, 0)$

13. (i) Intersects x-axis at $(0, 0), (1, 0)$ and $(3, 0)$; y-axis at $(0, 0)$
(ii) Intersects x-axis at $(-3, 0), (\frac{1}{2}, 0)$ and $(2, 0)$; y-axis at $(0, 6)$
(iii) Intersects x-axis at $(-2, 0), (1, 0)$ and $(4, 0)$; y-axis at $(0, -8)$
(iv) Intersects x-axis at $(-3, 0), (0, 0)$ and $(3, 0)$; y-axis at $(0, 0)$

(i)

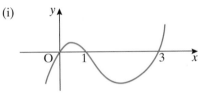

(ii)

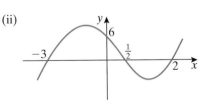

(iii)

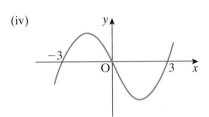

(iv)

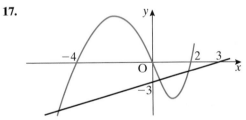

14. (i) Graph Ⓑ (ii) Graph Ⓒ
(iii) Graph Ⓑ (iv) Graph Ⓑ

15. $y = x^3 - x^2$ and Ⓒ ; $y = 1 - x^2$ and Ⓐ;
$y = x - x^2$ and Ⓑ ; $y = -\frac{3}{4}x + 3$ and Ⓕ;
$y = x^2 + 3x$ and Ⓔ ; $y = 9x - x^3$ and Ⓓ

16. (i) -27
(ii) $(-1, 5)$
(iii) $x = -2.8, x = 1.8, x = 3.9$
(iv) $-1 < x < 3$
(v) The line $y = 10$ intersects the graph at one point only
(vi) The line $y = -10$ intersects the graph at three points
(vii) $-27 < k < 5$

17.

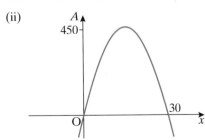

3 intersection points

18. $y = -\frac{2}{5}(x + 2)(x - 1)(x - 5)$

19. (i) $A = x(60 - 2x) \, \text{m}^2$

(ii)

(iii) $450 \, \text{m}^2$

20. (i) $-\frac{1}{2}(x-2)^2(x+1)$

    (ii) Because every output does not have a unique input.

    (iii) Yes, no element in the codomain is left unused.

    (iv) For every element in the range there is not a unique element in the domain (it is not injective and surjective)

    (v) Proof

21. (a)

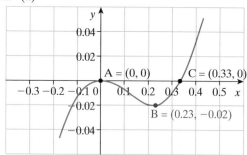

    (b)

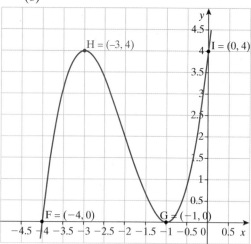

22.

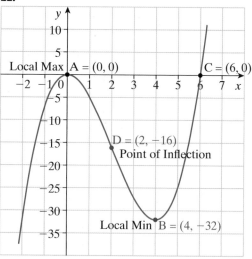

23. (i) Maximum, Minimum and Saddle points

    (ii) (a) Increasing: $x < 1$

        (b) Decreasing: $x > 1$

    (iii)

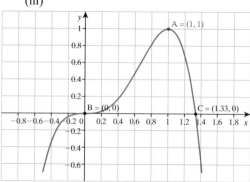

24. (i) $f(x) = (x-3)^2 + 9$

    (ii) $P = (0, 18)$, $Q = (3, 9)$

    (iii) $x = 3 + 4\sqrt{2}$ (as $x \geqslant 0$)

Exercise 8.6

1. (i) Ⓐ and the first; Ⓑ and the second

    (ii) $P = (0, 1)$

    (iii) Ⓐ: $y = 0$; Ⓑ: $y = 0$

2. $f(0.5) = 5.65$

3. A is $f(x) = 3.3^x$; B is $f(x) = 3^x$; C is $f(x) = 2^x$

4. (i) $k = 5$ (ii) $y = 5.2^x$

5. $a = \frac{3}{2}$

6. (i) 5.2

(ii) -1.25

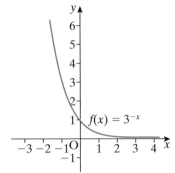

7. Range $= \left[2\frac{3}{4}, 26\right]$

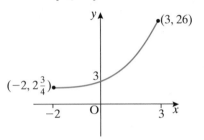

8. $a = \dfrac{14}{e - 1}, b = \dfrac{-14}{e - 1}$

9. (i) $a = \frac{1}{2}$ (ii) $b = \frac{3}{2}$

10. $x = 1.3$

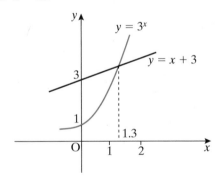

11.

12. $a = 2, b = 4$

13. $a = 3$

14. (c): $f(x) = \log_3(x - 3)$

15. Graph Ⓑ

16. $q = 13$

17. (i) $T_0 = 100$ (ii) $332°C$

18. (i) 4433   (ii) 347 years

19. (i) 180   (ii) 20   (iii) 200

20. $k = \dfrac{1}{10}\ln\left(\dfrac{10}{9}\right)(= 0.0105)$; half-life $= 65.8$ years

Exercise 8.7

1.

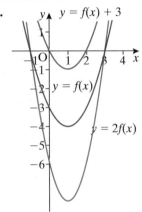

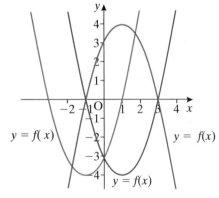

2. $g(x) = -f(x)$; $h(x) = f(x) + 3$

3.

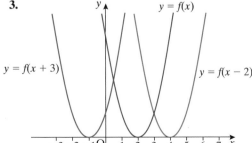

4. Graph Ⓓ

5. (i)

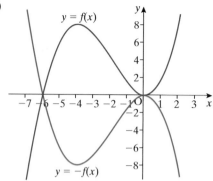

(ii)

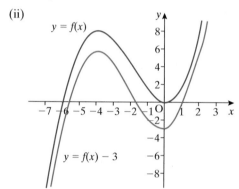

6. Graph Ⓒ

7. Graph Ⓐ

8.

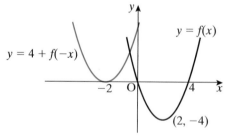

9. (i)

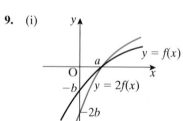

(ii)

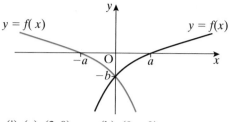

10. (i) (a) $(2, 0)$ (b) $(0, -2)$
    (ii) Graph Ⓓ

Revision Exercise 8 (Core)

1. $gf(x) = (2x - 3)^2$; $x = 0$ or $x = 3$

2. Ⓐ and $y = x^2 - 2$; Ⓑ and $y = 2 - x^2$;
    Ⓒ and $y = 2x$

3. Range $= \left\{ \dfrac{1}{2}, \dfrac{2}{3}, \dfrac{3}{4}, \dfrac{4}{5}, \dfrac{5}{6} \right\}$

4. $y = \dfrac{x}{11}(x + 7)$

5. $g^{-1}(x) = 2x - 10$;   (i) -14 (ii) $x = 10$

6. (i) $C = (0, 1)$ (ii) $a = 4$

7. (i) $x = -2, 1, 3$
    (ii) $x = 1.4$ or $x = 2.8$
    (iii) $x = -1.5$ or $x = 0$;
       No; a horizontal line will cut the graph at
       more than one point;
       Any horizontal line will cut the graph at
       least once.

8. (i) $m = 3$ (ii) $P = (0, 2)$

9. (i) proof
    (ii) $a = 3, b = 2$; $x = 0$(Min), $x = -2$(Max)

10. $(x + 1)^2 - 1$; $(-1, -1)$

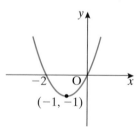

11. (i) (a) Domain $= \mathbb{R}$; Range is $y \geqslant -2$
       (b) Domain is $x \leqslant 2$; Range is $\mathbb{R}$
       (c) Domain is $-4 \leqslant x \leqslant 0$;
          Range is $0 \leqslant y \leqslant 4$
    (ii) (a) is the only function; a vertical line
       will intersect graphs (b) and (c) more
       than once

12. A and $y = \left(\frac{1}{2}\right)^x$; B and $y = 3^{-x}$;

C and $y = 5^x$; D and $y = 2^x$

13.

t	0	1	2	3	4
v	0·3	0·7	1·8	5·0	13·6

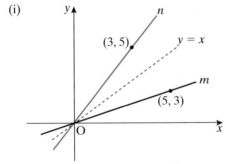

14. (i) $fg(x) = 10x + 30$;

$(fg)^{-1}(x) = \dfrac{x - 30}{10}$

15. (a) $fg(x) = x^2 + 8x + 19$; $gf(x) = x^2 + 7$

(b) $b^2 - 4ac = -36$ and so no real roots

16. (i) $y \geqslant 0$

(ii) $g^{-1}(x) = \dfrac{3x + 1}{2x}$

(iii) $x \in \mathbb{R}, x \neq \dfrac{3}{2}$

(iv) $x = \dfrac{5}{3}$ or $x = \dfrac{4}{3}$

Revision Exercise 8 (Advanced)

1. (i) $hf(x) = \log_3(x - 1)$;

$hg(x) = \log_3(2x^2 - x - 1)$

(ii) $x = 1$ or $x = 4$

2. (a) and Ⓒ; (b) and Ⓑ; (c) and Ⓓ; (d) and Ⓐ

3. (i)

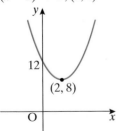

(ii) $-4 \leqslant x \leqslant 4$; $0 \leqslant y \leqslant 4$

4. $(x - 2)^2 + 8$; $(2, 8)$

5. $V = x(24 - 2x)(18 - 2x)$; $18 - 2x > 0$,

i.e. $x < 9$, i.e. $0 < x < 9$

6. (i) $a = 2, b = 3$

(ii) (a) $x = 1$

(b) $x \in \mathbb{R} \backslash \{1\}$

(c) Range $= \mathbb{R} \backslash \{0\}$

(d) Yes; a horizontal line will intersect the graph at most once

7. (ii)

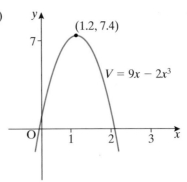

(iii) (a) $x = 1.2$ (b) $7.4 \, \text{m}^3$

8. (a) Range of g: $y \geqslant 1$ (c) $x = 3, x = -\dfrac{7}{3}$

(b) $x = 0, x = 1$ (d) $q = -\dfrac{3}{2}$

9. (i) $t = -5$; $k = -2$ (ii) $\dfrac{4}{3}$

10. (i) $-5 \leqslant x \leqslant 5$; $[0, 5]$

(ii) (a) $(0, 1)$

(b)

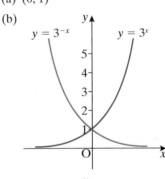

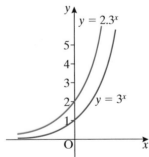

11. $A = 5$;

t	0	5	10	15	20
P	5	6.4	8.2	10.6	13.6

; $t = 13.9$ days for population to double

12. (i) $x \geqslant 4$ and $x \leqslant 3$

(ii) (a) A vertical line will intersect the graph once only

(b) No   (c) Yes   (d) $\dfrac{\pi}{2} \leqslant x \leqslant \dfrac{3\pi}{2}$

13. Graph Ⓒ

14. (i) You cannot have a negative number of predators or if $n = 0$, the population would not change.

(ii) Minimum number of birds = 50 when $n = 10$.

(iii)

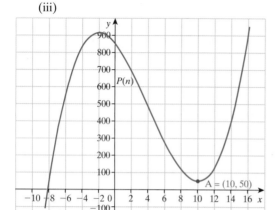

Revision Exercise 8 (Extended Response Questions)

1. (a) $a = 2, b = -6$; Turning point $= (-2, -6)$

(b) Intersects x-axis at -4.45 and 0.45; Intersects the y-axis at $(0, -2)$

(c) Discriminant $= \sqrt{24}$; since discriminant > 0, the curve will intersect the x-axis at two distinct points

(d) $k > 4$

2. (a) $a = -0.09, b = 9$

(b) $|DE| = 2.79\,m$

(c) Length of bar $= 2 \times \sqrt{30} = 10.95\,m$

3. (a) $a = 2, b = 3$

(b) (iii)

4. (a) Graph Ⓓ

(b) (i) (a) $N_0 = 20000$ (b) $k = -0.223$

(ii) 6.2 years

5. (a) $\mathbb{R}$

(b) (i) $fg(x) = \dfrac{1}{(x-3)^3}$ (ii) $x = \dfrac{13}{4}$

(c) (i) $g^{-1}(x) = \dfrac{1 + 3x}{x}$

(ii) Range of g^{-1} = domain of $g = \mathbb{R}$, $x \neq 3$

(iii) $gg^{-1}(x) = x$

(iv) Not continuous at $x = 0$

6. (i) €130,000 (ii) 0.064 (iii) €88,500

7. (a) Graph Ⓑ

(b) (i) $x = \dfrac{\log_a 9}{\log_a 12}$

(ii) $y = 3.4$ (choose any positive value for a)

8. (a) $(x - 2)^2 + 1$; Turning point $= (2, 1)$

(b) $f^{-1}(x) = 2 + \sqrt{x - 1}$

(c)

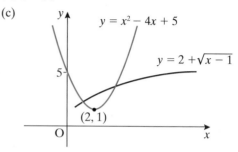

9. (i) $C_0 = 5$ and $k = 0.5798$ (ii) 5.6 years

Chapter 9: Statistics 2

Exercise 9.1

1. (i) C and E (ii) A and F (iii) B and D

(iv) A; negative correlation

2. (i) B (ii) C (iii) D

3. (i) Strong positive

(ii) The better a student does in the mock exams, the better he/she tends to do in the final exam.

4. (ii) Strong positive

(iii) On balance, there is a tendency for those who do better at statistics to also do better at maths.

5. (i) Negative (ii) Positive (iii) None

(iv) Negative (v) Positive

6. (i) B (ii) C (iii) A (iv) D

7. (i) Reasonably strong negative

(ii) Yes; as the age of the bike increases, it causes the price to decrease.

8. (ii) Strong negative

(iii) No; an increase in the sales of one does not cause a decrease in the sales of the other.

Exercise 9.2

1. A(0.6); B(−1); C(−0.4); D(0.8)

2. (i) 0.9 (ii) −0.8 (iii) 0

(iv) −1 (v) −0.1 (vi) 0.2

3. (i) Line of best fit.
   (ii) Approximately equal number of points on either side of line.
   (iii) 55 kg
   (iv) Strong positive
5. 0.86
6. (iii) -0.9
   (iv) $y = 41 - 1.1x$ (by calculator)
   (v) Approx. 12
7. (ii) Strong negative correlation
   (iv) $y = -1.7x + 98$ (exact)
   (v) Approx. 68
8. 0.85
9. (iii) $y = 1.9x - 16$ (by calculator)
   (iv) Approx. 15 hours
10. (ii) Strong negative correlation
   (iii) -0.9250
   (iv) $y = -3x + 18$
   (v) 0.9
11. (ii) Fairly strong positive correlation
   (iii) 0.8591
   (iv) $y = 0.63x - 2.2$ (by calculator)
   (v) Approx. €18

Exercise 9.3

1. (i) 68% (ii) 95% (iii) 81.5% (iv) 68%
2. (i) 34% (ii) 16% (iii) 81.5%
3. (i) 46 km/hr (ii) 73 km/hr
   (iii) 82 km/hr
4. (i) $55 < x < 65$ (ii) [50, 70]
5. (i) [162 cm, 178 cm] (ii) [146 cm, 194 cm]
6. (i) 95% (ii) 2.5% (iii) 570
7. (i) 8160 bulbs (ii) 5700 bulbs
   (iii) 300 bulbs
8. 25
9. (i) (a) 95% (b) 99.7% (ii) 97 portions
10. (i) 1 (ii) -2 (iii) 1.5 (iv) -2.5
11. (i) A value which lies 2 standard deviations above the mean.
   (ii) A value which lies $1\frac{1}{2}$ standard deviations below the mean.
12. (i) Karl's mark is 1.8 standard deviations above the mean.
   Tanya's mark is 0.6 standard deviations below the mean.
   (ii) Karl, 97 and Tanya, 61
13. Height: $z = -1.5$; Weight: $z = 0.5$

14. (i) Maths: $z = 0.417$; History: $z = -0.8$
   (ii) Maths; higher z-score
   (iii) 83
15. (i) Her mark was 1.8 standard deviations above the mean
   (ii) 58.4 (iii) -0.7
16. (i) 1.75 (ii) 77
17. (ii) History: $z = 2$; Physics: $z = 1.5$.
   Yes, she did better in History.
18. First beach: $z = 1.43$; Second beach: $z = 1.25$.
   Her claim is correct.

Exercise 9.4

1. (i) 0.8849 (ii) 0.1587
   (iii) 0.0274 (iv) 0.9282
2. 0.9222 **3.** 0.8133 **4.** 0.9793
5. 0.0228 **6.** 0.1056 **7.** 0.2266
8. 0.0107 **9.** 0.0968 **10.** 0.0166
11. 0.7123 **12.** 0.6826 **13.** 0.8664
14. 0.1980 **15.** 0.9534 **16.** 0.7159
17. 1.12 **18.** 0.34 **19.** 0.91
20. 1.42
21. (i) 0.8413 (ii) 0.6915 (iii) 0.6915
22. (i) 0.5948 (ii) 0.6844
23. (i) 0.1056 (ii) 0.0301
24. (i) 0.1370 (ii) 0.2902
25. (i) 0.1349 (ii) 0.0514
26. (i) 0.3830 (ii) 0.3721
27. (i) 0.0668 (ii) 0.3085
28. (i) 0.6554 (ii) 0.7257 (iii) 0.3056
29. (i) 0.0062 (ii) 0.1587 (iii) 0.6247
30. 0.5746
31. (i) 0.0764 (ii) 0.1895
32. (i) 6 (ii) 294
33. (i) 203 (ii) 111
34. (i) (a) 0.0668 (b) 0.7745
   (ii) 73%

Revision Exercise 9 (Core)

1. 81.5%
2. (i) B (ii) A (iii) C (iv) A (v) B
3. (i) $a = 160$ cm, $b = 170$ cm, $c = 180$ cm, $d = 190$ cm, $e = 200$ cm
   (ii) $z = 1$
   (iii) 16%
4. (ii) Strong positive
   (iv) $y = 0.713x + 9.74$ (exact)
   (v) 33

5. 7.5 cm

6. 0.1762

7. (i) A measure of the strength of the linear relationship between 2 sets of variables.

(ii) (a) $r = 0.916$

(b) It is very likely that a student who has done well in Test 1 will also have done well in Test 2.

8. (i) 95%   (ii) 47.5%

9. (i) 0.8   (ii) 0.66

(iii) Simon did better in French.

10. There may be a strong positive correlation between house prices and car sales but that does not imply that one increase **causes** the other.

Revision Exercise 9 (Advanced)

1. 0.7338

2. (i) 0.1359   (ii) $k = 1.12$

3. (i) 0.0668   (ii) 0.052

4. (i) $k = 1.42$

5. (i) 2.5%   (ii) 0.95   (iii) 5000 hours

6. (i) $r = 0.959$

(ii) Very strong positive correlation.

7. First tree: $z = 2$; Second tree $z = -0.67$
He is correct since $z = -0.67$ has a greater chance of happening on the normal curve than $z = 2$.

8. (ii) Strong negative correlation

(iii) $y = -1.12x + 41.6$

(iv) 38 mins

(v) $r = -1$

9. (i) 1.5   (ii) 153 cm

Revision Exercise 9 (Extended Response Questions)

1. (i) (a) 68%   (b) 81.5%

(ii) 8150 nails   (iii) 0.16

2. (ii) $y = 0.7x + 25$

(iii) $r = 0.737$

(iv) There is a strong positive correlation between maths and physics results.

3. (i) 0.0228   (ii) 0.0005

(iii) $\binom{n}{r}(0.0228)^r \, 0.9772^{n-r}$

(iv) 0.0206

4. (i) (a) 1.25   (b) -1 (c) 0   (d) 4

(ii) 2.5%

(iii) 80 years

(iv) Since $z = -2.5$, its very unlikely. The probability will be less than 1%.

5. (i) $r = -0.85$

(ii) 37 years; 139 bpm

(iii) 180 bpm

(iv) -0.8

(v) $MHR = 216 - (0.8 \times \text{age})$

(vi)

Age	Old rule	New rule
20	200	200
50	170	176
70	150	160

For a younger person (20 years) the MHR's are roughly the same; for an older person (50 years or 70 years) the new rule gives a higher MHR reading.

(vii) At 65 years of age, the old rule gives $MHR = 155$ and the new rule gives $MHR = 164$. To get more benefit from exercise, he should increase his activity to 75% of 164 instead of 75% of 155.

Chapter 10: Inferential statistics

Exercise 10.1

1. (i) 0.3   (ii) 0.04   (iii) $0.26 < p < 0.34$

2. (i) 34%

(ii) $0.29 < p < 0.39$; 95% of samples would give this result.

3. $0.35 < p < 0.37$

4. $0.218 < p < 0.382$

5. $0.176 < p < 0.398$

6. (i) 400   (ii) 1111   (iii) 4444

7. $0.35 < p < 0.49$

8. (i) $0.09 < p < 0.21$

(ii) If 100 samples were taken, we would expect 95 of them to have defective items ranging between 9% and 21% (or between 27 items and 63 items).

(iii) 190

9. $0.1096 < p < 0.1904$

10. $0.293 < p < 0.427$

11. $0.260 < p < 0.379$

12. $0.122 < p < 0.358$

13. $0.294 < p < 0.386$

14. (i) $0.654 < p < 0.812$

(ii) $0.765 < p < 0.917$

15. (i) 34%

(ii) $29.4\% < p < 38.6\%$; On 95% of samples the true proportion will lie in this interval.

(iii) 2156

16. $0.245 < p < 0.295$

17. (i) $0.08 < p < 0.22$

(ii) 2180

Exercise 10.2

1. $0.325 < p < 0.389$; No, as 0.4 is outside this range.

2. $0.489 < p < 0.579$; No, as 0.5 is within this range.

3. (i) 0.2166　(ii) 0.065

(iii) 0.1667　(iv) Dice is fair.

4. No

5. $2.4\% < p < 24.5\%$; claim correct

6. $0.61 < p < 0.723$; Yes, it's justified.

7. (i) $0.49 < p < 0.58$

(ii) The coin is not biased.

8. (i) 2213　(ii) 984

Exercise 10.3

1. (i) Sampling distribution

(ii) decrease

(iii) μ

(iv) $\frac{\sigma}{\sqrt{n}}$

2. Ⓐ Represents the distribution of the sample means

3. (i) Normal distribution; The Central Limit Theorem

(ii) Sample size is sufficiently large (i.e. >30)

(iii) Mean = 12;

Standard deviation $= \frac{2}{\sqrt{36}} = \frac{1}{3}$

4. (i) $(4, 6), (4, 8), (4, 10), (6, 8), (6, 10), (8, 10)$

(ii) Means are: 5, 6, 7, 7, 8, 9

(iii) Statistic

(iv) Both = 7

5. (i) Positively

(ii) Normal distribution

(iii) Sample size is sufficiently large ($n > 30$) to apply the theorem.

6. 0.0228

7. 0.0262

8. (i) 0.209　(ii) 0.1635

9. (i) 0.3　(ii) (a) 0.0228　(b) 0.4706

10. 0.894

11. $P(\bar{x} > 8 \text{ years 1 month}) = 0.0228$; Number of samples = 1

12. 0.3214

13. C = 80, D = 96, E = $78\frac{2}{3}$

14. $n = 26$

15. (i) 0.0793　(ii) $n > 170$

16. (i) 0.0228　(ii) 0.822　(iii) 0.086; Answer (iii)

Exercise 10.4

1. $62.17 < \mu < 63.83$

2. $279.1 < \mu < 288.9$

3. (i) $225.2 < \mu < 228.8$

(ii) 5%

4. $60.9 < \mu < 64.5$

5. (i) $5.097 < \mu < 5.143$

(ii) 5.10 and 5.14

(iii) The "95% confidence" means that the mean lies in the range 5.10 to 5.14 95 times out of 100.

6. €$269.71 < \mu <$ €290.29

7. (i) $28.99 \text{ cm} < \mu < 29.41 \text{ cm}$

(ii) No, as the sample size (180) is sufficiently large to apply The Central Limit Theorem.

8. (i) 0.0125

(ii) 0.932 g

(iii) $0.9075 < \mu < 0.9565$

(iv) The confidence interval would be $[0.9124 < \mu < 0.9516]$

(v) A larger sample results in a smaller confidence interval.

9. (i) $4.28 < \mu < 4.92$

(ii) 601 cars

10. (i) $747.42 < \mu < 748.58$

(ii) $n = 23$

11. (i) $68.12 < \mu < 69.88$

(ii) $n = 28$

12. (i) 0.629

(ii) $46.2 \text{ g} < \mu < 51.0 \text{ g}$

(iii) At least 70

13. (i) $\bar{x} = 57.4$

(ii) $\sigma = 15.1$

Exercise 10.5

1. No; $z = 1.68$; so not greater than 1.96
2. Yes; $z = -2.66$
3. (i) H_0: The mean age of the patients is 45 years.
   H_1: The mean age of the patients is not 45 years.
   (iii) $z = 1.89$
   (iv) No; $z = 1.89$; so not greater than 1.96
4. (i) H_0: The mean length is 210 cm
   H_1: The mean length is not 210 cm
   (iii) Yes: $z = 2.5$
   As $z = 2.5$ is in the critical region, we reject the null hypothesis.
5. No: $z = 1.955$; so z not greater than 1.96
6. Yes: $z = -2.11$, which is <-1.96
7. Yes: $z = -2.54$, which is less than -1.96
8. (i) 0.0836 (ii) 0.0562
   (iii) 0.099 (iv) 0.0394
9. (i) $z = 1.77$
   (ii) p-value $= 0.0768$
   (iii) No, as p-value > 0.05
10. (i) $z = -1.5$
    (ii) p-value $= 0.1336$
    (iii) No, as p-value > 0.05
11. (i) $z = 1.5$
    (ii) No, as $z \ngtr 1.96$
    (iii) p-value $= 0.1336$
    (iv) Yes, as p-value is not less than 0.05; so we accept H_0 that the mean time required is 12 mins.
12. (i) $z = 2.5$
    (ii) 0.0124
    (iii) Yes, as p-value < 0.05
13. Standard error $= 0.0036$; 4.993 mm $< \mu$ < 5.007 mm; Yes as $z = 2.22$ and so $z > 1.96$.

Revision Exercise 10 (Core)

1. 0.89
2. Mean $\mu = 2.85$;
   Standard error $= \dfrac{0.07}{\sqrt{20}} = 0.016$
3. $24.42 < \mu < 27.98$
4. 260.0 ml $< \mu < 272.2$ ml
5. $0.522 < p < 0.678$
6. $0.45 < p < 0.65$
7. Yes; $z = 2.113$ and $z > 1.96$

8. (i) The mean 460.3 g has not changed.
   (ii) $z = 2.18$
   (iii) Since $z = 2.18$ and $2.18 > 1.96 \Rightarrow$ the new mean is different from the known mean.
9. (i) Normal distribution; Central Limit Theorem
   (ii) Sample size is large (i.e. >30)
   (iii) None.
10. (i)

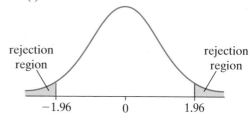

    (ii) $z < -1.96$ and $z > 1.96$
    (iv) p-value $= 0.1096$
11. (i) 0.06   (ii) $0.62 < p < 0.74$

Revision Exercise 10 (Advanced)

1. $n = 10$
2. (i) 0.401
   (ii) 0.691
   (iii) 0.494; unaffected as $n > 30$
3. 30.6 kg $< \mu < 32.2$ kg
4. (i) Since $n \geqslant 30$, the Central Limit Theorem can be applied.
   (ii) $0.057 < p < 0.343$
5. (i) If 100 samples of the same size are taken, then the true population mean or proportion will lie in the given interval on 95 occasions out of 100.
   (ii) 3.16 km $< \mu < 13.88$
6. (i) $H_0: \mu = 1.2$ sec; $H_1: \mu \neq 1.2$ sec
   (ii) Critical regions are: $z < -1.96$ and $z > 1.96$
   (iii) $z = -3$. Yes as $z < -1.96$ and so is in the critical region.
   (iv) p-value $= 0.0026$
   Since $p < 0.05$, we reject the null hypothesis that $\mu = 1.2$ sec.
7. (i) 0.118
   (ii) 0.69
   (iii) $0.576 < p < 0.812$
   (iv) The sample proportion, 0.8 is within the confidence limit and so we accept the school's claim.

8. (i) H_0: The mean weight is 25 kg.
H_1: The mean weight is not 25 kg.
(ii) $z = -2.36$
(iii) p-value $= 0.0182$
(iv) Yes, as the p-value < 0.05
(v) "The p-value is the smallest level of significance at which the null hypothesis could have been rejected".

9. (i) 68 kg; 0.6 kg
(ii) 17 samples

10. (i) 0.022 (ii) $0.241 < p < 0.286$

11. (i) 3%
(ii) $18\% < p < 24\%$; not sufficient to reject party's claim.

12. (i) 0.05
(ii) $11\% < p < 21\%$; no evidence to reject claim.

13. $66.9\% < p < 81.9\%$; NCCB's beliefs are borne out.

14. (i) 2% (ii) $\hat{p} = 0.1096$
(iii) $0.0896 < p < 0.1296$; yes, owner's claim is justified.

Revision Exercise 10 (Extended Response Questions)

1. (i) H_0: The mean weight is 500 g.
H_1: The mean weight is not 500 g.
(ii) $z = 1.666$
(iii) p-value $= 0.095$
(iv) Since p-value $\not< 0.05$, we accept the null hypothesis. The result is not significant.

2. (i) 0.0533
(ii) $0.245 < p < 0.454$

3. (i) $\bar{x} = 81.4$ g
(ii) $\sigma = 15$ g

4. (i) 10.6%; 6.7%
(ii) $z = -1.58$

(iii) p-value $= 0.114$
(iv) $p = 0.114$ is not less than $0.05 \Rightarrow$ the mean weight of the sample is not different from the population mean.

5. (a) Mean $= \mu$; Standard deviation $= \dfrac{\sigma}{\sqrt{n}}$
(i) Normal distribution.
(ii) Normal distribution.
The Central Limit Theorem can be applied to any distribution if n is large ($n > 30$). The distribution of the sample means will always be normal when the underlying population is normal.
(b) (i) 0.278 (ii) 695

6. (i) $\frac{3}{4}$
(ii) 0.2966
(iii) Normal distribution; $\mu = 22.05$; $\sigma = 0.7524$
(iv) 103

7. (i) 0.773 (ii) 0.631
(iii) 2.89 kg (iv) 0.936

8. (a) (i) 0.0228 (ii) 0.440
(iii) 0.785
(b) (i) Mean only 1.08 standard deviations above zero.
For a normal distribution this gives a probability of about 0.14 of negative times, which are impossible.
(ii) Large sample $\Rightarrow$ mean approximately normally distributed.

9. (i) 0.1587
(ii) 0.1736
(iii) 63 g

10. (i) 5%
(ii) $83\% < p < 93\%$; **no**, their claim is not justified as 81% is not within the confidence limit.